MW00607476

THE FUNCTIONAL EMOTIONAL ASSESSMENT SCALE (FEAS)

FOR INFANCY AND EARLY CHILDHOOD: CLINICAL AND RESEARCH APPLICATIONS

The Functional Emotional Assessment Scale (FEAS)

For Infancy and Early Childhood:

Clinical and Research Applications

Stanley I. Greenspan, M.D.

Georgia DeGangi, Ph.D., OTR

Serena Wieder, Ph.D.

Interdisciplinary Council on Developmental and Learning Disorders
Bethesda, MD

Copyright © 2001 by the Interdisciplinary Council on
Developmental and Learning Disorders
All rights reserved.
Printed in the U.S.A.

ISBN 0-9728925-1-6

This book is dedicated to children with special needs
and their families.

ACKNOWLEDGMENTS

Many people have helped us in the writing of this book. We are very grateful to Ruth Sickel, Betty Ann Kaplan, Andrea Santman Wiener, Diane Hopkins, Polly Craft, and Cecilia Breinbauer who collaborated on the Fussy Baby team at the Lourie Center in testing subjects and scoring parent-child interactions using the FEAS. Their camaraderie of spirit and intellectual curiosity spurred the development of test items, and their dedication and hard work enabled us to complete the various validity and reliability studies described in this book.

We also especially wish to thank Jan Tunney and Sue Morrisson for their heroic efforts in the formatting and manuscript preparation of this book.

In addition, we would like to thank Evelyn Stefansson Nef, who provided financial support, and the Reginald S. Lourie Center for Infants and Young Children in Rockville, Maryland, which made the research on the FEAS possible. We also gratefully acknowledge the Cecil and Ida Green Foundation, which provided financial support in research assessing and treating infants and children with regulatory disorders.

Contents

Introduction

Stanley I. Greenspan, M.D.

Our understanding of emotional and social functioning in infants and young children has grown enormously in the past 40 years. Clinical insights, observations, and research have all contributed. Yet, there are huge challenges to assessing emotional functioning (Greenspan & Meisels, 1996). Critical aspects of emotional functioning only occur in naturalistic settings. For example, the true intimacy of a parent and baby cuddling or playing together can't be created; it must be observed naturally. Attempts to create experimental, stimulus-driven, or question-answer type formats for these naturally occurring, dynamic, emotional interactions may change the very interaction one is attempting to learn about. In addition, vital aspects of emotional functioning occur in the inner emotional life of the child and/or his or her interactive partner. Such deeply felt personal feelings and associated thoughts may not be readily apparent from observed behaviors or verbalizations. Clues that are present in observed behaviors are often quite indirect and require a great deal of clinical experience to interpret (e.g., a child avoiding a caregiver because he is scared of being rejected).

Furthermore, there are many different traditions and psychological models that have informed our understanding of children's emotional and social functioning. For example, psychoanalytic and psychodynamic models have focused on play and inner feeling states. Complex clinical observations are made involving the sequence of the child's behavior, play, verbal productions, interactive patterns, and affective proclivities (Freud, A., 1965; Greenspan, Hatleberg, & Cullander, 1976). Cognitive developmental models have focused on aspects of social cognition, such as empathy, morality, and social reasoning. Behavioral models have attempted to look at discrete social behaviors and the conditions that shape them. Empirical models have emphasized observable, measurable aspects of children's emotional lives rather than deeper levels of feelings. Narrowly defined research approaches have looked at specific aspects of emotional functioning (e.g., Ainsworth's assessment of attachment using the strange situation [Ainsworth, Blehar, Waters, & Wall, 1978]).

The development of assessment tools for in-depth emotional development has been especially difficult to develop because emotional functioning covers many areas or variables. Each of these areas requires subtle clinical observations. For example, emotional functioning includes self-regulation, different levels of relating or attachments, emotional cueing and signaling, expressed affects, co-regulated social problem-solving, symbolizing or representing wishes and emotions, expressing wishes and feelings, elaborating emotional themes in pretend play, reasoning about feelings, and reflecting on one's own feelings and empathizing with the feelings of others. Emotional functioning also includes wishes, defenses, a sense of self, self-other boundaries, a sense of reality and reality testing, and identity (Ainsworth, Bell, & Stayton, 1974; Bowlby, 1951; Brazelton, Koslowski, & Main, 1974; Emde, Gaensbauer, & Harmon, 1976; Erikson, 1940; Escalona, 1968; Fogel, 1982; Freud, A. 1965; Freud, 1900; Greenspan, 1979; Kohut, 1971; Mahler, Pine, & Bergman, 1975; Murphy, 1974; Piaget, 1962; Spitz, 1945; Stern, 1985; Tomkins, 1963; Winnicott, 1931).

As can be seen, the complexity of emotional and social functioning makes it extraordinarily challenging to develop assessment tools to reliably measure its most important dimensions. In fact, as described in Chapter 4, current instruments are limited in their ability to systematically assess the full range of emotional capacities in infancy and early childhood. They focus on aspects of cognitive or motor functioning and only isolated surface aspects of emotional and social functioning. They generally do not measure the in-depth aspects of emotional functioning (i.e., the inner emotional life of a child). They also generally do not systematically assess the vital structure-building aspects of emotional interactions, such as the ability to relate to others, symbolize wishes and affects, and test reality.

Therefore, there is a need for assessment tools that can assess in-depth emotional and social functioning (e.g., the capacity for intimacy, fantasy and imagination, symbolizing different emotions, etc.), as well as easily observable emotional and social behaviors (e.g., social reciprocity). The challenge is to develop a reliable and valid tool that doesn't sacrifice complexity, subtlety, or depth of observation.

Guided by observations of normally developing and environmentally and biologically at-risk infants, young children, and their families, we developed a framework for the observation and assessment of emotional functioning. The first step involved creating an integrated framework. The framework synthesized psychoanalytic, cognitive, developmental and empirical models, as well as findings from observations of and clinical work with a variety of infants, toddlers, and families. Interestingly, it was the clinical work with infants, young children, and their families with both environmental and biological risks that lead to an understanding of how different aspects of development work together. This lead to the formulation of the Developmental Structuralist Theory and the Developmental, Individual-Difference, Relationship-Based model (DIR) (Greenspan, 1979, 1989, 1992, 1997; Greenspan & Lourie, 1981).

Based on this theory and model, we formulated the functional emotional developmental approach (Greenspan, 1992, 1997). The functional emotional developmental approach describes the critical emotional capacities that characterize development. It also serves as an organizing construct for the other aspects of development, including motor, sensory, language, and cognitive functioning. For example, when we describe the child's capacity for two-way interactive, emotional communication at around eight months (reciprocal affect-cueing), in addition to the emotional features of affect cueing, we take into account the cognitive component (cause and effect interaction), the motor component (reaching), the language component (exchanging vocalizations that convey affect), and the sensory component (using sight, touch, and perception of sound as part of a co-regulated, reciprocal emotional interaction). Therefore, as will be seen in Chapters 1 and 2, the functional emotional developmental approach provides a way of characterizing emotional functioning and, at the same time, a way of looking at how all the components of development (cognition, language, and motor skills) work together (as a mental team) organized by the designated emotional goals. In this model, therefore, emotional capacities serve as the "orchestra leader" that enables all the developmental components to work together in a functional manner (Greenspan, 1997). Chapter 1 describes this theoretical model and the stages of emotional development that are a part of it.

In addition, in this model there are two critical features of emotional and social functioning. One of these features relates to vital structure-building emotional and social interactions. This includes, for example, the ability to regulate emotions, form pleasurable relationships, use emotional signals for communication, develop a sense of self and psychological boundaries, and construct meaning and purpose. These structure-building aspects of emotional and social functioning are vital for essential personality or ego capacities, such as reality-testing, the ability to relate to others, and the capacity to communicate, process, and modulate feelings. A second feature of the model involves the content or themes of emotional life, for example, aggression, fears, pleasure, sexuality, and so forth. As will be seen, within this assessment model it will be possible to look for deficits or instabilities in the core structure-building emotional and social capacities, as well as constrictions and inflexibilities in the affective, thematic range of emotional life (including conflicts and defenses).

This integrated model lead to the development of a number of initial clinical assessment and intervention approaches for a variety of infants and young children, including those with emotional disorders, regulatory disorders, and pervasive or multisystem developmental disorders. A systematic, clinical approach to assessing emotional functioning in infancy and early childhood is described in Chapter 2. This approach builds on earlier work systematizing observations of emotional functioning (Greenspan et al., 1976; Greenspan & Lieberman, 1980; Greenspan & Lieberman, 1989). A brief observational and potential screening approach is described in Chapter 3.

The next goal was to further operationalize the variables in the functional emotional developmental approach, reliably code them from videotaped interactions between infants and children and their caregivers, and conduct a series of validation studies. This process is described in Chapters 4, 5, 6, and 7. In these chapters, we present the research version of the Functional Emotional Assessment Scale (FEAS) and the reliability and validity data. It will be seen that it was possible to operationalize complex emotional concepts sufficiently for raters to be trained to reliability.

Another goal involved describing the clinical features of a comprehensive evaluation of emotional functioning (as well as related areas of functioning) and a developmentally based approach to the classification and diagnosis of emotional problems. Not infrequently, individuals are tempted to use a research assessment of emotional functioning as an overall clinical assessment. Specific clinical or research tools, including the clinical or research version of the FEAS, constitute one part of a comprehensive clinical evaluation (as described in Chapter 8). In addition, if a formal diagnosis is required, it's important to understand the relationship between the child's unique emotional developmental profile and symptom-based diagnoses. Chapter 9 describes a developmental approach to the diagnostic process, including a developmentally based classification system for emotional problems in the early years of life.

The FEAS in its clinical and/or research formats can be used for circumscribed clinical or research purposes. However, if it is to be used in an overall clinical assessment, it should be a part of an overall evaluation and, if needed, a developmentally based diagnosis.

In conclusion, although there is a strong tradition in psychology to set up experimental situations or structured questions and then observe the responses, such approaches tend to limit and change the phenomena being observed. Such approaches tend to be based, broadly speaking, on a narrow, deterministic paradigm that goes back to Descartes and other Enlightenment philosophers (Greenspan & Shanker, in press). On the other hand, many investigators are now arguing that emotional phenomena needs to be conceptualized as part of naturally occurring dynamic interactions (e.g., dynamic systems models). Such models suggest the importance of observing spontaneous interactions between children and their caregivers. The challenge has been in creating a reliable and valid approach that can capture complex, dynamic, interactive processes. Toward this goal, the clinical and research tools presented in this volume will provide a comprehensive, systematic approach that is able to focus on the dynamic processes involved in the observation and assessment of emotional and social functioning in infancy and early childhood.

References

Ainsworth, M., Bell, S. M., & Stayton, D. (1974). Infant-mother attachment and social development: Socialization as a product of reciprocal responsiveness to signals. In M. Richards (Ed.), *The Integration of the Child into a Social World* (pp. 99–135). Cambridge, England: Cambridge University Press.

Ainsworth, M., Blehar, M., Waters, E., & Wall, S. (1978). *Patterns of attachment: A psychological study of the strange situation.* New York: Lawrence Erlbaum Associates.

Bowlby, J. (1951). Maternal care and mental health. *WHO Monograph, No. 51*. Geneva, World Health Organization.

Brazelton, T. B., Koslowski, B., & Main, M. (1974). The origins of reciprocity; the early mother-infant interaction. In M. Lewis & L. Rosenblum (Eds.), *The Effect of the Infant on Its Caregiver*. New York: Wiley & Sons.

Emde, R. N., Gaensbauer, T. J., & Harmon, R. J. (1976). Emotional expression in infancy: A biobehavioral study. *Psychological Issues* (Monograph No. 37). New York, International Universities Press.

Erikson, E. H. (1940). Studies in interpretation of play: I. Clinical observation of child disruption in young children. *Genetic Psychology* (Monograph No. 22).

Escalona, S. (1968). *The roots of individuality*. Chicago: Aldine.

Fogel, A. (1982). Affect dynamics in early infancy: Affective tolerance. In T. Field & A. Fogel (Eds.), *Emotion and Early Interaction*. Hillsdale, NJ: Erlbaum.

Freud, A. (1965). *Normality and pathology in childhood; assessments of development*. New York: International Universities Press.

Freud, S. (1900). *The interpretation of dreams*. Standard Edition. (1958) London: Hogarth Press.

Greenspan, S. I. (1979). Intelligence and adaptation: An integration of psychoanalytic and Piagetian developmental psychology. *Psychological Issues* (Monograph No. 47–48). New York, International Universities Press.

Greenspan, S. I. (1989). *The development of the ego: Implications for personality theory, psychopathology, and the psychotherapeutic process*. New York: International Universities Press.

Greenspan, S. I. (1992). *Infancy and early childhood: The practice of clinical assessment and intervention with emotional and developmental challenges*. Madison, CT: International Universities Press.

Greenspan, S. I. (1997). *The growth of the mind and the endangered origins of intelligence*. Reading, MA: Addison Wesley Longman.

Greenspan, S. I., Hatleberg, J. L., & Cullander, C. C. (1976). A systematic metapsychological assessment of the personality in childhood. *J.Am.Psychoanal.Assoc., 24*, 875–903.

Greenspan, S. I. & Lieberman, A. (1980). Infants, mothers, and their interaction: A quantitative clinical approach to developmental assessment. In S. I. Greenspan & G. H. Pollock (Eds.), *The Course of Life, Vol. I, Infancy* (pp. 503–560). Madison, CT: International Universities Press.

Greenspan, S. I. & Lieberman, A. (1989). A quantitative approach to the clinical assessment of representational elaboration and differentiation in children two to four. In S. I. Greenspan & G. H. Pollock (Eds.), *The Course of Life, Vol. II, Early Childhood* (pp. 387–442). Madison, CT: International Universities Press.

Greenspan, S. I. & Lourie, R. S. (1981). Developmental structuralist approach to the classification of adaptive and pathologic personality organizations: infancy and early childhood. *Am.J.Psychiatry, 138*, 725-735.

Greenspan, S. I. & Meisels, S. J. (1996). Toward a new vision for the developmental assessment of infants and young children. In *New Visions of Assessment*. Washington, DC: ZERO TO THREE.

Greenspan, S. I. & Shanker, S. (in press). *The evolution of intelligence: How language, consciousness, and social groups come about.* Reading, MA: Perseus Books.

Kohut, H. (1971). *The analysis of self: A systematic approach to the psychoanalytic treatment of narcissistic personality disorders.* New York: International Universities Press.

Mahler, M. S., Pine, F., & Bergman, A. (1975). *The psychological birth of the human infant: Symbiosis and individuation.* New York: Basic Books.

Murphy, L. B. (1974). The individual child. *Publication no. OCD 74–1032 .* Department of Health, Education and Welfare, Washington, DC, US Government Printing Office.

Piaget, J. (1962). The stages of intellectual development of the child. In S. Harrison & J. McDermott (Eds.), *Childhood Psychopathology* (pp. 157–166). New York: International Universities Press.

Spitz, R. A. (1945). Hospitalism: An inquiry into the genesis of psychiatric conditions in early childhood. *The Psychoanalytic Study of the Child, 1,* 53–74.

Stern, D. (1985). The interpersonal world of the infant: A view from psychoanalysis and developmental pscychology. New York: Basic Books.

Tomkins, S. (1963). *Affect, Imagery, Consciousness, Vol. 1.* New York: Springer Publishing.

Winnicott, D. W. (1931). *Clinical notes on the disorders of childhood.* London: Heineman.

I

Theoretical and Clinical Perspectives on Emotional Functioning In Infancy and Early Childhood

1

The Basic Model

Stanley I. Greenspan, M.D.
Serena Wieder, Ph.D.
Georgia DeGangi, Ph.D., OTR

In an attempt to understand early emotional development, we conducted a number of clinical, observational, and intervention studies on emotional development in infants, young children, and their families. These have included multirisk infants and families, infants and children with biologically based developmental problems, such as autism, and infants and families without challenges or problems (Greenspan, 1981; 1992; 1998; Greenspan & Wieder, 1998; Greenspan et al., 1987; Interdisciplinary Council on Developmental and Learning Disorders Clinical Practice Guidelines Workgroup, 2000). In order to understand the observed patterns, we formulated a broad theoretical perspective, a "developmental structuralist" model (Greenspan, 1979; 1981) that would accommodate both disturbed and adaptive emotional functioning as well as related cognitive, motor, and sensory capacities.

The clinical interest in early emotional development, including psychopathology in infancy and early childhood, is based on an impressive foundation. Constitutional and maturational patterns that influenced the formation of early relationship patterns were already noted in the early 1900s, with descriptions of "babies of nervous inheritance who exhaust their mothers" (Cameron, 1919) and infants with "excessive nerve activity and a functionally immature" nervous system (Rachford, 1905).

Winnicott, who as a pediatrician in the 1930s began describing the environment's role in early relationship problems (1931), was followed in the 1940s by the well-known studies describing the severe developmental disturbances of infants brought up in institutions or in other situations of emotional deprivation (Bakwin, 1942; Bowlby, 1951; Hunt, 1941; Lowery, 1940; Spitz, 1945). Spitz's films resulted in the passage of laws in the United States prohibiting institutional care for infants. (They were instead to be placed in foster care.)

Both the role of individual differences in the infant, based on constitutional-maturational and early interactional patterns, and the "nervous" infants described by Rachford in 1905 and Cameron in 1919, again became a focus of inquiry, as evidenced by the observations of Burlingham and Freud (1942); Bergman and Escalona's descriptions of infants with "unusual sensitivities" (1949); Murphy and Moriarty's description of patterns of vulnerability (1976); Thomas, Chess, and Birch's temperament studies (1968); Cravioto and Delicardie's descriptions of the role of infant individual differences in malnutrition (1973); and the early empirical literature on infants (Brazelton, Koslowski, & Main, 1974; Emde, Gaensbauer, & Harmon, 1976; Gewirtz, 1961; Lipsitt, 1966; Reingold, 1969; Sander, 1962; Sroufe, 1979; Stern, 1974a; Stern, 1974b).

Perhaps most widely known of these foundation-building efforts are Spitz's report (1946) on anaclitic depressions in institutionally reared infants and Bowlby's monograph, *Maternal Care and Mental Health* (1951), describing the now well-known "syndromes" of disturbed functioning in infancy. Child psychoanalysts' interest in disturbances in infants, as indicated by the work of Bernfeld (1929), Winnicott (1931), A. Freud and Burlingham (1942), and Anna Freud (1965), as well as the work of Erik Erikson (1959), amplified the complexity or multidimensional nature of early problems. Important for current approaches was the work relating individual differences in infants (constitutional and maturational patterns) to tendencies for psychopathology highlighted by the reports of Sybille Escalona and Lois Murphy and their colleagues (Escalona, 1968; Murphy, 1974) and Cravioto and Delicardie (1973).

Several existing developmental frameworks have provided enormous understanding of individual lines of development in infancy and early childhood; for example, Sigmund Freud (1905), Erikson (1959), Piaget (1962), Spitz and Cobliner (1966), Anna Freud (1965), Kohut (1971), Kernberg (1975), and Mahler, Pine, and Bergman (1975). These foundations, together with the rapidly growing body of clinical experience with infants and their families (Fraiberg, 1980; Provence & Naylor, 1983; Provence, 1983), provided direction for a much-needed integrated approach encompassing the multiple lines of development in the context of adaptive and disordered functioning.

Further clarification of the elements that needed to be involved in an integrated model includes the perspective offered by developmental psychopathology. This perspective combines knowledge about developmental processes (Bemesderfer & Cohler, 1983; Campos, Campos, & Barrett, 1989; Kovacs & Paulauskas, 1984), adaptive patterns (Als, 1981; Brazelton & Als, 1979), and characteristics of normal socioemotional development. This perspective is useful for the purposes of assessment because it provides a framework for evaluating adaptive and maladaptive behaviors (Digdon & Gotlib, 1985; Zahn-Waxler, Cummings, McKnew, & Radke-Yarrow, 1984), behavioral systems (Cicchetti & Aber, 1986; Cicchetti & Schneider-Rosen, 1984), and developmental tasks (Sroufe & Rutter, 1984).

One of these, the developmental processes of infancy that are associated with attachment, has been well studied and shows that early attachment patterns play a critical role in the level of later adaptive functioning (del Carmen & Huffman, 1996; Egeland & Farber, 1984; Erikson, Egeland, & Sroufe, 1985; Heuber & Thomas, 1995). In addition, inadequate attachment between child and parent is associated with psychopathology in adolescence (Rosenstein & Horowitz, 1996) and possibly into adulthood (Ricks, 1985). As can be seen, in order to adequately represent the richness of human experience, a developmental perspective of psychopathology should consider a range of etiological factors associated with childhood maladaptive behavior. These include interactive dynamics such as caregiver responsivity, contingency, and reciprocity; a range of biological phenomena such as sensory processing, temperament, and regulatory capacities; and environmental influences that impact the caregiver including quality of social support and family setting. These variables are important in evaluating the characteristics of the child and caregiver and their relationship (Wieder, Jasnow, Greenspan, & Strauss, 1983).

With the numerous contributing perspectives on early emotional development, the challenge was to construct a comprehensive, integrated model that could take into account the many contributing factors. In order to meet this challenge, we developed an approach that focuses on the organizational level of personality along multiple dimensions and on mediating processes or "structures." There are two assumptions that relate to this approach. One is that the capacity to organize experience is present very early in life and progresses to higher levels as the individual matures. The phase-specific higher levels in this context imply an ability to organize in stable patterns an ever-widening and complex range of experience. For example, it is now well documented that the infant is capable at birth, or shortly thereafter, of organizing experience in an adaptive fashion. He or she can respond to pleasure and displeasure (Lipsitt, 1966), change behavior as a function of its consequences (Gewirtz, 1965; Gewirtz, 1969), and form intimate bonds and make visual discriminations (Klaus & Kennell, 1976; Meltzoff & Moore, 1977). Cycles and rhythms, such as sleep-wake and alertness states, can be organized (Sander, 1962). The infant evidences a variety of affects or affect proclivities (Ekman, 1972; Izard, 1978; Tomkins, 1963) and demonstrates organized social responses in conjunction with increasing neurophysiologic organization (Emde et al., 1976). It is interesting to note that this empirically documented view of the infant is, in a general sense, consistent with Freud's early hypotheses (1905; 1900; 1911) and Hartmann's postulation (1939) of an early undifferentiated organizational matrix. That the organization of experience broadens during the early months of life to reflect increases in the capacity to experiences and tolerate a range of stimuli, including responding in social interactions in stable and personal configurations, is also consistent with recent empirical data (Brazelton et al., 1974; Emde et al., 1976; Escalona, 1968; Murphy et al., 1976; Sander, 1962; Sroufe, Waters, & Matas, 1974; Stern, 1974a; Stern, 1974b). There are a number of indications that increasingly complex patterns continue to emerge as the infant develops. Between 7 and 12 months complex emotional responses, such as surprise (Charlesworth, 1969) and affiliation, wariness, and fear (Ainsworth, Bell, & Stayton, 1974; Bowlby, 1969; Sroufe & Waters, 1977), have been observed. Exploration and "refueling" patterns (Mahler, Pine, & Bergman, 1975), and behavior suggesting functional understanding of objects (Werner & Kaplan, 1963), have been observed in the middle to latter part of the second year of life, along with the eventual emergence of symbolic capacities (Bell, 1970; Gouin-Decarie, 1965; Piaget, 1962).

The interplay between age-appropriate experience and maturation of the central nervous system (CNS) ultimately determines the characteristics of this organizational capacity at each phase. The active and experiencing child uses his maturational capacities to engage the world in ever-changing and more complex ways.

The organizational level of experience may be delineated along a number of parameters, including age or phase appropriateness, range and depth (i.e., animate and inanimate, full range of affects and themes), stability (i.e., response to stress), and personal uniqueness.

In addition to a characteristic organizational level, a second assumption is that for each phase of development there are also certain characteristic types of experience (e.g., interests or wishes, fears, and curiosities) that play themselves out, so to speak, within this organizational structure. Here one looks at the specific drive-affect derivatives, including emotional and behavioral patterns, or, later, thoughts, concerns, inclinations, wishes, fears, and so forth. The type of experience is, in a sense, the drama the youngster is experiencing, whereas the organizational level might be viewed metaphorically as the stage upon which this drama is being played out. To carry this metaphor a step further, it is possible to imagine some stages that are large and stable and can therefore support a complex and intense drama. In comparison, other stages may be narrow or small, able only to contain a very restricted drama. Still other stages may have cracks in them and may crumble easily under the pressure of an intense, rich, and varied drama.

According to the developmental-structuralist approach, at each phase of development there are certain characteristics that define the experiential organizational capacity, that is, the stability and contour of the stage. At the same time, there are certain age-expectable dramas, themes characterized by their complexity, richness, depth, and content.

The developmental-structuralist approach is unique in an important respect. In focusing on levels and organizations of experience, it alerts the clinician to look not only for what the infant or toddler is evidencing (e.g., specific emotions or symptoms), but for what he or she is not evidencing. For example, the 8-month-old who is calm, alert, and enjoyable, but who has no capacity for discrimination or reciprocal social interchanges, may be of vastly more concern than an irritable, negativistic, food-refusing, night-awakening 8-month-old with age-appropriate capacities for differentiation and reciprocal social interchanges. In other words, each stage of development may be characterized according to "expected" organizational characteristics.

The formulated developmental stages do not exist in a vacuum. During development they are influenced by both constitutional and maturational factors, as well as environmental factors. Each stage, in fact, can be understood as resulting from specific caregiver-child interaction patterns in which the child's behavior is influenced by his constitutional and maturational patterns and the caregiver is influenced by the family-cultural patterns.

This developmental model can be visualized with the infant's constitutional-maturational patterns on one side and the infant's environment, including caregivers, family, community, and culture, on the other side. Both of these sets of factors operate through the infant-caregiver relationship, which can be pictured in the middle. These factors and the infant-caregiver relationship, in turn, contribute to the organization of experience at each of six different developmental levels, which may be pictured just beneath the infant-caregiver relationship.

Each developmental level involves different tasks or goals. The relative effect of the constitutional-maturational, environmental, or interactive variables will, therefore, depend on and can only be understood in the context of the developmental level they relate to. The influencing variables, therefore, are best understood, not as they might be traditionally, as general influences on development or behavior, but as distinct and different influences on the six distinct developmental and experiential levels. For example, as a child is negotiating the formation of a relationship (engaging), his mother's tendency to be very intellectual and prefer talking over holding may make it relatively harder for him to become deeply engaged in emotional terms. If constitutionally he has slightly lower than average muscle tone and is hyposensitive with regard to touch and sound, his mother's intellectual and slightly aloof style may be doubly difficult for him, as neither she nor the child is able to take the initiative in engaging the other.

Let us assume, however, that he more or less negotiates this early phase of development. (Grandmother, who lives with him, as well as his father are very "wooing" caregivers.) At age 3, when the developmental phase and task is different, he may have an easier time, even though his mother hasn't changed. His intellectual mother is highly creative and enjoys pretend play as well as give-and-take logical discussions. No longer anxious about her son's dependency needs, she is more relaxed and quite available for play and chit-chat. The task is no longer simply one of forming a relationship but of learning to represent (or symbolize) experience and form categories and connections between these units of experience. Mother's verbal style is now quite helpful to him, especially given his need for lots of verbal interaction. In other words, the same caregiving pattern can have a very different impact, depending on the tasks of the particular developmental level. Each developmental level of experience is, therefore, a reference point for the factors that influence development. There have been very useful intervention models that focus on specific influences such as the caregiver's feelings, fantasies or support system, or on certain phases of early development (Brazelton et al., 1979; Fraiberg, 1980; Provence, 1983; Provence et al., 1983).

What is potentially unique about this particular clinical and research model (Greenspan, 1992; Greenspan et al., 1987; Greenspan, 1989) is the ability it gives us to look at the back-and-forth influence of highly specific and verifiable constitutional-maturational factors on interactive and family patterns and vice versa in relationship to specific developmental processes (and to relate these processes to later developmental and psychopathologic disorders). The goal of this model is to look at all the major influences throughout the different stages of development. Genetic, biological, or environmental influences do not influence behavior directly, but influence either the child's or the caregiver's behavior, which, in turn, influences their interaction, which eventually leads to adaptive or maladaptive organizations at each developmental level. This model, therefore, provides a range of dynamic pathways through which influences can be exerted on the organization of the personality.

The Developmental Levels of Emotional Functioning

As indicated above, the developmental structuralist approach focuses attention on the way in which the infant and young child organize experience. There are six early organizational levels of experience. For each of these developmental levels, there are two ways of considering how the infant organizes experience. These are the interrelated dimensions of sensory and affective-thematic experience. These two dimensions and their clinical implications for normal development and disturbances in development will be described for each of the developmental-structuralist organizational levels.

Self-Regulation and Interest in the World (Homeostasis): 0–3 Months

The first level of development involves regulation and shared attention, that is, self-regulation and emerging interest in the world through sight, sound, smell, touch, and taste. Children and adults build on this early developing set of capacities when they act to maintain a calm, alert, focused state, and organize behavior, affect, and thoughts. The infant is capable at birth or shortly thereafter of initial states of regulation to organize experience in an adaptive fashion. The infant's ability for regulation is suggested by a number of basic abilities involving forming cycles and establishing basic rhythms, perceiving and processing information, and exploring and responding to the world (Berlyne, 1960; Deci, 1977; Harlow, 1953; Hendrick, 1939; Hunt, 1965; White, 1963; Meltzoff et al., 1977; Sander, 1962).

The early regulation of arousal and physiological states is critical for successful adaptation to the environment. It is important in the modulation of physiological states including sleep-wake cycles and hunger and satiety. It is needed for mastery of sensory functions and for learning self-calming and emotional responsivity. It is also important for regulation of attentional capacities (Als, Lester, Tronick, & Brazelton, 1982; Brazelton et al., 1974; Field, 1981; Sroufe, 1979; Tronick, 1989). It is generally recognized that self-regulatory mechanisms are complex and develop as a result of physiological maturation, caregiver responsivity, and the infant's adaptation to environmental demands (Lachmann & Beebe, 1997; Lyons-Ruth & Zeanah, 1993; Rothbart & Derryberry, 1981; Tronick, 1989).

In the early stages of development, the caregiver normally provides sensory input through play and caretaking experiences such as dressing and bathing and soothes the young infant when distressed to facilitate state organization (Als, 1982). It is an interactive process of mutual coregulation whereby the infant uses the parent's physical and emotional state to organize himself (Feldman, Greenbaum, & Yirmiya, 1999; Sroufe, 1996). This synchronization of states that occurs between parent and child is the basis for affect attunement and is the precursor to social referencing and preverbal communication.

During this early stage, the infant learns to tolerate the intensity of arousal and to regulate his internal states so that he can maintain the interaction while gaining pleasure from it (Sroufe, 1979). This has been described as "affective tolerance," that is, the ability to maintain an optimal level of internal arousal while remaining engaged in the stimulation (Fogel, 1982). The parent first acts to help regulate this arousal, then works to facilitate the infant's responses once the infant can regulate himself. If the infant does not develop affective tolerance, withdrawal from arousing stimuli may occur with resulting challenges to the formation and stability of relationships. Brazelton and his colleagues (1974) observed how the mother attempts to adjust her behavior to be timed with the infant's natural cycles. For example, mothers generally reduce their facial expressiveness when the infant gazes away, but will maintain their expressiveness when the infant looks at them (Kaye & Fogel, 1980).

Field (1977; 1980) proposed an "optimal stimulation" model of affect and interaction. If the mother provides too much or too little stimulation, the infant withdraws from the interaction. The optimal level varies considerably from one infant to the next and depends upon the infant's threshold for arousal, tolerance for stimulation, and ability to self-control arousal.

To systematize these observations and the results of our clinical work with a variety of infants and families, we have been able to describe a number of individual differences in constitutional-maturational characteristics that contribute to an infant and child's regulatory capacities. These patterns may change as one develops, however. They include

- Sensory reactivity, including hypo- and hyperreactivity in each sensory modality (tactile, auditory, visual, vestibular, olfactory);
- Sensory processing in each sensory modality (e.g., the capacity to decode sequences, configurations, or abstract patterns);
- Sensory affective reactivity and processing in each modality (e.g., the ability to process and react to degrees of affective intensity in a stable manner);
- Muscle tone and motor planning and sequencing.

The Sensory Organization

The infant's first task in the developmental-structuralist approach sequence is simultaneously to take an interest in the world and regulate himself. In order to compare the ability of certain infants to simultaneously regulate and take an interest in the world with those who cannot, it has been clinically useful to examine each sensory pathway individually as well as the range of sensory modalities available for phase-specific challenges.

As indicated, each sensory pathway may be (a) hyperarousable (e.g., the baby who overreacts to normal levels of sound, touch, or brightness); (b) hypoarousable (e.g., the baby who hears and sees but evidences no behavioral or observable affective response to routine sights and sounds—often described as the "floppy" baby with poor muscle tone who is unresponsive and seemingly looks inward); or (c) neither hypo- nor hyperarousable but having a subtle type of early processing disorder (hypo- or hyperarousable babies may also have a processing difficulty). A processing disorder may presumably involve perception, modulation, and processing of the stimulus and/or integration of the stimulus with other sensory experiences (cross-sensory integration), with stored experience (action patterns or representations), or with motor proclivities. Although more immature in form, processing difficulties in infants may not be wholly dissimilar from the types of perceptual-motor or auditory-verbal processing problems we see in older children. In this context, the capacity of babies to habituate to and process the various inanimate sights and sounds may apply to the entire experiential realm of the child, including the affective-laden, interpersonal realm. It is important to note that the differences in sensory reactivity and processing were noted many years ago and continue to be discussed in the occupational therapy literature (Ayres, 1964).

If an individual sensory pathway is not functioning optimally, then the range of sensory experience available to the infant is limited. This limitation, in part, determines the options or strategies the infant can employ and the type of sensory experience that will be organized. Some babies can employ the full range of sensory capacities. At the stage of regulation and interest in the world (i.e., homeostasis), for example, one can observe that such babies look at mother's face or an interesting object and follow it. When this baby is upset, the opportunity to look at mother helps the baby become calm and happy (i.e., a calm smile). Similarly, a soothing voice, a gentle touch, rhythmic rocking, or a shift in position (offering vestibular and proprioceptive stimulation) can also help such a baby to relax, organize, and self-regulate. Also, there are babies who only functionally employ one or two sensory modalities. We have observed babies who brighten up, alert, and calm to visual experience, but who are either relatively unresponsive, become hyperexcitable, or appear to become "confused" with auditory stimuli (a 2-month-old baby may be operationally defined as confused when instead of looking toward a normal high-pitched maternal voice and alerting he makes some random motor movements—suggesting that the stimulus has been taken in—looks past the object repeatedly, and continues his random movements). Other babies appear to use vision and hearing to self-regulate and take an interest in the world but have a more difficult time with touch and movement. They often become irritable even with gentle stroking and are calm only when held horizontally (they become hyperaroused when held upright). Still other babies calm down only when rocked to their own heart rate, respiratory rate, or mother's heart rate. Studies of the role of vestibular and proprioceptive pathways in psychopathology in infancy are very important areas for future research.

As babies use a range of sensory pathways, they also integrate experiences across the senses (Spelke & Owsley, 1979). Yet, there are babies who are able to use each sensory pathway but have difficulty, for example, integrating vision and hearing. They can alert to a sound or a visual cue but are not able to turn and look at a stimulus that offers visual and auditory information at the same time. Instead, they appear confused and may even have active gaze aversion or go into a pattern of extensor rigidity and avoidance.

As higher levels of sensory integration are considered, one may also consider the difference between perception as a general construct and sensory-specific perceptions. In this discussion, the focus will be on individual sensory pathways with the understanding that as sensory and affective information is processed, it can be considered in terms of sensory-specific perceptions and more integrated perceptions.

The sensory pathways are usually observed in the context of sensorimotor patterns. Turning toward the stimulus or brightening and alerting involve motor "outputs." There are babies who have difficulties in the way they integrate their sensory experience with motor output. The most obvious case is a baby with severe motor difficulties. At a subtle level, it is possible to observe compromises in such basic abilities as self-consoling or nuzzling in the corner of mother's neck or relaxing to rhythmic rocking. In this context, Escalona's classic descriptions (1968) of babies with multiple sensory hypersensitivities require further study as part of a broader approach to assessing subtle difficulties in each sensory pathway, as well as associated master patterns.

Thematic Affective Organization

At this first stage the affective-thematic organizations can support the phase-specific task, which in turn can organize discrete affective-thematic inclinations into more integrated organizations. For example, the baby who wants to calm down is, at the same time, learning the means for obtaining dependency and comfort. The baby who is interested in the world can, with a certain posture or glance, often let his primary caregiver know he is ready for interesting visual, auditory, and tactile sensations.

In this first stage, there are babies who cannot organize their affective-thematic proclivities in terms of the phase-specific tasks. Babies who are uncomfortable with dependency often evidence specific sensory hyper-sensitivities or higher-level integrating problems, as well as maladaptive infant-caregiver interactions. Babies with a tendency toward hyper- or hypoarousal may not be able to organize the affective-thematic domains of joy, pleasure, and exploration. Instead, they may evidence apathy and withdrawal or a total disregard for certain sensory realms while over-focusing on others (e.g., babies who stare at an inanimate object while ignoring the human world).

Children with sensorimotor dysfunction typically have difficulty utilizing the range of sensory experiences available to them for learning, and as a result may be unable to organize purposeful, goal-directed movement as well as socially adaptive behaviors. These children oftentimes have maladaptive responses in forming affective relationships or attachments. For instance, an infant who is hyper-sensitive to touch, sound, and movement may avoid tactile contact, being held and moved in space, and may avert its gaze to avoid face-to-face interactions. A child may be unable to play with peers because of problems sequencing actions, a high need for physical contact, or inappropriate affect during interactions because of low muscle tone or poor sensorimotor feedback. Both are examples of how sensorimotor dysfunction may affect emotional behaviors

In addition, difficulties with muscle tone or coordination can affect the infant's ability to signal interest in the world. For example, the young infant who arches away from the mother's breast during feeding will affect the level of engagement that occurs during a normal feeding experience. In turn, these problems affect the caregiver's ability to consistently respond back or respond inconsistently to their infant's signal, particularly when they do not understand what the baby's responses mean. The mother whose baby arches away every time he is held may feel that she is a less capable mother, particularly if the baby's tactile hypersensitivities or increased muscle tone are not identified.

Some investigators explore sensory, motor, and affective differences in terms of temperament, which tends to look at overall patterns of behavior. Temperamental differences have been shown to influence the organization and regulation of inter/intrapersonal processes (Campos et al., 1989). Temperamental qualities characterizing the child as "difficult," for example, have been linked to later psychopathology (Thomas & Chess, 1984). The difficult temperament might create challenges in self-regulatory processes and potentially adversely affect infant-caregiver interaction. Of course, neither sensory nor temperamental characteristics alone necessarily predict pathology. As a transactional perspective indicates, the effects of particular sensory or temperamental characteristics can be mediated by the attention of a sensitive, responsive caregiver

Even when the infant is quite competent from a regulatory standpoint, a caregiver might fail to draw a baby into a regulating relationship. For example, dysregulation may occur with a caregiver who is exceedingly depressed or who is so self-absorbed that there is no soothing wooing of the new infant. A caregiver who is impatient with or threatened by the infant's manifestation of sensory or temperamental sensitivity and who reacts with abuse, withdrawal, or other maladaptive means may encourage infant reliance on ineffective patterns of behavior and further contribute to the infant's inability to achieve self-regulation.

Clinical Features

Sensory reactivity (hypo- or hyper-) and sensory processing can be observed clinically. Is the child or adult hyper- or hyposensitive to touch or sound? Do sounds of motors or of a noisy party overwhelm the individual? Is a gentle touch on the hand or face reacted to by a startled withdrawal? The same question must be asked in terms of vision and movement in space. In addition, in each sensory modality processing of sensations occurs. Does the 4-month-old "process" a complicated pattern of information input or only a simple one? Does the 4-year-old have a receptive language problem and is therefore unable to sequence words he hears together or follow complex directions? Is the young adult prone to get lost in his own fantasies because he has to work extra hard to decode the complex verbal productions of others? Is the 3-year-old an early comprehender and talker, but slower in visual-spatial processing? If spatial patterns are poorly comprehended, a child may be facile with words, sensitive to every emotional nuance, yet have no context, never see the "forest." Such children tend to get lost in the "trees." In the clinician's office, they may forget where the door is or have a hard time picturing that mother is only a few feet away in the waiting room. Similarly, adults may find it difficult to follow instructions or easily get lost in new settings. They also may have difficulty with seeing the emotional "big picture." For example, if the mother is angry, the child may think the earth is opening up and he is falling in, because he cannot comprehend that she was nice before and will probably be nice again. Similarly, adults may be over-whelmed with the emotion of the moment, losing sight of the past or future.

It is also necessary to look at the motor system, including muscle tone, motor planning (fine and gross), and postural control. A picture of the motor system will be provided by observing how a person sits or runs; maintains posture; holds a crayon or pen; hops, scribbles, or draws; and makes rapid alternating movements. Security in regulating and control-ling one's body plays an important role in how one uses gestures to com-municate. Regulatory motor patterns also include the ability to regulate dependency (being close or far away); the confidence in regulating aggression ("Can I control my hand that wants to hit?"); and the ability to comprehend social sequences and follow through on tasks or work activities.

Deficits, Distortions, and Constrictions

The constitutional and maturational variables described above (i.e., regu-latory factors) can contribute to difficulties with attending, remaining calm, and organizing or modulating affect or behavior and, therefore, can be a prominent feature of a disorder of behavior, affect, or thought. Such a disorder may be considered a "regulatory disorder" (Greenspan, 1992). Regulatory differences sometimes are attributed to "lack of motivation" or emotional conflicts. Observing carefully and obtaining a history of reg-ulatory patterns will make it possible to separate maturational variations from other factors and also observe how many factors often operate to-gether. In general, excessive hypersensitivities and sensory underreactiv-ity with a tendency toward withdrawal and apathy illustrate some of the dramatic, maladaptive patterns in this first stage of development. If there are maladaptive environmental accommodations, these early patterns may form the basis for later disorders, including avoidance of the human world, and defects in such basic personality functions as perception, inte-gration, regulation, and motility.

In many conditions these regulatory capacities are not well estab-lished. For example, the child with severe attentional difficulties may not be able to process information well. Some children with mild attentional difficulties have problems more in one sensory mode than in another. Some children with attentional problems are more distracted by sounds, others by visual stimuli, whereas still others have tactile defensiveness, a pattern that is not described well in the psychiatric literature. Sensory processing difficulties are also seen in child and adult schizophrenic populations. Separating and studying each processing capacity in terms of the sensory pathway involved, in relation to both impersonal and affective stimuli (i.e., the auditory, tactile, vestibular, olfactory, and proprioceptive systems, etc.) is an important research area.

Sensory processing difficulties may also involve problems in making discriminations. In addition to a sensory system being hypo- or hyper-arousable, we have observed infants in the first few months of life who, although not at these extremes, seem unable to tune in to the environment. When mother talks to them, instead of decoding her rhythmic sound and brightening up (as most infants do), they almost look confused. Clinically, we have observed that this is present in some children with regard to one sensory pathway, but not another. For example, an infant with intact hearing, unable to focus on rhythmic sound, may be able to focus on facial gesturing. When an infant looks confused in reaction to vocal stimuli, we may coach a mother to slow down, to talk very distinctly, not to introduce too much novelty too quickly (most infants love novelty), and to use lots of animated facial expressions, movements (to encourage the use of vision), and tactile sensations. Often this infant will begin to become alert, brighten up, and become engaged.

It is instructive to consider what happened to deaf children before they were diagnosed early in infancy. By 2 years, many often looked very withdrawn (some were diagnosed as autistic) and were functionally retarded as well. The early diagnosis of deafness led to the introduction of sensory input through the intact modes—visual, tactile, olfactory. With these compensatory experiences, deaf children developed well both cognitively and emotionally. In other words, it may be that critical ego functions follow a certain required sequence of experiential inputs.

What may have happened with many partially or fully deaf babies, however, was that their mothers did not know their infants could not hear. A concerned mother would understandably become anxious if she was not getting a brightening response for her new infant. She may have then talked even more, louder, and faster. Becoming discouraged, she may have become so anxious that she rigidly and repetitively tried the same pattern. Other sensory modes were not experimented with. The mother in this example is overwhelming the nonfunctioning auditory mode, not trying other modes, and her infant becomes more and more confused. On the other hand, the youngster who is hyporeactive may require a highly energetic caregiver. The fit is always a factor. By profiling individual sensory processing differences and motor and affect patterns in infancy, however, it may become possible through counseling to improve the flexibility or intuitive patterns of the caregiver. How well the "informed" environment can find a unique way to provide the stage-specific experiences even for the infants with significant maturational differences will be the focus of future research and is certainly, at this time, an open question. My clinical hunch is that we have not yet found the limits of human adaptability.

Forming Relationships, Attachment, and Engagement: 2–7 Months

Another early level concerns engagement, or a sense of relatedness, a lifelong capacity. Once the infant has achieved some capacity for regulation and interest in the world between 2 and 4 months of age, it becomes more engaged in social and emotional interactions. There is greater ability to respond to the external environment and to form a special relationship with significant primary caregivers. The infant's capacity for engagement is supported by early maturational abilities for selectively focusing on the human face and voice and for processing and organizing information from his senses (Meltzoff, 1985; Papousek, 1981; Papousek & Papousek, 1979; Stern, 1985). A sense of shared humanity, a type of synchrony of relating, is evident in the way both the infant and parent use their senses, motor systems, and affects to resonate with one another (Scaife & Bruner, 1975). The early quality of engagement has implications for later attachment patterns and behavior (Ainsworth et al., 1974; Bates, Maslin, & Frankel, 1985; Belsky, Rovine, & Taylor, 1984; Grossmann, Grossmann, Spangler, Suess, & Unzner, 1985; Lewis & Feiring, 1987; Miyake, Chen, & Campos, 1985; Pederson et al., 1990).

Bowlby (1969) described attachment as the affective bond between an infant and his or her primary caregiver. The infant is biologically prepared to use the primary caregiver as a secure base while exploring the environment, turning to the caregiver for comfort when challenges are experienced. The concept of attachment has been expanded to include the infant's capacity to self-regulate emotions and levels of arousal within the context of the parent-child relationship (Sroufe, 1996). When the infant experiences distress, he or she signals the caregiver and a sensitive and responsive caregiver reads the infant's signals and responds by regulating the infant's emotions.

Attachment or relating with the caregiver is important not only because it represents the capacity to form human relationships, but also because it's been shown that atypical attachment patterns can have a negative impact on developmental outcomes (Carew, 1980). Longitudinal studies have found that securely attached children tend to have better emotional adaptability, social skills, and cognitive functioning (Cassidy & Shaver, 1999). During the school-aged and adolescent years, children who were securely attached as infants were more likely to be accepted by their peers and were better able to form intimate relationships with peers (Sroufe, Egeland, & Carlson, 1999). In addition, a secure attachment seems to provide a protective mechanism for children whose families experience a high level of stress (Egeland & Kreutzer, 1991). The key element that underlies a secure attachment is sensitive and responsive caregiving (Ainsworth, Blehar, Waters, & Wall, 1978; De Wolff & van Ijzendoorn, 1997).

Attachment has a specific research meaning in terms of the studies cited above as well as others. In a clinical as well as normative developmental context, however, it is useful to consider a broader framework for relationships involving the overall pattern of relating between an infant and caregiver. As we will discuss, this involves the depth of pleasure, range of feelings, and meanings given to relationships. The processes that define relationships go significantly beyond definitions used in various research paradigms (Greenspan, 1997b).

The Sensory Organization

In this stage, which involves a growing intimacy with the primary caregiver(s), one can observe babies who are adaptively able to employ all their senses to orchestrate highly pleasurable affect in their relationship with their primary caregiver(s). The baby with a beautiful smile, looking at and listening to mother, experiencing her gentle touch and rhythmic movement, and responding to her voice with synchronous mouth and arm and leg movements is perhaps the most vivid example. Clinically, however, we observe babies who are not able to employ their senses to form an affective relationship with the human world. The most extreme case is where a baby actively avoids sensory and, therefore, affective contact with the human world. Human sounds, touch, and even scents are avoided either with chronic gaze aversion, recoiling, flat affect, or random or nonsynchronous patterns of brightening and alerting. We also observe babies who use one or another sensory pathway in the context of a pleasurable relationship with the human world but cannot orchestrate the full range and depth of sensory experience. The baby who listens to mother's voice with a smile but gaze averts and looks pained at the sight of her face is such an example.

Thematic Affective Organization

Forming an attachment or relationship organizes a number of discrete affective proclivities—comfort, dependency, pleasure, and joy, as well as assertiveness and curiosity in the context of a pleasurable caregiver-infant relationship. In the adaptive pattern, protest and anger are organized along with the expected positive affects as part of a baby's emotional interest in the primary caregiver. A healthy 4-month-old can, as part of his repertoire, become negative, but then also quickly return to mother's beautiful smiles, loving glances, and comforting. Relationship patterns, once formed, continue and further develop throughout the course of life.

Infants and children can already have major limitations in certain affect proclivities. Rather than evidencing joy, enthusiasm, or pleasure with their caregivers, they may instead evidence a flat affect. Similarly, rather than evidencing (periodic) assertive, curious, protesting, or angry behavior in relationship to their primary caregiver, they may only look very compliant and give shallow smiles. In addition to being constricted in their affective range, babies may also evidence a limitation in their organizational stability. An example is a baby who, after hearing a loud noise, cannot return to his earlier interests in the primary caregiver. Where environmental circumstances are unfavorable or for other reasons development continues to be disordered, early attachment or relationship difficulties may occur. If these are severe enough, they may form the basis for an ongoing deficit in the baby's capacity to form affective human relationships and to form the basic personality structures and functions that depend on the internal organization of human experience.

Clinical Features

Most clinicians have a great deal of experience in monitoring the quality of relatedness. But sometimes the clinician ignores the quality of engagement while working on specific ideas or thoughts, so that indifference, negative feelings, or impersonal or aloof patterns continue longer than necessary.

For example, the child who walks in and goes right for the toys, ignoring the clinician, is different from the child who looks at the clinician with a twinkle in his eye and points to the toys, waiting for a warm accepting smile. The adult who strides in the office and makes a beeline for the new painting on the wall with nary a wave or a nod in the therapist's direction may be eschewing any initial sense of engagement to cement a relationship. One observes if there is a range of affects used for trying to establish a sense of connectedness and relatedness—warmth, pleasure, a sense of intimacy and trust.

Deficits, Distortions, and Constrictions

As indicated earlier, within the developmental structuralist framework, negotiation of these first two stages—achievement of homeostasis (i.e., regulation and interest in the world) and achievement of an attachment to a primary caregiver—establishes the infant's ability to engage in the human world. Accordingly, variations in the capacity for engagement influenced by physical and/or ecological conditions play an important role in the emergence of psychopathology in later childhood and adulthood (Greenspan, 1989). If the early experience of the world is aversive, the affective interest in the human world may be compromised. Significant compromises in the attachment process are seen in autistic patterns, in certain types of withdrawn and regressed schizophrenics, and, intermittently, in children who are diagnosed as having pervasive developmental disturbances.

We also see shallow attachments. There is some involvement with the human world, but it is without positive affect or emotional depth. We see a compromise in the depth of human connectedness in some of the narcissistic character disorders, illustrating a subtle deficit in the range of emotion incorporated into an attachment pattern. A severe lack of regard for human relationships is seen in what used to be called the chronic psychopathic personality disorder (now the sociopathic or antisocial personality disturbance). Although some individuals are involved in sociopathic behavior because of neurotic conflicts or anxiety (i.e., acting out), in the primary sociopathic disturbances, there is a failure to see the human world as human. Human beings are seen as concrete objects, only as a means to concrete gratifications. Studies of hardened repeat offenders with histories of violent crimes against other individuals (i.e., showing a total disregard for other humans as human) should observe, in addition to the reports on neurologic problems and early abuse, the degree to which there are—and the nature of—different types of compromises in early relationship patterns (e.g., multiple foster care placements, disturbed and withdrawn parents, or unusual constitutional tendencies that interfered with the formation of warm relationships).

Bowlby (1958) and Main, Kaplan, and Cassidy (1985) have hypothesized that early disturbances in the attachment relationship between mother and child contribute to a child's working model of self as unlovable and of others as unresponsive and/or rejecting. The deleterious effects of deficient or disturbed mother-infant attachment on cognitive, social, and emotional development has been documented by many others as well (Bemesderfer et al., 1983; Davenport, Zahn-Waxler, Adland, & Mayfield, 1984; Egeland et al., 1984; Gaensbauer, Harmon, Cytryn, & McKnew, 1984).

In addition to increasing the possibility of developing a deficit in his or her capacity to form affective human relationships (Bowlby, 1958; Bretherton & Waters, 1985) as well as an impairment in those basic personality structures that depend on an internal organization of human experience (Greenspan & Lourie, 1981; Greenspan & Porges, 1984), problems in forming relationships may increase the risks that an infant may experience personal helplessness. Because of sensory deficits, temperamental characteristics, or exposure to repeated noncontingent situations, he or she may be unable to establish control over the environment during interactions with his or her caregiver (Lyons-Ruth & Jacobovitz, 1999; Weisz & Stipek, 1982; Zekoski, O'Hara, & Wills, 1987). Maternal depression (Gaensbauer, 1982; Radke-Yarrow, Cummings, Kuczynski, & Chapman, 1985), unstable caregiving environments (Gaensbauer, 1982), and physical maltreatment (Egeland & Sroufe, 1981; Schneider-Rosen & Cicchetti, 1984) are also likely to have a negative impact on caregiver-child relationships.

When children experience disorganized patterns of relating, they are likely to suffer from marked impairments in emotional, social, and cognitive functioning. This disorganized pattern is associated with the caregiver's frightening, frightened, or disoriented behavior with the child (Main & Hesse, 1990). Unresolved trauma or grief related to childhood experiences often causes the disoriented response in the parent (Hesse,

1999). The child experiences the parent as a source of alarm, fear, or terror rather than as soothing and nurturing. One type of psychopathology that has been suggested when disorganized attachment occurred during infancy is "dissociation," whereby the person does not function in an organized and coherent manner (Carlson, 1998; Ogawa, Sroufe, Weinfield, Carlson, & Egeland, 1997). Adolescents with disorganized attachments as infants were found to be at high risk for hostile and violent behavior (Lyons-Ruth et al., 1999) in addition to being at risk for psychopathology (Carlson, 1998). In addition, children with anxious attachments were more likely to experience behavioral and emotional problems from preschool through adolescence (Warren, Huston, Egeland, & Sroufe, 1997).

Two-Way, Purposeful Communication (Somatopsychological Differentiation): 3–10 Months

The next stage involves purposeful communication. It involves intentional, nonverbal communications or gestures. These gestures include affective communication, facial expressions, arm and leg movements, vocalizations, and spinal posture. From the middle of the first year of life onward, individuals rely on gestures to communicate. Initially during the stage of purposeful communication, simple reciprocal gestures such as head nods, smiles or other affective expressions, and movement patterns serve a boundary-defining role. The "me" communicates a wish or intention and the "other" or "you" communicates back some confirmation, acknowledgment, or elaboration on that wish or intention.

The stage of two-way, causal, intentional communication indicates processes occurring at the somatic (sensorimotor) and emerging psychological levels. It is evidenced in the infant's growing ability to discriminate primary caregivers from others and differentiate his or her own actions from their consequences—affectively, somatically, behaviorally, and interpersonally.

These capacities are first seen as the infant develops complex patterns of communication in the context of his or her primary human relationship. Parallel with development of the infant's relationship to the inanimate world in which basic schemes of causality (Piaget, 1962) are being developed, the infant becomes capable of complicated human emotional communication (Brazelton et al., 1974; Charlesworth, 1969; Stern, 1974a;

Tennes, Emde, Kisley, & Metcalf, 1972). There is both a historic and newly emerging consensus among clinicians, developmental observers, and researchers that affects are used for intentional communication (Bowlby, 1973; Brazelton & Cramer, 1990; Mahler et al., 1975; Osofsky & Eberhart-Wright, 1988; Spitz, 1965; Stern, 1985; Winnicott, 1965) and that these affective patterns, for example, for happiness, anger, fear, surprise, and disgust, are similar in different cultures and in both children and adults (Campos, Barrett, Lamb, Goldsmith, & Stenberg, 1983; Darwin, 1872; Ekman, 1972; Izard, 1971). Intentional communication, which involves both intuiting and responding to the caregiver's emotional cues, gradually takes on qualities that are particular to relationships, family, and culture (Brazelton et al., 1979; Bruner, 1982; Feinman & Lewis, 1983; Kaye, 1982; Kimmert, Campos, Sorce, Emde, & Svejda, 1983; Kleinman, 1986; Markus & Kitayama, 1990; Schweder, Mahapatra, & Miller, 1987; Stern, 1977; Trevarthen, 1979; Tronick, 1980).

Kopp (1987; 1989) further elaborates that during this time, the infant learns to modify actions in relation to events and object characteristics. According to Kopp, at approximately 9 months of age the infant shows intentionality in the context of an awareness of situations. For example, the baby learns to use verbal and contextual cues to distinguish between father putting on his coat to go to work or to take her for a stroller ride.

When there have been distortions in the emotional communication process, as occurs when a mother responds in a mechanical, remote manner or projects some of her own dependent feelings onto her infant, the infant may not learn to appreciate causal relationships between people at the level of compassionate and intimate feelings. This situation can occur, even though causality seems to be developing in terms of the inanimate world and the impersonal human world.

Sensory Organization

With the task during this stage to develop the capacity for cause-and-effect, or means-end type communications, we observe even more profoundly the differential use of the senses. Some babies do not possess the capacity to orchestrate their sensory experiences in an interactive cause-and-effect pattern. A look and a smile on mother's part does not lead to a consequential look, smile, vocalization, or gross motor movement on baby's part. This baby may perceive the sensory experiences mother is making available but seems unable to organize these experiences, and ei-

ther looks past mother or evidences random motor patterns. We also observe babies who can operate in a cause-and-effect manner in one sensory
pathway but not another. For example, when presented with an object,
they may clearly look at the object in a purposeful way and then examine
it. However, when presented with an interesting auditory stimulus, instead of responding vocally or reaching toward the person or the object,
the infant behaves chaotically with increased motor activity and discharge-
type behavior, such as banging and flailing. Similarly, with tactile experience, some babies, instead of touching mother's hand when she is stroking
their abdomen, begin evidencing random-seeming or chaotic motor responses that appear unrelated to the gentle stimulus. We observe even
more profoundly the differential use of the senses as infants are now also
learning to "process" information in each sensory mode and between
modes in terms of seeing relations between elements in a pattern. For example, some babies learn quickly and some slowly that a sound leads to a
sound or a look to a look. The implications for later learning problems of
certain sensory pathways not fully becoming incorporated into a cause-
and-effect level of behavioral organization are intriguing to consider (e.g.,
the differences between children with auditory-verbal abstracting and sequencing problems and those with visual-spatial problems). In organizing
cause-and-effect type communications, a compromise in a sensory pathway not only limits the strategies available for tackling this new challenge
but also may restrict the sensory modalities that become organized at this
new development level. Motor differences, such as high or low muscle
tone or lags in motor development or in motor planning, will also obviously influence the infant's ability to signal his wishes. In organizing
cause-and-effect type communications, therefore, a compromise in a sensory or motor pathway not only limits the strategies available for tackling
this new challenge, but also may restrict the sensory and motor modalities that become organized at this new developmental level and, as will be
discussed, the associated drive affect patterns as well.

As babies learn to orchestrate their senses in the context of cause-and-
effect type interactions, we observe an interesting clinical phenomenon—
in relationship to what has been described in the early neurological literature as "proximal" and "distal" modes. At this time, we may begin seeing
a shift toward distal rather than proximal modes of communication.
Proximal modes of communication may be thought of as direct physical
contact, such as holding, rocking, touching, and so forth. Distal modes
may be thought of as involving communication that occurs through

vision, auditory cueing, and affect signaling. The distal modes can obviously occur across space, whereas the proximal modes require, as the word implies, physical closeness. The crawling 8-month-old can remain in emotional communication with his primary caregiver through various reciprocal glances, vocalizations, and affect gestures. Some babies, however, seem to rely on proximal modes for a sense of security. Early limitations in negotiating space will be seen later on to affect the capacity to construct internal representations.

Thematic-Affective Organization

At this stage the full range of affective-thematic proclivities, evident in the attachment phase, become organized in the context of cause-and-effect (means-end) interchanges. The baby joyfully smiles or reaches out in response to a motor movement or affective signal, such as a funny look from the mother, in a reciprocal exchange.

If one divides the emotional terrain into its parts, one can see cause-and-effect signaling with the full range of emotions. In terms of dependency, the 8-month-old can make overtures to be cuddled or held. He shows pleasure with beatific smiles and love of touching (if he does not have a tactile sensitivity). There is also curiosity and assertiveness as the 8-month-old reaches for a rattle in mom's hand. There is also anger and protest as he throws his food on the floor in a deliberate, intentional manner and looks at his caregiver as if to say, "What are you gonna do now?" There is protest, even defiance (e.g., biting, banging, and sometimes butting, as an expression of anger because at 8 months children have better motor control of their mouths, heads, and necks than of their arms and hands).

Where the caregiver does not respond to the baby's signal, such as returning a smile or a glance, we have observed that the baby's affective-thematic inclinations may not evidence this differentiated organization. Instead he or she remain either synchronous, as in the attachment phase, or shift from synchrony to a more random quality. The expected range may be present but not subordinated into a cause-and-effect interchange.

There are also many babies who, because of a lack of reciprocal responses from their caregiver, seemingly evidence affective dampening or flatness and a hint of despondency or sadness. This may occur even after the baby has shown a joyfulness and an adaptive attachment. In some cases at least, it seems as though when not offered the phase-specific "experiential nutriments" (the cause-and-effect interactions he is now capable of), but only the earlier forms of relatedness, the baby begins a pattern of withdrawal and affective flattening. It is as though he needs to be met at his own level to maintain his affective-thematic range. Most interesting are the subtle cases where the baby can reciprocate certain affects and themes, such as pleasure and dependency, but not others, such as assertiveness, curiosity, and protest. Depending on the baby's own maturational tendencies and the specificity of the consequences in the caregiving environment, one can imagine how this uneven development occurs. For example, caregivers who are uncomfortable with dependency and closeness may not afford opportunities for purposeful reciprocal interactions in this domain but may, on the other hand, be quite "causal" in less intimate domains of assertion and protest.

The baby's own affective-thematic "sending power," and the degree of differential consequences he is able to elicit, may have important implications for how he differentiates his own internal affective-thematic life (as well as how he organizes these dimensions at the representational or symbolic level later on).

Clinical Features

During an interview, a child or adult demonstrates mastery of this stage by using purposeful gestures, such as facial expressions, motor gestures (showing you something), or vocalizations. Aimless behavior, misreading of the other person's cues, fragmented islands of purposeful interaction, together with aimless or self-absorbed behavior, indicate challenges at this level. In addition, the ability to be purposeful around some affects, but not others (i.e., around love, but not assertiveness), also indicates limitations.

Deficits, Distortions, and Constrictions

As indicated, early in this stage an infant seems capable of many human emotional expressions. What determines whether these affective inclinations develop and become differentiated from each other or remain undifferentiated, so that eventually pleasure, dependency, and aggression cannot be experienced as separate from one another? During the 4- to 8-month phase, the differential reciprocal signaling of the caregiver tells the child that pleasure is different from pain, that hunger for food is different from hunger to be picked up, that assertiveness is different from aggressiveness, and so forth. If each of the infant's feelings and expressions receives a different empathetic and overt response from the caregiver, the child experiences each of his own inclinations. Hilda Bruch (1973) anticipated what we now observe directly when she suggested that in some of the primary eating disturbances the dyadic signal system was not well formed because caregivers were rigid and unresponsive to the child's communications. For example, the child never learned to distinguish basic physical hunger from other sensations, such as dependency needs.

Therefore, during this stage, the affect system is differentiated to the degree to which the caregiving environment subtly reads the baby's emotional signals. Some infants do not experience reciprocity at all; others experience it selectively and have selective limitations. No family will be equally sensitive and responsive in all areas. Some families are conflicted around dependency, and others around aggression. Thus, there will be more anxiety in some areas than in others, and children will receive different feedback for different emotional areas. Although this is, in part, what makes people different, when a whole area like dependency, pleasure, or exploration does not receive reciprocal, purposeful cause-and-effect feedback, early presymbolic (prerepresentational) differentiations may be limited.

It is also useful to think of this stage of development as a first step in reality testing. At this time, prerepresentational causality is established. The child is learning that reaching out, smiling, vocalizing, pleasurable affect, and aggressive affect all have their consequences. Causality is the sense of one's own behavior and emotions as having consequences. Cause-and-effect experiences teach a child that the world is a purposeful place. When cause-and-effect behavioral patterns do not occur, the most fundamental aspect of the sense of causality may be compromised. Later in development, ideas or representations are also organized according to the cause-and-effect patterns. It may prove interesting to separate psychotic patients who have a failure of reality testing at the level of behavioral causality (4–8 months) from those who have a failure of reality testing at the later representational level (the 2 to 4-year level of representational causality). For example, some psychotic individuals tend to think and talk irrationally (they can be hallucinating, delusional, and have thought disorders), but they behave realistically. Other individuals talk in an organized way, but at the behavioral level, they seem to operate in an irrational way. It may prove useful, therefore, to consider two levels of reality testing and related disorders.

At the stage of somatopsychological differentiation, the fundamental deficit is in reality testing and basic causality. There are also subtle deficits, which may be part of a lack of differentiation along a particular emotional-thematic proclivity. In various character disturbances and borderline conditions, we observe patients who are undifferentiated when it comes to aggression but not dependency, or vice versa. Certain areas of internal life remain relatively undifferentiated; yet in other areas, differentiation and reality testing are progressing. This uneven pattern is part of many definitions of borderline syndromes.

A variety of symptoms may be seen in relationship to problems at this stage. They include developmental delays in sensorimotor functioning, apathy, intense chronic fear, clinging, lack of explorativeness and curiosity, lack of emotional reactions to significant caregivers, biting, chronic crying and irritability, and difficulties with sleeping and eating. Additional symptoms may be evident if, secondary to the lack of forming differentiated patterns, there are compromises in the infant-primary caregiver relationship (e.g., the infant becomes frustrated and irritable as his new capacities for contingent interactions are ignored or misread). If the basic comforting and soothing functions that support the baby's sense of security begin to falter, we may then see compromises in attachment and regulatory patterns leading to physiologic disorders and interferences in already achieved rhythms and cycles such as sleep and hunger. Where disorders of differentiation are severe and are not reversed during later development, they may set the foundation for later disorders. These disorders may include primary personality (ego) defects in reality testing, the organization and perception of communication and thought, the perception and regulation of affects, and the integration of affects, action, and thought.

Behavioral Organization, Problem-Solving, and Internalization (A Complex Sense Of Self): 9–18 Months

The next stage involves the child's capacity for engaging in a continuous flow of complex organized problem-solving interactions (e.g., taking mom to the refrigerator and pointing to the juice) and the formation of a presymbolic sense of self. With appropriate reading of cues and differential responses, the infant's or toddler's behavioral repertoire becomes complicated, and communications take on more organized, meaningful configurations. By 12 months of age, the infant is connecting behavioral units into larger organizations as he or she exhibits complex emotional responses such as affiliation, wariness, and fear (Ainsworth et al., 1974; Ainsworth et al., 1978; Bowlby, 1969; Sroufe et al., 1977). As the toddler approaches the second year of life, in the context of the practicing subphase of the development of individuation (Mahler et al., 1975), there is an increased capacity for forming original behavioral schemes (Piaget, 1962), imitative activity and intentionality, and behavior suggesting functional understanding of objects (Werner et al., 1963).

It is recognized that at this stage the infant takes a more active role in developing and maintaining the reciprocal relationship with his/her parent (Bell, 1977; Goldberg, 1977; Reingold, 1969). In addition, much has been written about the growing complexity of the reciprocal dyadic interaction (Cicchetti et al., 1984; Greenspan et al., 1984; Talberg, Couto, O'Donnell, & Cuoto Rosa, 1988; Tronick & Gianino, Jr., 1986). These types of complex interactions enable the child to utilize and respond to social cues and eventually achieve a sense of competence as an autonomous being in relationship with a significant other (Brazelton et al., 1979; Lester, Hoffman, & Brazelton, 1985).

There is now in evidence, therefore, a stage of behavioral organization or a complex sense of self as interactions become more complex and social patterns involve many circles of intentional communication that negotiate intimacy exploration, aggression, and limit setting, for example, using emotional signals to figure out if a behavior is acceptable or not (Dunn, 1988; Emde, Johnson, & Easterbrooks, 1988; Kagan, 1981; Radke-Yarrow, Zahn-Waxler, & Chapman, 1983; Zahn-Waxler & Radke-Yarrow, 1982).

Sensory Organization

This stage involves a baby's ability to sequence together many cause-and-effect units into a chain or an organized behavioral pattern (e.g., the 14-month-old who can take mother's hand, walk her to the refrigerator, bang on the door, and, when the door is opened, point to the desired food). Wish and intention are organized under a complex behavioral pattern. This organized behavioral pattern can be viewed as a task that involves coordinated and orchestrated use of the senses. Here the toddler who is capable of using vision and hearing to perceive various vocal and facial gestures, postural cues, and complex affect signals is able to extract relevant information from his objects and organize this information at new levels of cognitive and affective integration. A toddler who is not able to incorporate certain sensory experiences as part of his early cognitive and affective abstracting abilities (Werner et al., 1963) may evidence a very early restriction in how his senses process information.

Balanced reliance on proximal and distal modes of communication becomes even more important during this phase of development. The mobile toddler enjoying his freedom in space presumably can feel secure through his distal communication modes (e.g., looking and listening across space). It is interesting in this context to examine traditional notions of separation anxiety and the conflicts that some toddlers have over separation and individuation (Mahler et al., 1975). With the use of the distal modes, the toddler can "have his cake and eat it too." If he can bring the caregiving object with him through the use of distal contact with her, he does not have to tolerate a great deal of insecurity. He can "refuel" distally by looking at mother or listening to her voice and signal her back with vocalizations or arm gestures. He can use proximal contact, such as coming over for a cuddle when necessary. The youngster who has difficulty in using his distal modes to remain in contact with the primary caregiver may need more proximal contact. While this reliance on proximal contact can occur because of feelings of insecurity generated by an ambivalent primary caregiver, the limitations of a child's own sensory organization may also be an important factor in this pattern.

From a motor and sensory perspective, therefore, to master this stage, the toddler needs to be able to process sounds and sights, employ reciprocal motor gestures, and comprehend spatial relationships.

Thematic-Affective Organization

The piecing together of many smaller cause-and-effect units of experience involves a range of types of experience, such as pleasure, assertiveness, curiosity, and dependency, into an organized pattern. For instance, it is not unlikely for a healthy toddler to start with a dependent tone of cuddling and kissing his parents, shift to a pleasurable, giggly interchange with them, and then get off their laps and invite them to engage in an assertive chase game in which he runs to a room that is off-limits, such as the living room. When the parents say, "No, you can't go in there," protest and negativism may emerge. Under optimal circumstances, the interaction may come to a relative closure with the toddler back in the playroom, sitting on his parent's lap, pleasurably exploring pictures in his favorite book.

Here the child has gone full circle, suggesting that he has connected the many affective-thematic areas.

Around 18 months, as children begin to abstract the meaning of objects, their understanding of the functions of the telephone or brush may have its counterpart in their experiencing the caregiver as a "functional" being invested with many affective-thematic proclivities. Between 12 and 18 months, although children are able to integrate many behavioral units, they do not seem to be able to fully integrate intense emotions. For the moment at least, they do not fully realize that person they are mad at is the same person they love and experience pleasure with. By 18 to 24 months, the sense of split-off fury seems, at least in clinical observations, to be modified at some level by an awareness of love and dependency.

Clinical Features

This stage involves the many preverbal, behavioral interactions that begin in the second half of the first and beginning of the second year of life. Patterns that began with these early capacities can be seen in many behaviors in older children and adults, including simple gestural cues, involving eye contact, finger pointing, interjections or vocalizations, facial expressions, motor gestures, and different subtle affect expressions. The therapist should note whether the patient initiates such gestures and if she in turn responds to the clinician's countergesturing with a further gesture of her own.

The different emotions the patient reveals suggest the range and type of affect gestures they can communicate. The range and degrees of specific affects can be very broad. In the aggressive domain, for instance, there are gradations that run from assertive, competitive, and mildly aggressive behavior to explosive and uncontrolled rage. The same is true for the affectionate and caring domain, which ranges from promiscuous emotional hunger to mild affection, a sincere sense of warmth, compassion, and the other developmentally appropriate forms of caring. Affects can be combined with verbal themes showing a pattern during a session.

How does the person begin the session? What happens as he or she moves through the first third to the middle of the session, and then from the last third to saying good-bye? Follow the change in affect. For example, an individual may come in showing apprehension and tentativeness, become warm, and then competitive; show concern with issues of sibling or spousal jealousy and rivalry, and then express concern about separating from the therapist toward the end of the interview. Although several specific feelings have been elaborated in the above example, another patient may show only one or two affects during the entire interview.

The basic emotional messages of life—safety and security vs. danger, acceptance vs. rejection, approval vs. disapproval—can all be communicated through facial expressions, body posture, movement patterns, and vocal tones and rhythm. Words enhance these more basic communications, but most of us form quick, split-second judgments regarding a new person's dangerousness or approachability from his or her gestures before the conversation even gets started. In fact, if a person looks threatening and says, "You know, I'm your friend," we tend to believe the gestures and discount the words.

At a more subtle level, gestural communication also relays to us what aspects of our own emotions are being accepted, ignored, or rejected. The raised eyebrows and head nods we perceive quickly tell us whether the person hearing our message is reacting with excitement, anger, curiosity, or detachment. More importantly, our ever-emerging definition of the uniqueness of our very self is dependent on how others react to our own special tendencies with preverbal gestures. Differential responses stir different affects and are part of the process that refines and defines our maturing behavior and sense of self. How is our mischievous behavior and devilish grin responded to—with an accepting smile or a head-shaking frown? Our natural inclinations toward mischievousness, laziness, and a whole host of other personality traits are in part either accepted and supported, or refined or squelched, as a result of the impact of this nonverbal communication system. The nonverbal, gestural communication system is therefore a part of every dialogue contributing to our sense of who we are and what we perceive.

The clinician who only focuses on a person's words may miss an underlying, critical lack of organized gestural communication ability. For example, the "spacey" child who floats in and out of the room, or misreads the implied social rules of the playroom and hides toys, ignoring the therapist's facial expressions and sounds, and the adult who misreads the intentions of others, seeing, for example, assertiveness as anger or dependence as rejection, both betray an inability to fully process organized gestural communications.

As one observes gestures expressing a complex sense of self, one should take note not only of the range of affects but the richness and depth of affects observed. Are they superficial, as if the person is simply play-acting or imitating someone? Or do they convey a sense of personal depth? In other words, is one able to empathize with the way the patient is feeling?

As we have been describing, complex, self-defining gestures involving opening and closing many circles in a row (30 or 40) emerges in the second year of life and is seen thereafter in complex, nonverbal interactions, where patterns are communicated and comprehended.

Deficits, Distortions, and Constrictions

As the child moves closer to 18 months, the ability emerges to gradually relate to the world in a more functional way and to see objects according to their functional properties. Werner and Kaplan (1963) describe how babies can take a comb or toy telephone and use it purposefully. This is not yet imaginary play guided by mental representations or ideas; it is semirealistic play with an understanding of the functional use of the object. Children can also understand the emotional proclivities of their parents in a functional sense. They sense either nurturing, warm, supportive patterns or undermining, controlling, intrusive patterns. One little girl was able to see her mother as a teasing, envious person, although she did not understand what her mother was saying. She would pull away whenever her mother verbally teased her.

As indicated above, we have also observed that toddlers shift from an early stage (12–13 months), akin to ego splitting in adults, to a stage of greater integration of different self-object organizations by 18 to 19 months. When I am involved in therapeutic play with a 12- to 13-month-old and that child becomes angry, it feels as though if he had a gun at that moment he could shoot me. It feels much like it does with the adult patient who has a borderline personality or character structure. Connections between stages of childhood and adult pathology, however, are never so simple as a direct expression of a behavior or function from one age to another (it is more often an early capacity that is not established, or vulnerably established, that influences subsequent stages in terms of organization, flexibility, or context). For the early toddler, it appears that when you are the bad object, there is no simultaneous connection with you as the object of security and comfort. For that moment, you are all bad and your sense of the toddler's affect is one of rage. By the time a child is 18 months old, you may feel the toddler's anger, but you also sense that he sees you as an object of security, love, and dependency. You feel more like you would with a typical adult. There is anger, but the backdrop of security and relatedness is still there.

Thus, during the stage of behavioral organization, problem-solving, and internalization, we observe a progression from a type of ego splitting or part-object relatedness to a more cohesive sense of the functional, emotional proclivities of the object. Presumably, this integration is also occurring in the sense of self. Just as toddlers are sensing their parents as loving or undermining, or both, they are also abstracting their own patterns of feelings and behaviors. They no longer see themselves as islands of discrete behaviors or feelings, aggressive one moment and pleasurable the next. They are abstracting a pattern. These are higher-level abstractions of feelings and behaviors, but still at a prerepresentational level.

One way to think of the second year of life is as involving the development of a conceptual attitude toward the world. In the first year of life, what might be called a somatic attitude is in evidence because events are experienced somatically and physiologically and through sensorimotor and affect patterns.

As the toddler communicates more and more effectively by using gestures (e.g., facial expressions of affect—happy, sad, angry; motor movements—clenching fists, reaching out to be hugged; body postures—turning away or toward another person; vocal patterns—sound sequence, tone, rhythm, and so forth), gestural communication reaches a crescendo and creates a critical foundation for representational communication.

The importance of the gestural level of communication cannot be overestimated. Consider the critical information that is conveyed presymbolically; for example, safety vs. danger, acceptance vs. rejection, concern vs. indifference, respect vs. humiliation, support for a person's uniqueness vs. undermining and controlling patterns. The most basic emotional messages of life needed for survival (e.g., danger vs. safety) and for a sense of security (e.g., acceptance vs. rejection) are communicated presymbolically through the gestural system. In fact, we tend to trust this system more than the representational one. If someone says, "I am a nice person," but acts in a menacing fashion, we tend to trust what we perceive in terms of their gestures over the meaning of their words.

This gestural level, which we have in common with other members of the animal kingdom, is surprisingly well mastered by 18 to 24 months of age. Toddlers can make their own intentions known and are learning to comprehend the intentions of others.

When this system is not mastered and children progress to higher representational levels, they seem to try to use higher representational modes to master what for others have become automatic tasks. Rather than listening to the teacher's instructions on how to match the "ah" sound to the letter A, they might be working very hard to figure out what she intended with her stern look: "Is she dangerous?" "Will she hurt me?" Many adults with mental health problems evidence this same pattern of preoccupation with figuring out the basic intentions of others. A deficit in this system of gestural interaction is, therefore, a contributor to various types of psychopathology (Greenspan, 1997a).

The potential value of this line of thinking was highlighted recently when, while working with a group of children who had difficulties controlling their impulses, I noticed a subtle deficit in gestural communication. This was a group of bright, focused (not hyper) children who would suddenly poke another child or adult. Both these children and their parents showed very little affect variation in their facial expressions, looking like good poker players (poker-faced). Perhaps, the lack of gestural variation removes the early warning system, so to speak. Children don't learn to modulate their behavior because there is no graded gestural feedback, only all or nothing punishments, much like the all or nothing quality of their own behavior. Our gestures, in part, help us define our feelings (e.g., muscle tension and anger). Gestures also are a form of expression of feelings (it could be viewed as a very early form of sublimation as well as a safe form of affective discharge). The intricate posturing and signaling so characteristic of safe negotiations among both animals and people seemed to be missing in these families. We often expect to see impulsiveness in children who are distractible, overly active, and/or have information-processing problems. Perhaps they share a similar mechanism with the children described above. The "processing" problems of these children often make successful negotiation of the gestural level quite difficult. It was surprising to see "poker faces" in a group of maturationally advanced children and their families. For these children, it appeared that the lack of gestural communication was predominantly related to psychosocial issues and a failure of early learning.

There are many types of problems that stem from deficits or constrictions in the capacities ordinarily mastered during this stage. These include ego splitting, a lack of a cohesive sense of one's self, or a lack of an ability to abstract the range of emotional properties of self and others. These also include the tendency to remain concrete rather than to develop conceptual and, eventually, a representational self-object organization. Many adult patients, for example, talk of themselves in terms of discrete behavioral patterns (e.g., "I pushed her; she bit; I went out drinking"). Life is a series of interrelated but somewhat discrete behaviors. There is no sense of, "She is a frustrating person; therefore, I get upset," or "I go out drinking because I can't tolerate the pain and anguish of her frustrating me," or "She's a sweet person who loves me, but I get scared of the closeness, and therefore I can't handle it and I go out and drink."

In therapy, often one inadvertently supplies the missing piece. The patient says, "I hit her." We say, "You must have felt angry." In fact, the patient's problem is that he does not have the capacity for fully experiencing or labeling the affect states. He only feels the tendency to hit and not the feeling of anger in a gestural or representational mode. For many with severe character disorders and borderline conditions, life is a series of discrete behavior patterns. In normal development—as early as 18 to 19 months—a more conceptual attitude toward the world is developed. But many patients do not develop this capacity in the emotional spheres of their life. They possess it intellectually; they can do math and other abstract impersonal problems, but when it comes to emotions they are not able to operate at the 18- to 19-month level. Or they may operate at different developmental levels with different emotions, for example, pleasure and dependency at one level, assertion and anger at another (depending on their caregiving environment).

Therefore, two extremes were observed. At one extreme, the capacity for organizing behavior, emotions, and a conceptual stance toward the world is not formed at all. We see fragmented images of the self and the world. These individuals can relate to others, but they are at the mercy of moment-to-moment intentions or feelings. There is no integration of discrete experiences. It is not surprising that borderline patients have affect storms and keep shifting their behavioral and emotional inclinations. Their part-self and object images are not tied together; they have not made it to the 18-month level where they have a sense of themselves and their significant others as operating individuals. Their part-selves are fueled by unconnected drive-affect proclivities.

This is an especially interesting stage of development because most of the severe character and borderline conditions (which are probably the most frequent conditions we treat today) have important normative parallels in the second year of life.

We also see in the second year of life the emergence of an internal signaling system. Affect, as a signal, seems to develop both as part of a more general conceptual attitude toward the world and as an outgrowth of the gestural communications. By 18 to 19 months, we see a toddler who, when he does not get what he wants, is not necessarily driven to temper tantrums or other driven behavioral patterns. There is now a capacity to pause and make a judgment regarding what to do. The toddler can consider alternative behavioral patterns. Most 18- to 19-month-olds, for example, may pester mother, pull at her leg, and so forth, but with one look from mom they can go back to their play area and wait for a while longer. Or, a toddler will want to do something, and you will look at him and make the gesture, "No, no, no." He may stop in his tracks, challenge you, stop again, and so forth. The signal function of affects is in the process of being developed. To be sure, many toddlers may not use this new capacity at all or may not yet have it.

Nemiah (1977) has suggested that in certain psychosomatic conditions, and in many drug abuse and impulse disorders, there is the lack of a signal affect capacity. Hence, there is a lack of the transitional capacity to elevate dysphoric affect into a conceptual (i.e., a co-regulated, interactive) and, subsequently, representational, signal.

It is interesting to consider what helps the child develop a signal affect function. One component is the capacity to shift from proximal modes to distal modes of relating. An infant relates to the adult world relatively more with proximal modes, through being held and being touched, as distal modes are getting organized. These modes are proximal in the sense that the infant is using his skin, a sense of pressure, and so forth. By 4 to 8 months, one begins seeing the distal modes come into use more fully as vision and hearing are used in reciprocal signaling, and infants stay in touch by vision and hearing, as well as with direct touch. By 12 to 18 months, the toddler, although across the room, can stay connected to mother or father through these distal modes. Vocalizations, visual signals, and affect gestures (a grin or smile) are used to remain in emotional contact. The refueling that Mahler et al. (1975) discuss, therefore, as we discussed earlier, occurs not only through proximal modes (coming back and hugging mother), but also through distal modes. The youngster, while playing, looks, sees mother's alert attentiveness, and feels reassured. Studies on social referencing (Sorce & Emde, 1982) show that children are more exploratively confident when their mother is looking at them and taking an interest in their play, compared to when she is reading a newspaper in the same room. A child can explore, have the freedom of space, and still feel connected. Although the child, at this time, relates across space, he cannot yet relate across time. He does not possess the ideational or representational mode.

A child may not establish this distal communication capacity because a parent is overanxious, overprotective, or overly symbiotic. Or the child may not have optimal use of the distal modes because of a unique maturational pattern or processing problem. Consider, for example, the child who has an auditory processing problem; he may not be able to decode the emotional intent or tone of mother's "that's a good boy." Or he may have a visual-spatial processing limitation and have difficulty reading facial gestures or interpersonal distance. He may need to rely more on the proximal modes. He may have to be held to feel secure.

The use of distal modes may be an important key in the transition to the development of the ideational or representational mode. With the ideational or representational mode, one has mobility not only across space but also across time because one can create ideas (one can conjure up the object). As Mahler et al. (1975) suggests, one feels security through the fantasy of the object.

In adults, there is a balance between proximal modes (to be held and cuddled, in close tactile and physical contact with our loved ones) and distal modes (we enjoy warmth and security through the nodding and gesturing of a close friend in a good conversation, or even a new acquaintance at a cocktail party). Adults who cannot receive experience through the distal modes often feel deprived and isolated. They often resort to proximal modes. This makes adult life very difficult. As far as I know, this deficit has not been looked at as a significant part of borderline disturbances and severe character disorders in which there is an inordinate sense of isolation, emptiness, and loneliness. The transition to distal and then to ideational modes, therefore, creates flexibility. One can carry with one the love object, first over space and eventually over time. One sees a failure at this stage in deficits in the functional-conceptual self and object, and limitations in functional-conceptual self-object affective-thematic proclivities.

A special type of functional, conceptual self-object limitation at this age may be evidenced in the lack of an emerging sense of gender. Normally an abstracted sense of being more masculine or feminine appears to be emerging at this stage. A lack of abstracting a sexual gender sense, however, can be in evidence at this time in children who become fragmented with different sexually relevant body parts operating in isolation from an overall sense of gender (Greenspan, 1989).

In summary, a severe disorder at this phase affects the basic capacity for organizing behavior and affects. Most worrisome is the toddler who pulls away entirely from emotional relationships in the human world or remains fragmented as he develops his affective-thematic proclivities. A less severe disorder at this stage will be reflected in the narrowness of the child's range of experience organized, as seen in extreme character rigidities (e.g., the child who never asserts himself or is always negative, or has difficulties with affiliative behavior, or cannot use imitation in the service of temporary gratification and delay). As such children are tied to concrete and immediate states of need fulfillment, they may never form the intermediary warning and delay capacities that complex internal affects are used for. They often will tend to see people only as fulfilling their hunger for physical touch or candy, cake, or other concrete satisfactions.

Symptomatic problems at the stage of behavioral organization are chronic temper tantrums, inability to initiate even some self-control, lack of motor or emotional coordination, extreme chronic negativism, sleep disturbance, hyperirritability, withdrawal, delayed language development, and relationships characterized by chronic aggressive behavior. In addition, if basic attachments and comforting functions are secondarily disrupted, one may see attachment and regulatory or homeostatic disorders.

Representational Capacity: 18–30 Months

The next level involves the creation, elaboration, and sharing of symbols and meanings. The individual's ability to represent or symbolize experience is illustrated in the pretend play, the verbal labeling of feelings ("I feel happy"), and the functional use of language.

This level begins as the toddler approaches the end of the second year. Internal sensations and unstable images become organized as multisensory, affective images or representations that can be evoked and are somewhat stable (Bell, 1970; Fenson & Ramsay, 1980; Gouin-Decarie, 1965; Piaget, 1962). While this capacity is fragile between 16 and 24 months, it soon becomes a dominant mode in organizing the child's behavior.

Related to the ability to create representations is the capacity for "object permanence." This capacity, which is relative and goes through a series of stages, refers to the toddler's ability to search for hidden inanimate objects (Gouin-Decarie, 1965).

Infants progress from engaging in actions with themselves (e.g., feeding self) to using themselves as the agents to act upon others (e.g., toddler uses a doll to feed another doll). The development of language and the capacity to share meanings with others facilitates children's capacity to describe themselves and to understand the difference between themselves and others. This development of perspective coincides with the early stages of empathy and prosocial behavior (Butterworth, 1990; DesRosiers & Busch-Rossnagel, 1997; Meltzoff, 1990; Pipp-Siegel & Pressman, 1996; Stern, 1983).

The elaboration of ideas or representations gradually becomes more complex as does the sense of self, which now involves symbols, not just behaviors (e.g., use of words for intent and descriptions, use of personal pronouns, improved recognition of self in mirror; Fein & Apfel, 1979; Fenson, Kagan, Kearsely, & Zelazo, 1976; Inhelder, Lezine, Sinclair, & Stambak, 1972; Pipp, Fischer, & Jennings, 1987; Rubin, Fein, & Vandenberg, 1983). Pretend play and intentional interpersonal use of language illustrate these new capacities (Erikson, 1940; Fein, 1975; Kraus & Glucksberg, 1969; Lowe, 1975; Nelson, 1973; Peller, 1954; Waelder, 1933).

Over time, causal schemes are developed at a representational level (McCune-Nicholich, 1977; Sinclair, 1970), leading to thinking capacities. In addition, as ideas and behaviors are being elaborated, they reflect not only ongoing relationships, but prior negotiations as well. A large number of studies on early attachment patterns and later behavior illustrate the importance of early patterns as well as later relationships (Aber & Baker, 1990; Arend, Gove, & Sroufe, 1979; Cassidy, 1990; Cassidy & Marvin, 1988; Easterbrooks & Goldberg, 1990; Egeland et al., 1984; Goldberg & Easterbrooks, 1984; Main, Kaplan, & Cassidy, 1985; Marvin & Stewart, 1991; Maslin-Cole & Spieker, 1990; Matas, Arend, & Sroufe, 1978; Pastor, 1981; Sroufe, 1983; Sroufe, Fox, & Pancake, 1983; Waters, Wippman, & Sroufe, 1979). As children elaborate their ideas, they use them to make more sense of their experiences and themselves (Bretherton & Beeghly, 1982; Dore, 1989; Dunn, 1988; Dunn, Bretherton, & Munn, 1987; Nelson & Gruendel, 1981; Schank & Abelson, 1977).

Sensory Organization

A mental representation or idea is a multisensory image that involves the construction of objects from the perspective of all the objects' properties (including levels of meaning abstracted from experiences with the object).

Therefore, the range of senses and sensorimotor patterns the youngster employs in relationship to his objects is critical, for the object is at once an auditory, visual, tactile, olfactory, vestibular, proprioceptive object, and an object that is involved in various affective and social interchanges. Where the range, depth, and integration of sensory experiences are limited, the very construction of the object and representation will obviously be limited in either its sensory range and depth or affective investment and meaning. Therefore, in such a situation, important limitations in the child's early representational world may result.

Thematic-Affective Organization

As the child learns to construct his own multisensory, affective-thematic image of his experiential world, he organizes affective-thematic patterns at a level of meanings. This new level of organization can be thought of as operating in two ways. The youngster with a representational capacity now has the tool to interpret and label feelings rather than simply act them out. A verbal 2-year-old can evidence this interpretive process by saying "Me mad," or "Me happy." Pretend play is, perhaps, an even more reliable indicator than language of the child's ability to interpret and label. Pretend play is an especially important indicator because many children have language delays. For example, a child soon provides a picture of his representational world as he plays out dramas in different thematic realms, for example, dependency (two dolls feeding or hugging each other), etc.

The representational capacity also provides a higher-level organization with which to integrate affective-thematic domains. Therefore, we observe new experiences as the child develops from 2 to 5 years of age. These include empathy, more consistent love (including object constancy, a love for self and others that is stable over time and survives separations and affect storms such as anger; Mahler et al., 1975), and later on the ability to experience loss, sadness, and guilt.

Because of the complexities of representational elaboration, the conceptualization of this stage may be aided by subdividing the representational capacity into three levels or subcategories. The first level is the descriptive use of the representational mode (the child labels pictures and describes objects). The second level is the limited interactive use of the representational mode (the child elaborates one or two episodes of thematic-affective interactions, such as statements of "Give me candy," "Me hungry," or a play scene with two dolls feeding, fighting, or nuzzling). The third level is elaboration of representational, affective-thematic interactions.

Clinical Features

One can observe the representational capacity by engaging a child in pretend play and seeing if he can elaborate ideas, such as having the dolly eating or hugging. Often by the age of 2 or 3, the child sequences a number of representational units into a drama—the doll eats, goes to sleep, awakens, goes to school, spanks the teacher, comes home and has a tea party, becomes overexcited, is comforted by mommy, and then goes back to sleep. Initially, the elements in the complex drama may not be logically connected. Over time, along with representational differentiation (the next stage), the causal-logical infrastructure of the child's representational world emerges in his pretend play and use of language. Over time, the child's thematic elaboration can be observed to include a range of themes, including dependency, pleasure, assertiveness, curiosity, aggression, self-limit-setting, and eventually empathy and love.

This level in relating not only involves using representations or symbols in both play and verbal communication, but also sometimes is evidenced by the use of subtle spatial communications, such as building complicated towers or houses with passages in them. Older children and adults can sometimes use a picture to convey a feeling or complex meaning. Adults often use descriptions of visual imagery from dreams or free associations. One can obscure the depth and range of themes developed at the representational level. Are there only shallow, repetitive dramas or rich deep ones with a range of emotions?

Deficits, Distortions, and Constrictions

If, for any reason, the child is not getting practice through interactive pretend play and/or functional language use, we often see the beginnings of a deficit or constriction in representational capacity. Deficits or constrictions may occur because mother or father becomes anxious in using ideas in emotionally relevant contexts. For example, they may be afraid of emotional fantasy in general, or in specific thematic-affective areas such as separation or rejection, aggression, or assertiveness. Many adults are more frightened or conflicted by the representation of a theme such as sexuality or aggression than the behaving or acting out of the same theme.

Parental anxiety often leads to overcontrolling, undermining, hyperstimulating, withdrawn, or concrete behavioral patterns (i.e., let's not talk or play; I will feed you). In addition, because of unique constitutional-maturational patterns or early experiences, the child may become overly excited and thus afraid of his own use of ideas and new feelings (e.g., sexual themes in the play). As a result, he may regress to concrete prerepresentational patterns. If the parent cannot help the child return to the ideational level (i.e., the child is beating the ground and cannot reorganize and get back into the play), the child does not practice affective-thematic proclivities at the ideational level, and remains at the behavioral action pattern mode (acting out).

The ideational mode allows for trial action patterns in thought (to contemplate and choose among alternatives). One can reason with ideas better than with actual behaviors. Therefore, one has an enormous deficit if a sensation or series of sensations that are distinctly human do not have access to the ideational plane. Parents often ask about aggression ("Should I take away aggressive toys?"). If parents ignore elevating aggression to the representational plane, they are leaving aggression to the behavioral discharge mode. As children go from the conceptual mode to being able to label affects, they learn to talk about feelings. Adaptive 4-year-olds can label most of the basic feelings and begin to deal with them in their pretend play.

The capacity for mindsight or the ability to take another's perspective may be disturbed when there are problems in forming representation. Children with autism often evidence this challenge (Baron-Cohen, 1994). The child with autism often has problems at earlier levels that form a foundation for representing experience as well (e.g., the ability to imitate gestures, facial expressions, and vocalizations of others; Hobson, 1986; 1989). A deficit in connecting affect, gesture, and language (Harlow, 1953) may contribute to why autistic children struggle with developing representational and empathic responses, evidence deficits in organizing joint attention, and have difficulty in perceiving the emotional states of others (Atlas, 1986; Hoffman, 1998; Roth-Hanania, Busch-Rossnagel, & Higgins-D'Alessandro, 2000).

Using a chart review of 200 cases of children on the autism spectrum, Greenspan and Wieder (1997) documented differences in children with this disorder in the areas of sensory processing and reactivity, object use, and symbolic play capacities. Specific problems with play interactions included an absence of any play, odd use of toys, inability to generate symbolic play, and difficulties sequencing symbolic play actions.

In addition, children with parents who are overly intrusive may also have a diminished capacity to represent thought (Fonagy & Target, 1997). It has been suggested that the ability to form mindsight (e.g., representational thinking, theory of mind, social cognition) develops from an intact, neurologically sound person who experiences joint, collaborative, nonintrusive, and supportive attachments (Siegel, 2001).

In summary, disorders in this phase include children who remain concrete and never learn to use the representational mode and show impulsive or withdrawn behavior. They also include children who have developed a representational capacity in both the inanimate and animate spheres but show severe limitations or regressions with even minor stress in certain areas of human experience. For example, they may be able to use symbolic modes only around negativism, dominance, and aggression and consequently look solemn, stubborn, and angry, showing little range of representational elaboration in the pleasurable or intimate domain.

Representational Differentiation (Building Logical Bridges Between Ideas and Emotional Thinking): 30–48 Months

The next level involves creating logical bridges between ideas. Shared meanings are used both to elaborate wishes and feelings and to categorize meanings and solve problems. The child elaborates and eventually differentiates those feelings, thoughts, and events that emanate from within and those that emanate from others. The child begins to differentiate the actions of others from his or her own. This process gradually forms the basis for the differentiation of self-representations from representations of the external world, animate and inanimate. It also provides the basis for such crucial personality functions as knowing what is real from unreal, impulse and mood regulation, and the capacity to focus attention and concentrate in order to learn and interact.

As logical bridges between ideas are established, reasoning and appreciation of reality grow, including distinguishing what's pretend from what's believed to be real, dealing with conflicts and finding prosocial outcomes (Dunn & Kendrick, 1982; Flavell, Green, & Flavell, 1986; Harris, Brown, Marriott, Whittall, & Harmer, 1991; Harris & Kavanaugh, 1993; Wolf, Rygh, & Altshuler, 1984; Wooley & Wellman, 1990). As children become capable of emotional thinking, they begin to understand relationships between their own and others' experiences and feelings. They also illustrate these relationships in their narratives. Emotional thinking also enables children to begin to reason about right and wrong (Buchsbaum & Emde, 1990; Emde & Buchsbaum, 1990; Harris, 1989; Nelson, 1986; Smetana, 1985; Stewart & Marvin, 1984; Wolf, 1990). As children move into subsequent stages—for example, latency—and become more concerned with peers, they begin to appreciate emotional complexity such as mixed feelings (Donaldson & Westerman, 1986; Harter & Whitesell, 1989).

The capacity for differentiating internal representations becomes consolidated as object constancy is established (Mahler et al., 1975). As the child moves into the Oedipal stage, both reality and fantasy become more complex (Bruner, 1986, 1990; Dore, 1989; Fivush, 1991; Greenspan & Salmon, 1993; Singer & Singer, 1990). In middle childhood, representational capacity becomes reinforced with the child's ability to develop derivative representational systems tied to the original representation and to transform them in accordance with adaptive and defensive goals. This permits greater flexibility in dealing with perceptions, feelings, thoughts, and emerging ideals. Substages for these capacities include representational differentiation, the consolidation of representational capacity, and the capacity for forming limited derivative representational systems and multiple derivative representational systems (structural learning; Greenspan, 1979). Throughout these stages, but especially in the last three (the formation of complex behavior patterns and rituals, the elaboration of ideas, and in creating bridges between ideas), one observes cultural influences, for example, in the way girls and boys construct aspects of their inner worlds (Reiss, 1989). The now-well-known finding that in Western cultures men tend to be more assertive and competitive and women more caring and relationship-oriented (Gilligan, 1982) is evident during development with, for example, greater early signs of empathy in girls' and parents' inclinations to talk more to boys about anger and girls about sadness (Zahn-Waxler, Robinson, & Emde, 1992).

At the level of building bridges between ideas, the child can make connections between different ideas and feelings ("I am mad because you took my toy") and balance fantasy and reality. An adult using capacities begun during this stage can similarly hold logical conversations about wishes and feelings and make connections. ("I feel lonely and needy, and I get helpless when I feel that way. Sometimes I get mad because I can't stand being so vulnerable.")

Sensory Organization

For the child to meet the challenges of organizing and differentiating his internal world according to "self" and "other," "inside" and "outside," dimensions of time and space and affective valence, he is, in part, dependent on the integrity of the sensory organization that underlies his experiential world. Now, as earlier, the capacity to process sensory information is critical, including sequencing auditory-verbal and visual-spatial patterns according to physical, temporal, and spatial qualities in the context of abstracting emerging cognitive and affective meanings. The child is now challenged to understand what he hears, sees, touches, and feels, not only in terms of ideas, but in terms of what is me and not-me; what is past, present, and future; what is close and far; and so forth. These learning tasks depend on the ability to sequence and categorize information through each of the sensory systems and through all of them working together. Therefore, if anywhere along the pathway of sensory processing there are difficulties, the subsequent ability to organize impersonal or affective information will likely be compromised. For example, if sounds are confused, words will not be easily understood. Similarly, if spatial images are confused, spatial configurations will not be easily negotiated. If short-term memory for either verbal or spatial symbols is vulnerable, information will be lost before it can be combined with, and compared to, other information to abstract meanings. And if higher level auditory-verbal symbolic or visual-spatial symbolic abstracting capacities are less than age-appropriate, the very capacity to categorize experience will be limited. When one considers that the challenge is now to process and organize not only impersonal, cognitive experiences, but also highly emotional, interpersonal experiences (which keep moving, so to speak), this challenge to the sensory system is formidable. Furthermore, categories such as "me," "not me," "real," and "make-believe" are high-level constructs that depend on organizing sensory information.

Thematic-Affective Organization

The child appears to use his new representational capacity to simultaneously elaborate and differentiate experience, in contrast to earlier views by Freud (1900) and Mahler et al. (1975). There does not appear to be a period of magical representational thinking followed by one of reality thinking. The child continually differentiates affective-thematic organizations along lines that pertain to self and other, inner-outer, time, space, and so forth. This differentiation is based on the child's capacity to experience the representational consequences of his representational elaborations with the emotionally relevant people in his world, usually parents, family, and friends. The parent who interacts with the child using emotionally meaningful words and gestures, and engages in pretend play in a contingent manner (offering, in other words, logical representational feedback), provides the child with consequences that help him differentiate his representational world. In this view, reality testing—the capacity to separate magical from realistic thought—appears to be a gradual process beginning with the onset of the representational capacity proper and reaching some degree of selective stabilization prior to the child's formal entry into school.

One observes the child's elaborate representational themes along two dimensions. In the horizontal dimension, the child broadens the range of his or her themes to eventually include a range of emotional domains or drive-affect realms, including closeness or dependency, pleasure and excitement, assertiveness, curiosity, aggression, self-limit-setting, the beginnings of empathy, and consistent love. For example, not infrequently one observes repetitive pretend play of a feeding or hugging scene suggesting nurturance and dependency. Over time, however, the dramas the child may initiate (with parental interactive support) will expand to include scenes of separation (one doll going off on a trip and leaving the other behind), competition, assertiveness, aggression, injury, death, recovery (the doctor doll trying to fix the wounded soldier), and so forth. At the same time, the logical infrastructure of the child's pretend play and functional use of language becomes more complex and causally connected. The "he-man" doll is hurt by the "bad guys" and therefore "gets them." After the tea party, the little girl doll goes to the "potty" and then decides it is time to begin cooking dinner. In discussions, the 3-year-old sounds more and more like a lawyer with "buts" and "becauses"—"I don't like that food because it looks yucky and will make me sick." There is, therefore, both thematic elaboration and differentiation. Even though the themes may be pretend and phantasmagoric, the structure of the drama becomes more and more logical. The rocket ship to the land of "he-man" uses NASA rocket fuel.

As indicated, representational differentiation depends not only on a child being representationally engaged in thematic-affective areas but experiencing cause-and-effect feedback at the representational level. Parents have to be able not only to engage but also to interpret experiences correctly. The parents who react to play with a gun as aggression one day, as sexuality another day, and as dependency on a third day, or who keep shifting meanings within the same thematic play session, will confuse the child. This child may not develop meanings with a reality orientation. Parents who confuse their own feelings with the child's feelings, or cannot set limits, may also compromise the formation of a reality orientation.

Clinical Features

Shared differentiated meanings involve the communication of ideas to another person and building on the other person's responses. Some people only communicate their own ideas, never building on the responses of the other person. In both childhood dramas and adult conversations they talk, but do not easily absorb or reply to someone else's ideas and comments. For example, whenever a 4-year-old little girl came home from preschool, she played out scene after scene of being a princess, letting her mother hold her imaginary ermine robe, while her mother's casual questions, such as "What does the princess want me to do next?" and "Who did you play with today?" were ignored. Similarly, a 40-year-old businessman seen in therapy could elaborate at great length about how "No one satisfies me." He was unable to wrench his thoughts away from this theme and would obsessively return to it, regardless of the therapist's comments or questions. Without the ability to form bridges between various feelings states, including his own and someone else's, that patient was incapable of exploring a fuller range of feelings. Other individuals are just the opposite; diligently following instructions, listening to every word, but rarely elaborating their own feelings about events or their understanding of them.

Children operating at the level of creating logical bridges between different islands of symbolic or representational communication do not just negotiate via pretend dramas. They also begin to negotiate the terms of their relationship with the clinician in a more reality-based way. "Can I do this?" or "Can I do that?" the child may say. "What will you do if I kick the ball into the wall?" the child may further inquire. The child may also want to know if he and the clinician can play after the session is over because he enjoys the playroom so much (and seems to yearn for a little extra contact with other people). A child's negotiations about bringing parents into the playroom, wanting either to continue or end the session early, or curiosity about where the clinician lives and what his family is like, clearly indicate a use of symbols or words in a logical interactive way. These logical bridges between one thought and another suggest that this more advanced level of negotiating relationships has been mastered. The adult who shifts between free associations and logical reflection, or who wonders about how two feelings are connected, or who makes such connections, also reveals this level.

The stages of representational elaboration and differentiation can be observed and further assessed as one looks at the way in which individuals organize the content of their communications and deal with anxiety. First it is important to look at the overall organization in terms of the presence or absence of logical links connecting the thematic elements. A certain level of thinking can be expected with adults. With a child, however, the standards vary according to age, and the organization of themes must be weighed against the age-expectations.

Deficits, Distortions, and Constrictions

The child needs to learn how to shift gears between the make-believe and the real world. Ordinarily, we see this occur gradually between the ages of 2 and 4. As part of this process, we see more planning in children's play, as Piaget (1962) highlighted (e.g., going upstairs to get just the right cup for the tea party). What happens if there are failures of development during this stage? Earlier it was suggested that if representational elaboration is not occurring, the child is left with a pre-ideational or prerepresentational, somatic, and behavioral orientation. If there are limitations in representational differentiation (confused meanings), a child's self and object differentiation at the representational level may be compromised. It is interesting to consider those people who can engage others warmly (have mastered attachment) and organize their behavior, but who have irrational thoughts. They often cannot separate their own thoughts from someone else's. They may have organized delusions, but are extremely warm and can relate to others.

On the other hand, one may also see constrictions; that is, individuals who cannot represent or differentiate aggression or sexuality and are left only with the behavioral-action mode who are confused about their own and others' ideas or feelings in these thematic areas but not other thematic areas. Constrictions at this stage may be associated with relatively more differentiated and internalized conflicts (i.e., between opposing differentiated tendencies).

It is also interesting to discuss psychosexual trends at this stage. The phallic trend is clearly present beginning at ages 2 to 4. Kids love to build towers, pretend to be Superman, and undress to show off their bodies. One does not see an equal preoccupation with the anal concerns (eliminative or retentive patterns). Therefore, the anal body interest may not be elaborated as much in the representational sphere as is the phallic one (i.e., may be part of prerepresentational behaviors).

It may be useful to consider the oral, anal, and phallic stages of psychosexual inclinations in terms of observable thematic-affective inclinations. There may be a sensory, tactile, or oral mode early in life. In the second year of life, muscle control may predominate (better gross and fine motor coordination, including anal control by the end of the second year). Then, by 2 years, one sees the phallic inclinations as part of the ever-increasing body control and investment in the body and its parts (which begins at 17 to 18 months). The phallic inclinations become part of an emerging more differentiated sense of childhood sexuality as the interest in the genitals becomes integrated with the overall emerging sense of the body as part of an internal bodily representation. In summary, even though there is fascination with feces, I have not observed the representational derivatives of anal body interest in normal children to the same degree as phallic derivatives. On the other hand, where development is not progressing optimally, either exaggerated phallic trends or excessive anal preoccupation is not uncommon.

To return to the earlier discussion, inclinations that do not have access to the representational mode and its differentiation, even in mild degrees, are perhaps sowing the seeds for severe character pathology and/or neurotic conflicts. What is often referred to as magical thinking is more probable where representational elaboration and differentiation have not fully occurred. Later on, in the triangular, Oedipal, and latency phases of development, earlier patterns obviously are reenacted and reworked.

In summary, it is useful to clinically observe and assess the representational capacity along the two simultaneous dimensions of representational elaboration and representational differentiation. Clinically one observes defects and constrictions in both domains. These are evidenced by the child who

- remains concrete and never learns to use the representational mode to elaborate "inner sensations" to the level of meanings;
- is severely constricted and is only able to represent a few of the affective-thematic domains characteristic of human functioning;

- evidences the full range of representational affective-thematic life but remains undifferentiated along the dimensions of ideas or thoughts (thought disorder), affective proclivities (mood disturbances), self and object organizations (reality testing and "self" and 41 "other" boundary disturbances), intentionality (impulse disorders), and sense of time and space (disorders of learning, concentration, and planning);
- in order to differentiate a representational world, gives up or avoids certain affective-thematic realms, such as aggression or competition, because they are potentially disruptive (e.g., character disorders).

Contributing to these limitations is the caregiver who cannot engage representationally and logically in all domains because he or she is fearful of certain affective-thematic realms and therefore withdraws or becomes disorganized. The child's own limitations from earlier maturationally based processing problems and psychosexual difficulties also contribute to representational disorders.

Summary of Developmental Levels

The organizational levels described and discussed above are not difficult to observe in either children or adults, but are often taken for granted. When a child comes into the playroom ready to play or talk, there is often some rapport or emotional relatedness that soon develops between therapist and child. As soon as the therapist opens the door and the child makes eye contact with him or her, or perhaps follows a few facial or arm gestures, indicating where the toys are kept, we have an intentional, preverbal communication system going. Therapist and child are engaged and intentional with each other.

As the child begins complex play, staging mock battles with appropriate sound effects—or making noises and pointing to indicate "Get me that!"—more complex intentional communication is occurring. When the child puts feelings into words and elaborates pretend play themes, the level of shared meanings or representational elaboration is reached. The next level will be reached when the child not only elaborates themes, but constructs bridges between domains of experience: "I'm scared when I'm mad." The ability to categorize experience indicates emotional thinking (i.e., representational differentiation). A symbolic "me" and a symbolic "you" are now in evidence: "I always get so scared of everything." Most importantly, the capacity for categorizing experience helps an individual elaborate feelings and build on another's communications. The individual can have a logical two-way dialogue and tell the difference between fantasy and reality.

Individuals may have clear compromises in their attainment of these organizational levels, such as the adult who comes in to therapy and can only partially engage. When anxious or frightened, this person typically disengages and becomes aloof or withdrawn. Not infrequently, he also gets disorganized and cannot even gesture purposefully and intentionally. His gestures and speech both become disjointed. His capacity for representational elaboration is limited to either disorganized emotional communications or organized descriptions of impersonal events. There is little capacity for balancing subjective elaborations and an appreciation of reality. The person then uses words in a fragmented way, tends to be concrete and impersonal in his descriptions of the world, gesturally signals in a disorganized and chaotic way, and, while capable of engaging with others, easily disengages and becomes aloof.

As the clinician looks at the tendency to use verbal descriptions of behavior and organize these descriptions rather than put them into acting out behaviors,[1] he further looks to see if the person can represent global, somatically based affects; simple, general affects; polarized affect states; or more differentiated, abstracted affects (i.e., specific feelings). He also looks for the ability to make connections between different affective domains and categories of feelings and behaviors, and the ability for self-observation and reasoning about one's emotional inclinations and tendencies. One can further look at this last category in terms of the ability to observe oneself and reason in different dimensions: in the here-and-now, which is the easiest in a historical sense, to anticipate the future, to do all the above as part of an active exploration, and, obviously, finally to integrate them.

Also, as a person is involved in more differentiated self-observing capacities, he or she can apply this to different types of relationship patterns. Therefore, in terms of comprehending relationships, various levels of representational differentiation can also be noticed. An early level has to do

---

[1] The acting out behaviors are usually characteristic of the person who hasn't yet mastered the complex interchange of behavioral intentions and expectations and who is somewhat arrested between the simple gestural and complex gestural stages.

with being able to explore feelings that occur in dyadic relationship patterns, a later one has to do with triangular relationship patterns. A still later level involves group patterns that have many different dyads and triads as well as the relationship between all the members of the group and the group as a whole. Finally, signposts of higher levels of organization can be seen in the ability to move into explorations of feelings having to do with stable internal values and principles, and being able to look at an emerging sense of self against these aspirations and principles.

(See the following tables for an overview of this developmental framework. Also see chapters 8 and 9 for further discussion of these issues.)

Table 1-1.
Developmental-Structural Delineation of Stage-Specific Capacities[2]

Stage	Illustrative Adaptive Capacities	Illustrative Maladaptive (Pathologic) Capacities	Adaptive Caregiver	Maladaptive Caregiver
Self-regulation and interest in the world (homeostasis): 0–3 months	Internal regulation (harmony) and balanced interest in the world	Unregulated (e.g., hyperexcitable) or withdrawn (apathetic) behavior	Invested, dedicated, protective, comforting, predictable, engaging, and interesting	Unavailable, chaotic, dangerous, abusive; hypo- or hyperstimulating; dull
Forming relationships, attachment, and engagement: 2–7 months	Rich, deep, multisensory emotional investment in animate world (especially with primary caregivers)	Total lack of or nonaffective, shallow, impersonal involvement (e.g., autistic patterns) in animate world	In love and woos infant to "fall in love"; effective, multimodality, pleasurable involvement	Emotionally distant, aloof, and/or impersonal (highly ambivalent
Two-way purposeful communication (Somatopsychological differentiation): 3–10 months	Flexible, wide-ranging, affective, multisystem contingent (reciprocal) interactions (especially with primary caregivers)	Behavior and affects random and/or chaotic or narrow, rigid, and stereotyped	Reads and responds contingently to infant's communications with a range of senses and affects	Ignores or misreads (e.g., projects) infant's communications (e.g., is overly intrusive, preoccupied, or depressed)
Behavioral organization, problem-solving, and internalization (a complex sense of self): 9–18 months	Complex, organized, assertive, innovative, integrated behavioral and emotional patterns	Fragmented, stereotyped, and polarized behavior and emotions (e.g., withdrawn, compliant, hyperaggressive, or disorganized behavior)	Admiring of toddler's initiative and autonomy, yet available, tolerant, and firm; follows toddler's lead and helps him organize diverse behavioral and affective elements	Overly intrusive, controlling; fragmented, fearful (especially of toddler's autonomy); abruptly and prematurely "separates"
Representational elaboration and differentiation: 18–48 months	Formation and elaboration of internal representations (imagery); organization and differentiation of imagery pertaining to self and nonself, emergence of cognitive insight; stabilization of mood and gradual emergence of basic personality functions	No representational (symbolic) elaboration; behavior and affect concrete, shallow, and polarized; sense of self and "other" fragmented, undifferentiated, or narrow and rigid; reality testing, impulse regulation, mood stabilization compromised or vulnerable (e.g., borderline psychotic and severe character problems).	Emotionally available to phase-appropriate regressions and dependency needs; reads, responds to, and encourages symbolic elaboration across emotional and behavioral domains (e.g., love, pleasure, assertion) while fostering gradual reality orientation and internalization of limits.	Fears or denies phase-appropriate needs; engages child only in concrete (nonsymbolic) modes generally or in certain realms (e.g., around pleasure) and/or misreads or responds uncontingently or unrealistically to emerging communications (i.e., undermines reality orientation) overly permissive or punitive

Source: Greenspan (1981), Psychopathology and Adaptation in Infancy and Early Childhood: Principles of Clinical Diagnosis and Preventive Intervention. *Clinical Infant Reports,* No. 1. New York: International Universities Press

[2]This chart is an illustrative summary and should not imply a level of precision or finality to this conceptualization beyond a relative approximation of important events in early development

Table 1-2.
Overview of Functional Emotional Developmental Levels with Descriptions of Different Degrees of Maladaptive and Adaptive Patterns

Self-Regulation and Interest in the World (Homeostasis)
0–3 Months

Maladaptive ⟶ Adaptive

Attention is fleeting (a few seconds here or there) and/or very active or agitated or mostly self-absorbed and/or lethargic or passive	When very interested or motivated or captivated can attend and be calm for short periods (e.g., 30 to 60 seconds).	Focused, organized, and calm except when over-stimulated or understimu-lated (e.g., noisy, active, or very dull setting); challenged to use a vulnerable skill (e.g., a child with weak fine motor skills asked to write rapidly), or ill, anxious, or under stress.	Focused, organized, and calm most of the time, even under stress.

Forming Relationships, Attachment, and Engagement
2–7 Months

Maladaptive ⟶ Adaptive

Aloof, withdrawn, and/or indifferent to others	Superficial and need-oriented, lacking intimacy.	Intimacy and caring is present but disrupted by strong emotions, like anger or separation (e.g., person withdraws or acts out).	Deep, emotionally rich capacity for intimacy, caring, and empathy, even when feelings are strong or under stress.

Two-Way Purposeful Communication (Somatopsychological Differentiation)
3–10 Months

Maladaptive ⟶ Adaptive

Mostly aimless, frag-mented, unpurposeful behavior and emotional expressions (e.g., no purposeful grins or smiles or reaching out with body posture for warmth or closeness).	Some need-oriented, purposeful islands of behavior and emotional expressions. No cohesive larger social goals.	Often purposeful and or-ganized, but not with a full range of emotional expressions (e.g., seeks out others for closeness and warmth with appropriate flirtatious glances, body posture, and the like, but becomes chaotic, frag-mented or aimless when very angry).	Most of the time purposeful and organized behavior and a wide range of subtle emotions, even when there are strong feelings and stress.

Behavioral Organization, Problem-Solving, and Internalization (Complex Sense of Self)
9–18 Months

Maladaptive ⟶ Adaptive

Distorts the intents of others (e.g., misreads cues and, therefore, feels suspicious, mis-treated, unloved, angry, etc.)	In selected relation-ships can read basic in-tentions of others (such as acceptance or rejection) but unable to read subtle cues (like respect or pride or partial anger).	Often accurately reads and responds to a range of emotional signals, ex-cept in certain circum-stances involving selected emotions, very strong emotions, or stress or due to a difficulty with pro-cessing sensations, such as sights or sounds, e.g., cer-tain signals are confusing.	Reads and responds to most emotional signals flexibly and accurately even when under stress (e.g., comprehends safety vs. danger, ap-proval vs. disapproval, acceptance vs. rejec-tion, respect vs. humili-ation, partial anger, etc.).

Table 1-2. *Continued*

Representational Elaboration and Differentiation
18–48 Months

Maladaptive ———————————————————————————▶ Adaptive

Puts wishes and feelings into action or into somatic states ("My tummy hurts"). Unable to use ideas to elaborate wishes and feelings (e.g., hits when mad, hugs or demands physical intimacy when needy, rather than experiencing idea of anger or expressing wish for closeness). Ideas are experienced in a piecemeal or fragmented manner (e.g., one phrase is followed by another with no logical bridges).	Uses ideas in a concrete way to convey desire for action or to get basic needs met Does not elaborate idea of feeling in its own right (e.g., "I want to hit but can't because someone is watching" rather than "I feel mad"). Thinking is polarized, ideas are used in an all-or-nothing manner (e.g., things are all good or all bad. There are no shades of gray).	Often uses ideas to be imaginative and creative and express range of emotions, except when experiencing selected conflicted or difficult emotions or when under stress (e.g., cannot put anger into words or pretend). Thinking is constricted (i.e., tends to focus mostly on certain themes like anger and competition). Often thinking is logical, but strong emotions, selected emotions, or stress can lead to polarized or fragmented thinking.	Uses ideas to express full range of emotions. Is imaginative and creative most of the time, even under stress. Thinking is logical, abstract, and flexible across the full range of age-expected emotions and interactions. Thinking is also relatively reflective at age-expected levels and in relationship to age-expected endeavors (e.g., peer, spouse, or family relationship). Thinking supports movement into the next stages in the course of life.

Additional Functional Developmental Stages
Throughout the life cycle, these stages build on emotional thinking

- *Triangular Thinking*—Triadic interactions among feeling states ("I feel left out when Susie likes Janet better than me").
- *Relativistic Thinking (Playground Politics)*—Shades and gradations among differentiated feeling states (ability to describe degrees of feelings around anger, love, excitement, love, disappointment—"I feel a little annoyed.")
- *Internalized sense of self (the world inside me)*—Reflecting on feelings in relationship to an internalized sense of self. ("It's not like me to feel so angry." Or "I shouldn't feel this jealous.")
- *Extending representational capacity to new realms of biological, psychological, and social experience*—Expanding reflective feeling descriptors into new realms, including sexuality, romance, closer and more intimate peer relationships, school, community, and culture, and emerging sense of identity ("I have such an intense crush on that new boy that I know it's silly; I don't even know him.").
- *Extending representational capacities in time and space*—Using feelings to anticipate and judge future possibilities in light of current and past experience ("I don't think I would be able to really fall in love with him because he likes to flirt with everyone and that has always made me feel neglected and sad.") Broadening reflective capacities to include the larger community and culture.
- *Extending representational capacities into the stages of adulthood, middle age, and the aging process*—Expanding feeling states to include reflections and anticipatory judgment with regard to new levels and types of feelings associated with the stages of adulthood, including
    ability to function independently from, and yet remain close to, and internalize many of the capacities initially provided by one's nuclear family
        inner sense of security
        judgment and self-monitoring of behavior and impulses
        regulation of mood
        reality-based, organized thinking;
    intimacy (serious long-term relationships);
    the ability to nurture and empathize with one's children without over-identifying with them;
    the ability to broaden one's nurturing and empathetic capacities beyond one's family and into the larger community;
    the ability to experience and reflect on the new feelings of intimacy, mastery, pride, competition, disappointment, and loss associated with the family, career, and intra-personal changes of mid-life and the aging process.

References

Aber, J. & Baker, A. J. (1990). Security of attachment in toddlerhood: Modifying assessment procedures for joint clinical and research purposes. In M. T. Greenberg, D. Cicchetti, & E. M. Cummings (Eds.), *Attachment in the Preschool Years* (pp. 427–463). Chicago: University of Chicago Press.

Ainsworth, M., Bell, S. M., & Stayton, D. (1974). Infant-mother attachment and social development: Socialization as a product of reciprocal responsiveness to signals. In M. Richards (Ed.), *The Integration of the Child into a Social World* (pp. 99–135). Cambridge, England: Cambridge University Press.

Ainsworth, M., Blehar, M., Waters, E., & Wall, S. (1978). *Patterns of attachment: A psychological study of the strange situation.* New York: Lawrence Erlbaum Associates.

Als, H. (1981). Infant individuality: Assessing patterns of very early development. In J. D. Call, E. Galenson, & R. Tyson (Eds.), *Frontiers of Infant Psychiatry* (pp. 363–378). New York: Basic Books.

Als, H. (1982). Patterns of infant behavior: Analogs of later organizational difficulties? In F. H. Duffy & N. Geschwind (Eds.), *Dyslexia: A neuroscientific approach to clinical evaluation* (pp. 67–92). Boston: Little, Brown, & Co.

Als, H., Lester, B. M., Tronick, E., & Brazelton, T. B. (1982). Towards a research instrument for the assessment of preterm infants' behavior (APIB). In H. Fitzgerald & M. W. Yogman (Eds.), *Theory and Research in Behavioral Pediatrics* (pp. 35–132). New York: Plenum Press.

Arend, R., Gove, F. L., & Sroufe, L. A. (1979). Continuity of individual adaptation from infancy to kindergarten: a predictive study of ego-resiliency and curiosity in preschoolers. *Child Dev., 50,* 950–959.

Atlas, J. A. (1986). Self-other differentiation in the psychoses. *New Ideas in Psychology, 3,* 17–82.

Ayers, A. J. (1964). Tactile functions: Their relation to hyperactive and perceptual motor behavior. *The American Journal of Occupational Therapy, 18,* 6–11.

Bakwin, H. (1942). Loneliness in infants. *Amer.J.Dis.Child., 63,* 30–42.

Baron-Cohen, S. (1994). *Mindblindness: An essay on autism and theories of mind.* Cambridge, MA: MIT Press.

Bates, J. E., Maslin, L. A., & Frankel, K. A. (1985). Attachment, security, mother-child interaction, and temperament as predictors of problem behavior ratings at age 3 years. *Monographs of the Society for Research in Child Development,* 50 (1–2, Serial No. 209).

Bell, R. (1977). Socialization findings re-examined. In R. Bell & L. Harper (Eds.), *Child Effects on Adults.* New York: John Wiley & Sons.

Bell, S. M. (1970). The development of the concept of the object as related to infant-mother attachment. *Child Development, 41,* 219–311.

Belsky, J., Rovine, M., & Taylor, D. G. (1984). The Pennsylvania Infant and Family Development Project, III: The origins of individual differences in infant-mother attachment: Maternal and infant contributions. *Child Dev., 55,* 718–728.

Bemesderfer, S. & Cohler, B. (1983). Depressive reactions during separation period: Individuation and self among children of psychotic, depressed mothers. In H. L. Morrison (Ed.), *Children of Depressed Parents: Risk, Identification, and Intervention* (pp. 159–188). New York: Grune & Stratton.

Bergman, P. & Escalona, S. (1949). Unusual sensitivities in very young children. *The Psychoanalytic Study of the Child, 3–4,* 333.

Berlyne, D. E. (1960). *Conflict, arousal, and curiosity.* New York: McGraw Hill.

Bowlby, J. (1958). The nature of the child's tie to its mother. *International Journal of Psychoanalysis, 39,* 350–373.

Bowlby, J. (1951). Maternal care and mental health. Geneva, World Health Organization. *WHO Monograph, 51.*

Bowlby, J. (1969). *Attachment and Loss (Vol. 1).* London: Hogarth Press.

Bowlby, J. (1973). *Attachment and Loss.* (Vol. 2) New York: Basic Books.

Brazelton, T. B. & Als, H. (1979). Four early stages in the development of mother-infant interaction. *The Psychoanalytic Study of the Child, 34,* 349–369.

Brazelton, T. B. & Cramer, B. (1990). *The earliest relationship: Parents, infants, and the drama of early attachment.* Reading, MA: Addison-Wesley Publishing Co.

Brazelton, T. B., Koslowski, B., & Main, M. (1974). The origins of reciprocity; the early mother-infant interaction. In M. Lewis & L. Rosenblum (Eds.), *The effect of the infant on its caregiver.* New York: John Wiley & Sons.

Bretherton, I. & Beeghly, M. (1982). Talking about inner states: The acquisition of an explicit theory of mind. *Developmental Psychology, 18,* 906–921.

Bretherton, I. & Waters, E. (1985). Growing pains of attachment theory and research. *Monographs of the Society for Research in Child Development, 50* (1–2, Serial No. 209).

Bruch, H. (1973). *Eating disorders: Obesity, anorexia nervosa, and the person within.* New York: Basic Books.

Bruner, J. S. (1982). *Child's talk: Learning to use language.* New York: Norton.

Bruner, J. S. (1986). *Actual minds, possible worlds.* Cambridge, MA: Harvard University Press.

Bruner, J. S. (1990). *Acts of meaning.* Cambridge, MA: Harvard University Press.

Buchsbaum, H. K. & Emde, R. N. (1990). Play narratives in 36-month-old children. Early moral development and family relationships. *Psychoanal.Study Child, 45,* 129–155.

Burlingham, D. & Freud, A. (1942). *Young children in wartime; a year's work in a residential war nursery.* London: Allen & Unwin.

Butterworth, G. (1990). Self-perception in infancy. In D. Cicchetti & M. Beeghly (Eds.), *The Self in Transition: Infancy to Childhood.* Chicago: Chicago University Press.

Cameron, H. S. (1919). *The nervous child.* London: Oxford Medical Publications.

Campos, J., Barrett, K., Lamb, M. E., Goldsmith, H. H., & Stenberg, C. (1983). Socioemotional development. In M. M. Haith & J. Campos (Eds.), *Handbook of child psychology, Vol. II.* New York: John Wiley & Sons.

Campos, J., Campos, R., & Barrett, K. (1989). Emergent themes in the study of emotional development and emotion regulation. *Developmental Psychology, 25,* 394–402.

Carew, J. V. (1980). Experience and the development of intelligence in young children at home and in day care. *Monographs of the Society for Research in Child Development, 45* (6–7), 1–115.

Carlson, E. A. (1998). A prospective longitudinal study of attachment disorganization/disorientation. *Child Dev., 69,* 1107–1128.

Cassidy, J. (1990). Theoretical and methodological considerations in the study of attachment and self in young children. In M. T. Greenberg & D. Cicchetti (Eds.), *Attachment in the Preschool Years* (pp. 87–120). Chicago: Chicago University Press.

Cassidy, J. & Marvin, R. (1988). with the Attachment Working Group of the John D. and Catherine T. MacArthur Network on the Transition from Infancy to Early Childhood. A system for coding the organization of attachment behavior in 3 or 4 year old children. Paper presented at the International Conference on Infant Studies. Washington, DC.

Cassidy, J. & Shaver, P. R. (1999). *Handbook of attachment.* New York: Guilford Press.

Charlesworth, W. R. (1969). The role of surprise in cognitive development. In D. Elkind & J. H. Flavell (Eds.), *Studies in Cognitive Development: Essays* (pp. 257–314). London: Oxford University Press.

Cicchetti, D. & Aber, J. (1986). Early precursors of later depression: An organizational perspective. *Advances in Infancy Research, 4,* 87–137.

Cicchetti, D. & Schneider-Rosen, K. (1984). Toward a transactional model of childhood depression. *New Directions for Child Development, 26,* 5–27.

Cravioto, J. & Delicardie, E. (1973). Environmental correlates of severe clinical malnutrition and language development survivors from kwashiorkor or marasmus. [PAHO Scientific Publication No. 251]. Washington, DC.

Darwin, C. (1872). *The expression of emotions in man and animals.* London: Murray (Republished by University of Chicago Press, 1965).

Davenport, Y. B., Zahn-Waxler, C., Adland, M. L., & Mayfield, A. (1984). Early child-rearing practices in families with a manic-depressive parent. *Am.J.Psychiatry, 141,* 230–235.

De Wolff, M. S. & van Ijzendoorn, M. H. (1997). Sensitivity and attachment: a meta-analysis on parental antecedents of infant attachment. *Child Dev., 68,* 571–591.

Deci, E. (1977). *Intrinsic motivation.* New York: Plenum.

Del Carmen, R. & Huffman, L. (1996). Epilogue: Bridging the gap between research on attachment and psychopathology. *J.Consult Clin.Psychol., 64,* 291–294.

DesRosiers, F. S. & Busch-Rossnagel, N. A. (1997). Self-concept in toddlers. *Infants and Young Children, 10,* 15–26.

Digdon, N. & Gotlib, I. (1985). Developmental considerations in the study of childhood depression. *Developmental Review, 5,* 162–199.

Donaldson, S. & Westerman, M. (1986). Development of children's understanding of ambivalence and causal theories of emotions. *Developmental Psychology, 22,* 655–662.

Dore, J. (1989). Monologue as reenvoicement of dialogue. In K. Nelson (Ed.), *Narratives from the crib* (pp. 27–73). Cambridge, MA: Harvard University Press.

Dunn, J. (1988). *The beginnings of social understanding.* Cambridge, MA: Harvard University Press.

Dunn, J., Bretherton, I., & Munn, P. (1987). Conversations about feeling states between mothers and their young children. In I. Bretherton (Ed.), *Symbolic Play: The Development of Social Understanding.* New York: Academic Press.

Dunn, J. & Kendrick, C. (1982). *Siblings.* Cambridge, MA: Harvard University Press.

Easterbrooks, M. A. & Goldberg, W. A. (1990). Security of toddler-parent attachment: Relation to children's sociopersonality functioning during kindergarten. In M. T. Greenberg, D. Cicchetti, & E. M. Cummings (Eds.), *Attachment in the Preschool Years* (pp. 221–245). Chicago: University of Chicago Press.

Egeland, B. & Farber, E. A. (1984). Infant-mother attachment: Factors related to its development and changes over time. *Child Dev., 55,* 753–771.

Egeland, B. & Kreutzer, T. (1991). A longitudinal study of the effects of maternal stress and protective factors on the development of high risk children. In A. L. Green, E. M. Cummings, & K. H. Karraker (Eds.), *Life-span developmental psychology: Perspectives on stress and coping* (pp. 61–84). Hillsdale, NJ: Lawrence Erlbaum Associates.

Egeland, B. & Sroufe, L. A. (1981). Attachment and early maltreatment. *Child Dev., 52,* 44–52.

Ekman, P. (1972). Universals and cultural differences in facial expressions of emotion. Paper presented at the Nebraska Symposium on Motivation. Lincoln: University of Nebraska Press.

Emde, R. N. & Buchsbaum, H. K. (1990). "Didn't you hear my mommy?": Autonomy with connectedness in moral self-emergence. In D. Cicchetti & M. Beeghly (Eds.), *The Self in Transition: Infancy to Childhood* (pp. 35–60). Chicago: University of Chicago Press.

Emde, R. N., Gaensbauer, T. J., & Harmon, R. J. (1976). Emotional expression in infancy: A biobehavioral study. *Psychological Issues Monograph No. 37.* New York, International Universities Press.

Emde, R. N., Johnson, W. F., & Easterbrooks, M. A. (1988). The do's and don'ts of early moral development: Psychoanalytic tradition and current research. In J. Kagan & S. Lamb (Eds.), *The Emergence of Morality* (pp. 245-277). Chicago: University of Chicago Press.

Erikson, E. (1959). *Identity and the life cycle; selected papers, with a historical introduction by David Rapaport.* New York: International Universities Press.

Erikson, E. H. (1940). Studies in interpretation of play: I. Clinical observation of child disruption in young children. *Genetic Psychology* (Monograph 22).

Erikson, M., Egeland, B., & Sroufe, L. The relationship between quality of attachment and behavior problems in preschool. *Monographs of the Society for Research in Child Development, 50* (1–2, Serial No. 209).

Escalona, S. (1968). *The roots of individuality.* Chicago: Aldine.

Fein, G. G. (1975). A transformational analysis of pretending. *Developmental Psychology, 11,* 291–296.

Fein, G. G. & Apfel, N. (1979). Some preliminary observations on knowing and pretending. In N. Smith & M. Franklin (Eds.), *Symbolic Functioning in Childhood.* Hillsdale, NJ: Lawrence Erlbaum Associates.

Feinman, S. & Lewis, M. (1983). Social referencing at ten months: A second-order effect on infants' responses to strangers. *Child Dev., 54,* 878–887.

Feldman, R., Greenbaum, C. W., & Yirmiya, N. (1999). Mother-infant affect synchrony as an antecedent of the emergence of self-control. *Dev. Psychol., 35,* 223–231.

Fenson, L., Kagan, J., Kearsely, R. B., & Zelazo, P. R. (1976). The developmental progression of manipulative play in the first two years. *Child Development, 47,* 232–235.

Fenson, L. & Ramsay, D. (1980). Decentration and integration of play in the second year of life. *Child Development, 51,* 171–178.

Field, T. (1977). Effects of early separation, interactive deficits, and experimental manipulation on infant-mother face-to-face interaction. *Child Dev., 48,* 763–771.

Field, T. (1980). Interactions of high risk infants: Quantitative and qualitative differences. In D. Sawin, R. Hawkins, I. Walker, & J. Penticuff (Eds.), *Current Perspectives on Psychosocial Risks During Pregnancy.* New York: Brunner/Mazel.

Field, T. (1981). Gaze behavior of normal and high-risk infants and during early interactions. *J. Am. Acad. Child Psychiatry, 20(2);* 308–317.

Fivush, R. (1991). Gender and emotion in mother-child conversations about the past. *Journal of Narrative and Life History, 1,* 325–341.

Flavell, J. H., Green, F. L., & Flavell, E. R. (1986). Development of knowledge about the appearance-reality distinction. With commentaries by M. W. Watson and J. C. Campione. *Monographs of the Society for Research in Child Development, 51* (1, Serial No. 212).

Fogel, A. (1982). Affect dynamics in early infancy: Affective tolerance. In T. Field & A. Fogel (Eds.), *Emotion and Early Interaction.* Hillsdale, NJ: Lawrence Erlbaum Associates.

Fonagy, P. & Target, M. (1997). Attachment and reflective function: Their role in self-organization. *Dev.Psychopathol., 9,* 679–700.

Fraiberg, S. (1980). *Clinical studies in infant mental health: The first year of life.* New York: Basic Books.

Freud, A. (1965). *Normality and pathology in childhood; assessments of development.* New York: International Universities Press.

Freud, S. (1900). *The Interpretation of Dreams.* Standard Edition. (1958) London: Hogarth Press.

Freud, S. (1905). Three essays on the theory of sexuality. In Standard Edition pp. 135–242. London: Hogarth Press.

Freud, S. (1911). *Formulations on the two principles of mental functioning.* (Standard Edition) London: Hogarth Press.

Gaensbauer, T. J. (1982). Regulation of emotional expression in infants from two contrasting caretaking environments. *J.Am.Acad.Child Psychiatry, 21,* 163–170.

Gaensbauer, T. J., Harmon, R. J., Cytryn, L., & McKnew, D. H. (1984). Social and affective development in infants with a manic-depressive parent. *Am.J.Psychiatry, 141,* 223–229.

Gewirtz, J. L. (1961). A learning analysis of the effects of normal stimulation, privation and deprivation on the acquisition of social motivation and attachment. In B. M. Foss (Ed.), *Determinants of Infant Behavior, Vol. 1* (pp. 28–35). London: Methuen.

Gewirtz, J. L. (1965). The course of the infant smiling in four child rearing environments in Israel. In B. M. Foss (Ed.), *Determinants of infant behavior* (pp. 205–220). London: Methuen.

Gewirtz, J. L. (1969). Levels of conceptual analysis in environment-infant interaction research. *Merrill-Palmer Quarterly, 15,* 9–47.

Gilligan, C. (1982). *In a different voice: Psychological theory and women's development.* Cambridge, MA: Harvard University Press.

Goldberg, S. (1977). Social competence in infancy: A model of parent-infant interaction. *Merrill-Palmer Quarterly, 23,* 163–177.

Goldberg, W. A. & Easterbrooks, M. A. (1984). Toddler development in the family. Impact of the father involvement and parenting characteristics. *Developmental Psychology, 55,* 740–752.

Gouin-Decarie, T. (1965). *Intelligence and affectivity in early childhood: An experimental study of Jean Piaget's object concept and object relations.* New York: International Universities Press.

Greenspan, S. (1979). Intelligence and adaptation: An integration of psychoanalytic and Piagetian developmental psychology. [Monograph 47/68]. Psychological Issues. New York, International Universities Press.

Greenspan, S. (1981). Psychopathology and adaptation in infancy and early childhood: Principles of clinical diagnosis and preventive intervention. Clinical Infant Reports [1]. New York, International Universities Press.

Greenspan, S. I. (1989). *The development of the ego: Implications for personality theory, psychopathology, and the psychotherapeutic process.* Madison, CT: International Universities Press.

Greenspan, S. I. (1992). *Infancy and early childhood: The practice of clinical assessment and intervention with emotional and developmental challenges.* Madison, CT: International Universities Press.

Greenspan, S. I. (1997a). *Developmentally based psychotherapy.* Madison, CT: International Universities Press.

Greenspan, S. I. (1998). Commentary: Guidance for constructing clinical practice guidelines for developmental and learning disorders: Knowledge vs. evidence-based approaches. *Journal of Developmental and Learning Disorders, 2,* 171–192.

Greenspan, S. I. (1997b). *The growth of the mind and the endangered origins of intelligence.* Reading, MA: Addison Wesley.

Greenspan, S. I. & Lourie, R. S. (1981). Developmental structuralist approach to the classification of adaptive and pathologic personality organizations: Infancy and early childhood. *Am.J.Psychiatry, 138,* 725-735.

Greenspan, S. I. & Porges, S. W. (1984). Psychopathology in infancy and early childhood: Clinical perspectives on the organization of sensory and affective-thematic experience. *Child Dev., 55,* 49–70.

Greenspan, S. I. & Salmon, J. (1993). *Playground politics: Understanding the emotional life of your school-age child.* Reading, MA: Addison Wesley.

Greenspan, S. I. & Wieder, S. (1997). Developmental patterns and outcomes in infants and children with disorders in relating and communicating: A chart review of 200 cases of children with autistic spectrum diagnoses. *Journal of Developmental and Learning Disorders, 1,* 87–141.

Greenspan, S. I. & Wieder, S. (1998). *The child with special needs: Intellectual and emotional growth.* Reading, MA: Addison Wesley.

Greenspan, S. I., Wieder, S., Lieberman, A., Nover, R., Lourie, R., & Robinson, M. (1987). Infants in multirisk families: Case studies in preventive intervention. Clinical Infant Reports. [No. 3]. New York, International Universities Press.

Grossmann, K., Grossmann, K. E., Spangler, G., Suess, G., & Unzner, L. (1985). Maternal sensitivity and newborns' orientation responses as related to quality of attachment in Northern Germany. *Monographs of the Society for Research in Child Development, 50* (1–2, Serial No. 209).

Harlow, H. F. (1953). Motivation as a factor in the acquisition of new responses. In Nebraska Symposium on Motivation (pp. 24–29). Lincoln: University of Nebraska.

Harris, P. L. (1989). *Children and emotion.* Oxford: Basil Blackwell.

Harris, P. L., Brown, E., Marriott, C., Whittall, S., & Harmer, S. (1991). Monsters, ghosts, and witches: Testing the limits of the fantasy-reality distinction in young children. *British Journal of Developmental Psychology, 9,* 105–123.

Harris, P. L. & Kavanaugh, R. (1993). Young children's understanding of pretense. *Monographs of the Society for Research in Child Development, 58* (1, Serial No. 231).

Harter, S. & Whitesell, N. (1989). Developmental changes in children's emotion concepts. In C. Saarni & P. L. Harris (Eds.), *Children's Understanding of Emotion.* New York: Cambridge University Press.

Hartmann, H. (1939). *Ego psychology and the problem of adaptation.* New York: International Universities Press.

Hendrick, I. (1939). *Facts and theories of psychoanalysis.*

Hesse, E. (1999). The adult attachment interview: Historical and current perspectives. In J. Cassidy & P. R. Shaver (Eds.), *Handbook of Attachment* (pp. 395–433). New York: Guilford Press.

Heuber, R. & Thomas, K. (1995). The relationship between attachment, psychopathology, and childhood disability. *Rehabilitative Psychology, 40,* 111–124.

Hobson, R. P. (1986). The autistic child's appraisal of expressions of emotion: A further study. *Journal of Child Psychology and Psychiatry, 27*, 671–680.

Hobson, R. P. (1989). On sharing experiences. *Developmental Psychopathology, 1*, 197–204.

Hoffman, M. I. (1998). Varieties of empathy-based guilt. In J. Bybee (Ed.), *Guilt and Children*. New York: Academic Press.

Hunt, J. M. (1941). Infants in an orphanage. *Journal of Abnormal & Social Psychology, 36*, 338.

Hunt, J. M. (1965). Intrinsic motivation and its role in psychological development. In D. Levine (Ed.) Nebraska Symposium on Motivation, Lincoln: University of Nebraska Press.

Hurwitz, R. (1929). *The psychology of the infant, by Dr. Siegfried Bernfeld; translated by Rosetta Hurwitz*. New York: Brentano's.

Inhelder, B., Lezine, I., Sinclair, H., & Stambak, M. (1972). Le debut de la function symbolique. In E. M. Hetherington & P. H. Mussen (Eds.), *Handbook of Child Psychology, Vol. 4* (4th Ed. ed., pp. 187–243). New York: John Wiley & Sons.

Interdisciplinary Council on Developmental and Learning Disorders Clinical Practice Guidelines Workgroup. (2000). *Interdisciplinary council on developmental and learning disorders' clinical practice guidelines: Redefining the standards of care for infants, children, and families with special needs*. Bethesda, MD: Interdisciplinary Council on Developmental and Learning Disorders.

Izard, C. E. (1971). *The face of emotion*. New York: Meredith & Appleton-Century-Crofts.

Izard, C. E. (1978). On the development of emotions and emotion-cognition relationships in infancy. In M. Lewis & L. Rosenblum (Eds.), *The Development of Affect*. New York: Plenum Press.

Kagan, J. (1981). *The second year: The emergence of self-awareness*. Cambridge, MA: Harvard University Press.

Kaye, K. & Fogel, A. (1980). The temporal structure of face-to-face communication between mothers and infants. *Developmental Psychology, 16*, 454–464.

Kaye, K. (1982). *The mental and social life of babies: How parents create persons*. Chicago: University of Chicago Press.

Kernberg, O. F. (1975). *Borderline conditions and pathological narcissism*. New York: Jason Aronson.

Kimmert, M. D., Campos, J., Sorce, F. J., Emde, R. N., & Svejda, M. J. (1983). Social referencing: Emotional expressions as behavior regulators. In R. Plutchik & H. Kellerman (Eds.), *Emotion: Theory, Research and Experience: Vol. 2. Emotions in Early Development* (pp. 57–86). Orlando: Academic Press.

Klaus, M. & Kennell, J. (1976). *Maternal-infant bonding: The impact of early separation or loss on family development*. St. Louis, MO: C. V. Mosby.

Kleinman, A. (1986). *Social origins of distress and disease*. New Haven, CT: Yale University Press.

Kohut, H. (1971). *The analysis of self: A systematic approach to the psychoanalytic treatment of narcissistic personality disorders*. New York: International Universities Press.

Kopp, C. B. (1987). The growth of self-regulation: Caregivers and children. In M. Eisenberg (Ed.), *Contemporary Topics in Developmental Psychology* (pp. 34–55). New York: John Wiley & Sons.

Kopp, C. B. (1989). Regulation of distress and negative emotions: A developmental view. *Developmental Psychology, 25,* 343–354.

Kovacs, M. & Paulauskas, S. (1984). Developmental stage and the expression of depressive disorders in children: An empirical analysis. *New Directions for Child Development, 26,* 59–80.

Kraus, R. & Glucksberg, S. (1969). The development of communication: Competence as a function of age. *Child Development, 40,* 255–266.

Lachmann, F. M. & Beebe, B. (1997). The contribution of self- and mutual regulation to therapeutic action: A case illustration. In M. Moskowitz, C. Monk, C. Kaye, & S. Ellman (Eds.), *The Neurobiological and Developmental Basis for Psychotherapeutic Intervention* (pp. 94–121). Northvale, NJ: Jason Aronson, Inc.

Lester, B. M., Hoffman, J., & Brazelton, T. B. (1985). The rhythmic structure of mother-infant interaction in term and preterm infants. *Child Dev., 56,* 15–27.

Lewis, M. & Feiring, M. (1987). Infant, maternal and mother-infant interaction behavior and subsequent attachment. *Child Dev., 60,* 831–837.

Lipsitt, L. (1966). Learning processes of newborns. *Merrill-Palmer Quarterly, 12,* 45–71.

Lowe, M. (1975). Trends in the development of representational play in infants from one to three years—an observational study. *J.Child Psychol.Psychiatry, 16,* 33–47.

Lowery, L. G. (1940). Personality disorders and early institutional care. *American Journal of Orthopsychiatry, 10,* 546–555.

Lyons-Ruth, K. & Jacobovitz, D. (1999). Attachment disorganization: Unresolved loss, relational violence and lapses in behavioral and attentional strategies. In J. Cassidy & P. R. Shaver (Eds.), *Handbook of Attachment Theory and Research.* New York: Guilford Press.

Lyons-Ruth, K. & Zeanah, C. (1993). The family context of infant mental health: I. Affective development in the primary caregiving relationship. In C. Zeanah (Ed.), *Handbook of Infant Mental Health* (pp. 14–37). New York: Guilford Press.

Mahler, M. S., Pine, F., & Bergman, A. (1975). *The psychological birth of the human infant: Symbiosis and individuation.* New York: Basic Books.

Main, M. & Hesse, E. (1990). Parents' unresolved traumatic experiences are related to infant disorganized status: Is frightened or frightening parental behavior the linking mechanism? In Chicago (Ed.), *Attachment in the Preschool Years* (pp. 161–182). The University of Chicago Press.

Main, M., Kaplan, N., & Cassidy, J. (1985). Security in infancy, childhood and adulthood: A move to the level of representation. *Monographs of the Society for Research in Child Development, 50,* (1–2, Serial No. 209), 66-104.

Markus, H. & Kitayama, S. (1990). Culture and the self: Implications for cognition, emotion, and motivation. *Psychological Review, 98,* 224–253.

Marvin, R. & Stewart, R. B. (1991). A family systems framework for the study of attachment. In M. T. Greenberg, D. Cicchetti, & E. M. Cummings (Eds.), *Attachment in the Preschool Years* (pp. 51–87). Chicago: University of Chicago Press.

Maslin-Cole, C. & Spieker, S. J. (1990). Attachment as a basis of independent motivation: A view from risk and nonrisk samples. In M. T. Greenberg, D. Cicchetti, & E. M. Cummings (Eds.), *Attachment in the Preschool Years* (pp. 245–272). Chicago: University of Chicago Press.

Matas, L., Arend, R., & Sroufe, L. (1978). Continuity of adaptation in the second year: The relationship between quality of attachment and later competence. *Child Development, 49,* 547–556.

McCune-Nicholich, L. (1977). Beyond sensorimotor intelligence: Measurement of symbolic sensitivity through analysis of pretend play. *Merrill-Palmer Quarterly, 23,* 89–99.

Meltzoff, A. (1985). The Roots of Social and Cognitive Development: Models of Man's Original Nature. In T. M. Field & N. A. Fox (Eds.), *Social Perception in Infants.* Norwood, NJ: Ablex Publishing Co.

Meltzoff, A. (1990). Foundations for developing a concept of self: The role of imitation in relating self to other and the value of social mirroring, social modeling, and self practice in infancy. In D. Cicchetti & M. Beeghly (Eds.), *The Self in Transition: Infancy to Childhood.* Chicago: Chicago University Press.

Meltzoff, A. & Moore, K. (1977). Imitation of facial and manual gestures by human neonates. *Science, 198,* 75–78.

Miyake, K., Chen, S., & Campos, J. (1985). Infant temperament, mother's mode of interaction, and attachment in Japan: An interim report. *Monographs of the Society for Research in Child Development, 50* (1–2, Serial No. 209).

Murphy, L. B. (1974). The individual child. [Publication no. OCD 74–1032]. Washington, DC, US Government Printing Office. Department of Health, Education, and Welfare.

Murphy, L. B. & Moriarty, A. (1976). *Vulnerability, coping, and growth.* New Haven, CT: Yale University Press.

Nelson, K. (1973). Structure and strategy in learning to talk. *Monographs of the Society for Research in Child Development, 38* (1–2, Serial No. 149).

Nelson, K. (1986). *Even knowledge: Structure and function in development.* Hillsdale, NJ: Lawrence Erlbaum & Associates.

Nelson, K. & Gruendel, J. M. (1981). Generalized even representations: Basic building blocks of cognitive development. In A.L.Brown & M. E. Lamb (Eds.), *Advances in Developmental Psychology, Vol. 1.* Hillsdale, NJ: Lawrence Erlbaum & Associates.

Nemiah, J. C. (1977). Alexithymia: Theories and models. In the Proceedings of the Eleventh European Conference on Psychosomatic Research. Basel, Switzerland: Karger.

Ogawa, J. R., Sroufe, L. A., Weinfield, N. S., Carlson, E. A., & Egeland, B. (1997). Development and the fragmented self: Longitudinal study of dissociative symptomatology in a nonclinical sample. *Dev.Psychopathol., 9,* 855–879.

Osofsky, J. D. & Eberhart-Wright, A. (1988). Affective exchanges between high risk mothers and infants. *Int.J.Psychoanal., 69. (Pt 2),* 221–231.

Papousek, H. (1981). The common in the uncommon child. In M. Lewis & L. Rosenblum (Eds.), *The Uncommon Child* (pp. 317–328). New York: Plenum Press.

Papousek, H. & Papousek, M. (1979). Early ontogeny of human social inter-action: Its biological roots and social dimensions. In K. Foppa, W. Lepenies, & D. Ploog (Eds.), *Human Ethology: Claims and Limits of a New Discipline* (pp. 456–489). New York: Cambridge University Press.

Pastor, D. (1981). The quality of mother-infant attachment and its relation-ship to toddlers' initial sociability with peers. *Developmental Psychology, 23,* 326–335.

Pederson, D. R., Moran, G., Sitko, C., Campbell, K., Ghesquire, K., & Acton, H. (1990). Maternal sensitivity and the security of infant-mother attachment: A Q-sort study. *Child Dev., 61,* 1974–1983.

Peller, L. (1954). Libidinal phases, ego development, and play. In *The Psychoanalytic Study of the Child* (pp. 178–198). New York: International Universities Press.

Piaget, J. (1962). The stages of intellectual development of the child. In S. Harrison & J. McDermott (Eds.), *Childhood Psychopathology* (pp. 157–166). New York: International Universities Press.

Pipp-Siegel, S. & Pressman, L. (1996). Developing a sense of self and others. *ZERO TO THREE, 17,* 17–24.

Pipp, S., Fischer, K. W., & Jennings, S. (1987). Acquisition of self-and-mother knowledge in infancy. *Developmental Psychology, 47,* 86–96.

Provence, S. & Naylor, A. (1983). *Working with disadvantaged parents and their children: Scientific and practical issues.* New Haven, CT: Yale University Press.

Provence, S. E. (1983). Infants and parents: clinical case reports. Clinical Infant Reports: No. 2. New York, International Universities Press.

Rachford, B. K. (1905). *Neurotic disorders of childhood.* New York: E. B. Treat & Company.

Radke-Yarrow, M., Cummings, E. M., Kuczynski, L., & Chapman, M. (1985). Patterns of attachment in two- and three-year-olds in normal families and fami-lies with parental depression. *Child Dev., 56,* 884–893.

Radke-Yarrow, M., Zahn-Waxler, C., & Chapman, M. (1983). Children's prosocial dispositions and behavior. In E. M. Hetherington & P. H. Mussen (Eds.), *Handbook of Child Psychology, Vol. 4* (4th Ed. ed., pp. 469–545). New York: John Wiley & Sons.

Reingold, H. (1969). The social and socializing infant. In D. Goslin (Ed.), *Handbook of Socialization Theory and Research.* Chicago: Rand McNally.

Reiss, D. (1989). The represented and practicing family: Contrasting visions of family continuity. In A. J. Sameroff & R. N. Emde (Eds.), *Relationship Disturbances in Early Childhood* (pp. 191–220). New York: Basic Books.

Ricks, M. (1985). The social transmission of parental behavior: Attachment across generations. *Monographs of the Society for Research in Child Development, 50* (1–2, Serial No. 209).

Rosenstein, D. & Horowitz, H. (1996). Adolescent attachment and psychopathology. *Journal of Consulting & Clinical Psychology, 64,* 244–253.

Roth-Hanania, R., Busch-Rossnagel, N., & Higgins-D'Alessandro, A. (2000). Development of self and empathy in early infancy: Implications for atypical development. *Infants and Young Children, 13,* 1–14.

Rothbart, M. K. & Derryberry, D. (1981). Development of individual differences in temperament. In M. E. Lamb & A. L. Brown (Eds.), *Advances in Developmental Psychology, Vol. 1.* Hillsdale, NJ: Lawrence Erlbaum & Associates.

Rubin, K. H., Fein, G. G., & Vandenberg, B. (1983). Play. In E. M. Hetherington & P. H. Mussen (Eds.), *Handbook of Child Psychology, Vol. 4* (4th Ed, pp. 136–148). New York: John Wiley & Sons.

Sander, L. (1962). Issues in early mother-child interaction. *J.Am.Acad.Child Adolesc.Psychiatry, 1,* 141-166.

Scaife, M. & Bruner, J. S. (1975). The capacity for joint visual attention in the infant. *Nature, 253,* 265-266.

Schank, R. C. & Abelson, R. P. (1977). *Scripts, Plans, Goals and Understanding.* Hillsdale, NJ: Lawrence Erlbaum and Associates.

Schneider-Rosen, K. & Cicchetti, D. (1984). The relationship between affect and cognition in maltreated infants: Quality of attachment and the development of visual self-recognition. *Child Dev., 55,* 648–658.

Schweder, R., Mahapatra, M., & Miller, J. (1987). Cultural and moral development. In J. Kagan & S. Lamb (Eds.), *The Emergence of Morality in Young Children* (pp. 1–90). Chicago: University of Chicago Press.

Siegel, D. J. (2001). Interpersonal neurobiology of the developing mind. *Infant Mental Health Journal, 22,* 67–94.

Sinclair, H. (1970). The transition from sensorimotor to symbolic activity. *Interchange, 1,* 119–126.

Singer, D. G. & Singer, J. L. (1990). *The house of make-believe: Children's play and developing imagination.* Cambridge, MA: Harvard University Press.

Smetana, J. (1985). Preschool children's conceptions of transgressions: Effects of varying moral and conventional domain-related attributes. *Developmental Psychology, 21,* 18–29.

Sorce, J. F. & Emde, R. N. (1982). The meaning of infant emotional expressions: Regularities in caregiving responses in normal and Down's syndrome infants. *J.Child Psychol.Psychiatry, 23,* 145–158.

Spelke, E. S. & Owsley, C. (1979). Intermodal exploration and knowledge in infancy. *Infant Behavior and Development, 2,* 13–27.

Spitz, R. A. (1945). Hospitalism: An inquiry into the genesis of psychiatric conditions in early childhood. *The Psychoanalytic Study of the Child, 1,* 53–74.

Spitz, R. A. (1965). *The first year of life: A psychoanalytic study of normal and deviant development of object relations.* New York: International Universities Press.

Spitz, R. A. & Cobliner, W. G. (1966). *First year of life: A psychoanalytic study of normal and deviant development of object relations.* New York: International Universities Press.

Sroufe, L. A. (1979). Socioemotional development. In J. Osofsky (Ed.), *Handbook of infant development.* New York: John Wiley & Sons.

Sroufe, L. A. (1983). Infant-caregiver attachment and patterns of adaptation in preschool: The roots of maladaptation and competence. In (pp. 41–83). Hillsdale, NJ: Erlbaum.

Sroufe, L. A. (1996). *Emotional development: The organization of emotional life in the early years*. New York: Cambridge University Press.

Sroufe, L. A. & Waters, E. (1977). Attachment as an organizational construct. *Child Development, 48,* 1184-1199.

Sroufe, L. A., Egeland, B., & Carlson, E. (1999). One social world: The integrated development of parent-child and peer relationships. In W. A. Collins & B. Laursen (Eds.), *Relationships as Developmental Context: The 29th Minnesota Symposium on Child Psychology*. Hillsdale, NJ: Erlbaum.

Sroufe, L. A., Fox, N. A., & Pancake, V. (1983). Attachment and dependency in developmental perspective. *Child Development, 54,* 1615–1627.

Sroufe, L. A. & Rutter, M. (1984). The domain of developmental psychopathology. *Child Dev., 55,* 17–29.

Sroufe, L. A., Waters, E., & Matas, L. (1974). Contextual determinants of infant affective response. In M. Lewis & L. Rosenblum (Eds.), *The Origins of Fear* (pp. 49–72). New York: Wiley & Sons.

Stern, D. N. (1974a). Mother and infant at play: The dyadic interaction involving facial, vocal, and gaze behaviors. In M. Lewis & L. Rosenblum (Eds.), *The Effect of the Infant on Its Caregiver*. New York: John Wiley & Sons.

Stern, D. N. (1974b). The goal and structure of mother-infant play. *J.Am.Acad.Child Psychiatry, 13,* 402-421.

Stern, D. N. (1977). *The first relationship: Mother and infant*. Cambridge, MA: Harvard University Press.

Stern, D. N. (1983). The early development of schemas of self, of other, and of various experiences of `self with other'. In J. Lichtenberg & S. Kaplan (Eds.), *Reflections on Self Psychology*. Hillsdale, NJ: The Analytic Press.

Stern, D. N. (1985). *The interpersonal world of the infant: A view from psychoanalysis and developmental psychology*. New York: Basic Books.

Stewart, R. B. & Marvin, R. (1984). Sibling relations: The role of conceptual perspective-taking in the ontogeny of sibling caregiving. *Child Development, 55,* 1322–1332.

Talberg, G., Cuoto, R. J., O'Donnell, M. L., & Cuoto Rosa, J. A. (1988). Early affect development: empirical research. *Int.J.Psychoanal., 69 (Pt 2),* 239–259.

Tennes, K., Emde, R. N., Kisley, A., & Metcalf, D. (1972). The stimulus barrier in early infancy: An exploration of some formulations of John Benjamin. In R. Hold & E. Peterfreund (Eds.), *Psychoanalysis and Contemporary Science, Vol. 1* (pp. 206–234). New York: Macmillan.

Thomas, A., Chess, S., & Birch, H. G. (1968). *Temperament and behavior disorders in children*. New York: New York Universities Press.

Thomas, A. & Chess, S. (1984). Genesis and evolution of behavioral disorders: from infancy to early adult life. *Am.J.Psychiatry, 141,* 1–9.

Tomkins, S. (1963). *Affect, Imagery, Consciousness, Vol. 1*. New York: Springer Publishing.

Trevarthen, C. (1979). Communication and cooperation in early infancy: A description of primary intersubjectivity. In M. Bullowa (Ed.), *Before Speech: The Beginning of Interpersonal Communication* (pp. 321-347). Cambridge, England: Cambridge University Press.

Tronick, E. (1980). The primacy of social skills in infancy. In D. B. Sawin, R. C. Hawkins, L. O. Walker, & J. Penticuff (Eds.), *Exceptional Infant, Vol. 4* (pp. 144–158). New York: Brunner/Mazel.

Tronick, E. Z. (1989). Emotions and emotional communication in infants. *Am.Psychol., 44,* 112–119.

Tronick, E. Z. & Gianino, A. F., Jr. (1986). The transmission of maternal disturbance to the infant. *New Dir.Child Dev.* 5–11.

Waelder, R. (1933). The psychoanalytic theory of play. *Psychoanalytic Quarterly, 2,* 208–224.

Warren, S. L., Huston, L., Egeland, B., & Sroufe, L. A. (1997). Child and adolescent anxiety disorders and early attachment. *J.Am.Acad.Child Adolesc.Psychiatry, 36,* 637–644.

Waters, E., Wippman, J., & Sroufe, L. A. (1979). Attachment, positive affect, and competence in the peer group: Two studies in construct validation. *Child Dev., 50,* 821–829.

Weisz, J. R. & Stipek, D. J. (1982). Competence, contingency, and the development of perceived control. *Hum.Dev., 25,* 250–281.

Werner, H. & Kaplan, B. (1963). *Symbol Formation.* Wiley.

White, R. W. (1963). Ego and reality on psychoanalytic theory. Psychological Issues. 11. New York, International Universities Press.

Wieder, S., Jasnow, M., Greenspan, S., & Strauss, M. (1983). Identifying the multi-risk family prenatally: Antecedent psychosocial factors and infant developmental trends. *Infant Mental Health Journal* 165–201.

Winnicott, D. W. (1931). *Clinical notes on the disorders of childhood.* London: Heineman.

Winnicott, D. W. (1965). Ego distortion in terms of true and false self. In *The Maturational Processes and the Facilitating Environment* (pp. 140–152). New York: International Universities Press.

Wolf, D. (1990). Being of several minds. In D. Cicchetti & M. Beeghly (Eds.), *The Self in Transition* (pp. 183–213). Chicago: University of Chicago Press.

Wolf, D., Rygh, J., & Altshuler, J. (1984). Agency and experience: Actions and states in play narratives. In I. Bretherton (Ed.), *Symbolic Play* (pp. 195–217). Orlando, FL: Academic Press.

Wooley, J. D. & Wellman, H. M. (1990). Young children's understanding of realities, nonrealities, and appearances. *Child Development, 61,* 946–964.

Zahn-Waxler, C., Cummings, E. M., McKnew, D. H., & Radke-Yarrow, M. (1984). Altruism, aggression, and social interactions in young children with a manic-depressive parent. *Child Dev., 55,* 112–122.

Zahn-Waxler, C. & Radke-Yarrow, M. (1982). The development of altruism: Alternative research strategies. In M.Eisenberg (Ed.), *the Development of Prosocial Behavior.* New York: Academic Press.

Zahn-Waxler, C., Robinson, J. D., & Emde, R. N. (1992). The development of empathy in twins. *Developmental Psychology, 28,* 1038–1047.

Zekoski, E. M., O'Hara, M. W., & Wills, K. E. (1987). The effects of maternal mood on mother-infant interaction. *J.Abnorm.Child Psychol., 15,* 361–378.

II

The Clinical Application
of the Functional Emotional
Assessment Scale

2

The Clinical Applications of the FEAS

Stanley I. Greenspan, M.D.
Serena Wieder, Ph.D.

In addition to helping clinicians and researchers understand early development, the functional emotional developmental capacities described in Chapter 1 can be used to guide and systematize clinical observations. Developmentally based clinical observations, in turn, can enrich approaches to assessment and intervention.

To facilitate this process, we developed a clinical and research version of the Functional Emotional Assessment Scale (FEAS). The clinical version was developed first. It operationalizes the functional emotional developmental capacities described in Chapter 1 into clinically useful categories. The research version of the FEAS operationalizes the functional emotional developmental capacities into specific behaviors that can be reliably rated and validated and, therefore, used for a variety of research purposes. The research version, including reliability and validity studies and rating guidelines, is presented in Chapters 4, 5, 6, and 7.

The clinical version is presented in this chapter. It is an update of Chapter 9 in *Infancy and Early Childhood: The Practice of Clinical Assessment and Intervention with Emotional and Developmental Challenges* (Greenspan, 1992). This clinical approach to assessment emphasizes understanding the infant and young child's emotional and social functioning in the context of relationships with his or her caregivers and family. The emotional capacities of the infant and young child relate to the infant's ability to deal with his or her real world. This approach to the infant and young child's functioning can be contrasted to a formal structured test approach. The formal test approach looks at what an infant can and cannot do in relationship to a defined set of stimuli or test procedures.

In assessing infants and young children, especially those with atypical or challenging developmental patterns, the formal structured test approach covers only a small part of the infant's real capacities. Many formal tests were, for the most part, developed and standardized with infants and young children who were not evidencing unusual challenges or special needs. In addition, many formal tests are not geared toward bringing out a challenging child's unique ability and potential. Many infants and young children have difficulty in attending, relating, and conforming to the tests' most basic expectations. Skilled examiners aware of these factors may use only the challenging infant or child's general behavior around the test situation as an indicator of his or her abilities. The less experienced examiner often mistakenly attempts to derive and draw conclusions from a limited range of performance behaviors. In either case, the test situation is often not the best context within which to observe the full range of an infant or child's functional developmental capacities.

Incorrect and misleading formal test data often lead to incorrect recommendations for services and educational placements and programs. A delayed or atypical child may regress with the wrong placement, hardly a desirable outcome for such a laudable goal as early identification and appropriate early intervention. Unfortunately, as states and communities have been attempting to assess and offer services to more and more infants and young children in need of appropriate special services, the problem of incorrect service recommendations may be becoming greater. Recently, we have been seeing more and more toddlers and preschoolers who have been misdiagnosed and offered incorrect services and educational placements based on misleading early evaluations. Sometimes, test results have been six to seven months off in comparison to more complete clinical evaluation. Since many of these children have been under the age of 2, the error is quite significant.

All evaluations of infants, young children, and their families must begin with a clinical assessment of the infant and/or young child's functional capacities as described earlier. Specific structured tests, however reliable, valid, and easy to administer, must only be used to build on the overall clinical functional assessment. Often time can be saved and resources conserved by only using formal structured assessments selectively, for example, when there are critical questions that have not been answered by the clinical assessment. More importantly, however, errors in educational placement and service recommendations will be minimized with an approach that has as its foundation a clinical functional developmental assessment of the infant, young child, and his or her caregivers and family.

This chapter presents a method of systematizing the clinical functional developmental assessment of the infant and young child. It focuses on the infant's core emotional and social capacities at each stage in his or her development. It also outlines the related motor, sensory, language, and cognitive capacities that go along with each of the core emotional and social capacities. The data from which the clinician will make judgments are derived from a free, unstructured interaction between the infant or child and his or her caregiver, as well as the clinician. These unstructured interactions are started by simply asking the caregiver to interact or play with the infant or child as he/she might at home. If further suggestions are needed, phrases such as, "Just the way you like to interact with each other"; "The way you like to enjoy each other"; "The way you like to be together"; and so on, may be useful. If necessary, a series of semistructured interactive opportunities are offered to the infant or child to help elicit their core competencies. (These interactive opportunities, which can be suggested to caregivers or carried out by the clinician or both, will be described later in this chapter.) These free, unstructured, and, if necessary, semistructured interactions are close to the infant's natural way of interacting with his world. They can be done both in the office and at home and can be repeated as many times as necessary in order to gain a true picture of the infant/young child and caregiver's capacities. It is often very helpful to see the infant/young child and his caregiver(s) interacting on at least two separate occasions. In reaching an overall clinical judgment, one must also include historical data and caregiver reports of current functioning. Although this scale was developed to systematize the observable clinical data part of the evaluation, the clinician may also use it to systematize historical and/or current functioning data and integrated judgments using all sources of data.

The scale that follows can be used in two ways. It can be used descriptively to profile the infant and young child's emotional, social, and related developmental capacities. It can also be used to clinically rate each capacity on a 0 to 4 scale. However, the reader should be aware that the clinical version of the FEAS is intended to systematize clinical thinking. The research version of the FEAS, which is presented in Chapters 4, 5, 6, and 7, should be used for research purposes. The reliability and validity studies on the FEAS, presented in these later chapters, were conducted on the research version.

Rating Scale:

    0 = Capacity not present
    1 = Capacity fleetingly present
    2 = Capacity intermittently present
    3 = Capacity present most of the time
    4 = Capacity present all the time in all circumstances
    N/A = Not applicable, because there was no opportunity to observe the presence or absence of this capacity

For each item the child may receive an N/A, 0, 1, 2, 3, or 4 rating. These ratings can then be added together. Adding together each item observed at the 4 level can derive a potential score. This is the child's potential age-expected capacity. The score attained can be put over the possible score and a percentage derived.

Whereas this procedure can be carried out for each area of functioning, only the Primary Functional Emotional and Emotional Range categories may be described quantitatively. The other categories should only be used in a qualitative descriptive manner. The areas of functioning that will comprise the scale are as follows:

- *Primary Emotional Capacities:* The attainment of primary emotional capacities at each developmental level determines if a child has progressed to his/her age-expected functional emotional developmental capacity. When a primary functional emotional capacity is not present it suggests the infant has not achieved his/her age-expected developmental level.
- *Emotional Range-Sensorimotor (including speech)*: This area focuses on the range of sensory and motor equipment, including speech, the infant or child is able to employ in mastering his/her primary functional emotional capacities (e.g., using motor gestures, touch, words, etc.). At later ages these capacities will involve the use of sensory, motor, and speech capacities to support higher level functional and conceptual abilities.

- *Emotional Range-Affective:* This area focuses on the different affective themes (e.g., dependency, aggression) that the child can organize at his/her age-expected developmental level (e.g., one child can use words and pretend play in relationship to the theme of dependency-the dolls hugging-while another child can only use play and words for aggression).
- *Related Motor, Sensory, Language, and Cognitive Capacities:* This area comprises selected developmental items not already covered in the primary emotional capacities. Many capacities that would ordinarily fall in one of the cognitive categories will be seen to be covered as part of a functional emotional capacity.
- *General Infant Tendencies:* These are constitutionally and maturationally based capacities.
- *Overall Caregiver Tendencies:* These are facilitating and undermining caregiver patterns.

At present, the quantitative use of the scale should only be for descriptive purposes. Although based on the developmental model described in this work, this particular scale has not yet been used with a large number of normal, delayed, and dysfunctional infants and young children and their caregivers. The categories that are used in this scale, however, have been rated reliably, discriminate between clinical and nonclinical groups, and evidence age-related stability and expected shifts with developmental progression (Doherty, 1991, 1983; Hofheimer, Strauss, Poisson, & Greenspan, 1981) and are related to the (G.L.O.S.) scales (Greenspan & Lieberman, 1989a, 1989b; Chapter 5, this book).

In using the FEAS, the clinician should first assess the age-expected primary emotional capacities of the infant or young child. He should then assess all the prior primary emotional capacities, which, one hopes, were mastered at earlier ages, but continue as part of the child's basic capacities. He should then assess emotional range (sensorimotor) and emotional range (affective). If the infant or young child evidences an optimal emotional range in both emotional range categories for his age level, the clinician need not assess developmentally earlier categories of emotional range. On the other hand, if the infant or young child evidences constrictions in his emotional range, the clinician should keep assessing the developmentally earlier category of emotional range (one or both) to see if the infant or young child was ever able to establish a broad and flexible emotional range in the sensorimotor or affective areas. The clinician should next observe how the child functions in terms of motor, sensory, language, and cognitive capacities to see if these are consistent with, behind, or advanced for the child's functional emotional capacities. These should only be used qualitatively. Next, the clinician should assess the infant's constitutional tendencies and the caregiver's capacities.

The clinician arrives at a number of judgments regarding the infant's capacities, which includes the developmental level in terms of primary functional emotional capacities; the sensory motor range; and affective range. He also gains an understanding of contributions from the infant's constitutional and maturational tendencies and the caregiving patterns.

The clinician will see if a child is at or below the age-expected functional emotional development, as well as how well earlier functional emotional capacities have been mastered. Also, the clinician will gain an impression about the infant's emotional range. A child who is, for example, at a developmental level lower than expected with regard to functional emotional capacities, but has an optimal emotional range at that level, is not necessarily at greater risk than a child who is at his or her age-expected functional emotional developmental level, but with a constricted sensorimotor and affective range. The clinical interpretation of the child's profile must be a clinical judgment based on the child's overall adaptation. A child who, because of a medical illness, is a little delayed but is now developing at an appropriate rate in all areas may be at less risk than a child who is already chronically constricted in his emotional range (e.g., a 2½ -year-old who talks and does some pretend play, but avoids pleasure and only deals with dependency through physical touch and impulsive behavior may be more at risk than another 2½ -year-old who operates in all ways fully like a 2-year-old).

In general, one first determines the child's developmental level in terms of primary functional emotional capacities. This provides a sense of where the child is developmentally.

Then one determines how flexible or wide-ranging his/her adaptive and coping capacities are at that level (i.e., his/her sensorimotor and affective emotional range). If one wants to see how stable his/her capacities are, one looks at the ratings themselves. Lots of 1s and 2s ("fleeting" or "intermittent") suggest unstable capacities; 3s and 4s ("most" or "all of the time") suggest stable capacities. A stability score can be derived if needed by dividing the sum of the rating numbers by the highest possible score (i.e., all 4s for ratable capacities).

One then may look at the associated sensory, motor, language, and cognitive items to see which areas are ahead, at, or behind the functional emotional capacities. For example, fine motor and motor planning capacities may be behind while receptive language and cognition are advanced. If this child is also constricted in her emotional range, especially in dealing with aggression, one may wonder if the lag in fine motor and motor planning is contributing (i.e., a lack of security in the fine control of her motor system). Another child may evidence lags in her primary functional emotional capacities and her affective emotional range and be advanced in his/her motor, sensory, language, and cognitive areas. Here, one may wonder about her interactive opportunities with his/her caregivers and her family functioning.

After one gains a sense of the child's developmental levels in different areas, one should look at the infant's constitutional and maturational patterns (e.g., over- or undersensitive to touch or sound) and his/her caregiver's capacities. One now wonders about how each of these may contribute to the developmental profile. For example, an intrusive caregiver coupled with a tactilely and auditorily hypersensitive child may contribute to a certain developmental profile (e.g., a fearful, cautious child who avoids assertive behavior).

While it is always tempting to use rating scales to simplify complex clinical judgments, it should be clear that the goal of the Clinical Functional Emotional Assessment Scale is to assist the clinician in systematizing and fine-tuning clinical judgments, and in incorporating judgments about functional emotional capacities into research protocols. In working up a case, the scale is of assistance in pointing out critical areas for further clinical inquiry.

For example, an infant's profile evidences the following: a delay in achieving intentional communication (i.e., opening and closing circles of communication); a narrow emotional range (not using vocalization or evidencing assertive exploratory behaviors); auditory underreactivity; and a withdrawn depressed caregiver. Such a profile would alert the clinician to explore the infant's constitutional and maturational pattern of underreactivity and look for related constitutional and maturational patterns, including motor capacities dealing with vocalizing and sensory processing capacities dealing with auditory processing. It would also alert the clinician to explore the caregiving capacities, learning more about the depressed caregiver, other caregivers, and the family. Most importantly, it would alert the clinician that he or she should explore in great depth the interactive patterns that were not supporting intentional, purposeful communication. It would also create an immediate concrete goal for the potential intervention once the diagnostic workup was complete, namely to foster intentional interactions and initiative.

Therefore, the goal of this scale is to operationalize complex clinical judgments about what is often considered to be the vague and difficult to describe world of emotional capacities. Functional emotional capacities can be described just as can motor, sensory, language, and cognitive capacities. The goal is now for each clinician to routinely do it!

The Clinical Version of the Functional Emotional Assessment Scale

Self-Regulation and Interest in the World

By 3 months, the infant can be calm; recovers from crying with comforting; is able to be alert; looks at one when talked to; and brightens up when provided with appropriate visual, auditory, and/or tactile experiences.

Primary Emotional

1. Shows an interest in the world by looking (brightening) at sights or listening to (turning toward) sounds. Can attend to a visual or auditory stimulus for three or more seconds.
2. Can remain calm and focused for two or more minutes at a time, as evidenced by looking around, sucking, cooperating in cuddling (e.g., melding with caregiver), or other age-appropriate activities.

Emotional Range: Sensorimotor

1. Looks at interesting sights for three or more seconds (brightens or turns to sights).
2. Listens to interesting sounds for three or more seconds (brightens or turns to interesting sounds).
3. In response to touch (light or firm), relaxes, smiles, vocalizes, or looks.
4. In response to moving infant's arms and/or legs, relaxes, smiles, vocalizes, or looks at caregiver or own limbs.
5. Tolerates and/or shows pleasure (e.g., smiles) in gentle horizontal and vertical movement in space (e.g., caregiver moving infant up and down and side to side).
6. Tolerates or evidences pleasure in routine smells (e.g., a fruit odor like lemon, an after-shave lotion, or perfume).
7. When held firmly, relaxes or evidences pleasure.
8. When rhythmically rocked, relaxes or evidences pleasure.
9. Recovers from distress, with help from caregiver (e.g., holding, rocking) within 20 minutes.

Emotional Range: Affective

1. Shows an interest in the caregiver by looking, listening, or evidencing curiosity and pleasure (as compared to only being interested in inanimate objects or nothing).
2. Shows interest, through looking, listening, or signs of pleasure, when the caregiver makes happy, joyful facial expressions and vocal tones (e.g., caregiver smiling and laughing with great joy).
3. Shows interest when caregiver is assertive and reaches out by means of his or her facial expressions and vocal tones (caregiver talking in a regular tone of voice about, for example, "What a wonderful nose and mouth and little chin you have"; "Will you hold this rattle? You can do it! You can do it!").

Selected Associated Motor, Sensory, Language, and
Cognitive Capacities Not Already Included Above

1. Motor:
    a. Holds head upright on own;
    b. Lifts head by leaning on elbows while on stomach;
    c. Hands open 75 percent of the time;
    d. Rolls from side to back or stomach to back;
    e. Reaches for rattle or other toy;
    f. Manipulates rattle or other toy.
2. Sensory:
    a. Follows objects in horizontal plane (e.g., light);
    b. Follows objects in vertical plane;
    c. Responds to a variety of sounds;
    d. Tolerates deep pressure-type touch.
3. Language:
    a. Watches lips and mouth of speaker;
    b. Vocalizes with at least one type of sound.
4. Cognitive: (same as sensory and language)

Forming Relationships, Attachments, and Engagement

By five months, infant evidences positive loving affect toward primary caregiver and other key caregivers; looks and/or smiles spontaneously and responds to their facial expressions, voices, or touch with signs of pleasure such as smiling, relaxing, "cooing."

Primary Emotional

1. Responds to social overtures with an emotional response of any kind, which may include pleasure (a smile), but also may include a frown, other facial expressions, vocalizations, arm or leg movements, or postural shifts.
2. Responds to social overtures with an emotional response of pleasure (e.g., smile, joyful vocalizations, etc.).

Emotional Range: Sensorimotor

Shows emotional interest or pleasure in caregiver's:
1. Vocalizations (indicate which type works best—high or low pitch; loud, medium, or soft tone);
2. Facial expressions;
3. Touch (indicate part of body—back, abdomen, face, arms or legs— and type of touch—light or firm, that works best);
4. Gently moving the infant's arms or legs;
5. Moving infant horizontally or vertically in space (indicate rhythm that works best—fast, slow, etc.).

Emotional Range: Affective

1. Evidences a relaxed sense of security and/or comfort when held or rocked.
2. Evidences signs of pleasure (e.g., smiles, happy sounds) when either talked to, held, looked at, moved around, touched, or all of the above.
3. Evidences a curious, assertive interest in the caregiver (e.g., looks and studies caregiver's face).
4. Anticipates with curiosity or excitement the re-presentation of an interesting object that has been presented a moment earlier (e.g., a smiling, vocalizing caregiver making interesting sounds leads to anticipatory looks and facial expressions).

5. Evidences signs of discomfort or lack of pleasure or sadness when during interactive play caregiver is unresponsive for 30 to 60 seconds (e.g., while playing, caregiver stops interacting and is silent and still-faced).
6. Evidences anger or protest when frustrated (e.g., angry cry or facial expression).
7. Can recover from distress with caregiver's social overtures, such as vocalizing and making interesting facial expressions, within 15 minutes.

Selected Associated Motor, Sensory, Language, and Cognitive Capacities Not Already Included Above

1. Motor:
   a. Pushes up on extended arms;
   b. Shifts weight on hands and knees;
   c. Readies body for lifting while being picked up;
   d. Can reach for a toy;
   e. Can roll from back to front;
   f. Sits with support;
   g. Can cooperate in being pulled to a sitting position;
   h. Can bring hands together;
   i. Can grasp objects voluntarily;
   j. Can hold rattle.
2. Sensory:
   a. Reacts to paper on face;
   b. Looks toward sound;
   c. Tolerates roughhouse type play.
3. Language:
   a. Regularly localizes source of voice with accuracy;
   b. Vocalizes two different sounds;
   c. Vocalizes to caregiver's facial expressions and sounds.
4. Cognitive:
   a. Can focus or attend for 30 or more seconds;
   b. Looks and scans for objects and faces;
   c. Smiles at face in mirror;
   d. Looks toward object that goes out of visual range;
   e. Looks at own hand;
   f. Manipulates and plays with toys, such as a rattle or ring.

Two-Way, Purposeful Communication

By 9 months the infant is able to interact in a purposeful (i.e., intentional, reciprocal, cause-and-effect) manner; is able to initiate signals and respond purposefully to another person's signals. Uses multiple sensory modalities, the motor system, and a range of emotions in these intentional interactions.

Primary Emotional

1. Responds to caregiver's gestures with intentional gestures of his or her own (when caregiver reaches out to pick up infant, infant may reach up with his own arms; a flirtatious caregiver vocalization may beget a playful look and a series of vocalizations).
2. Initiates intentional interactions (e.g., spontaneously reaches for caregiver's nose, hair, or mouth; uses hand movements to indicate wish for a certain toy or to be picked up).

Emotional Range; Sensorimotor

Responses intentionally to caregiver's:
1. Vocalizations;
2. Facial expressions;
3. Touch (e.g., holds caregiver's hand when being touched or tickled);
4. Moving infant around in space.

Emotional Range: Affective

Uses gestures to initiate:
1. Closeness. The infant reaches out to be picked up or hugs back when hugged.
2. Pleasure and excitement. Can be playful and smile and vocalize joyfully while putting finger in caregiver's mouth or taking a rattle out of caregiver's mouth and putting it in own mouth.
3. Assertive exploratory behavior. Infant touches and explores caregiver's hair.
4. Protest or anger. Infant pushes undesired food off table with an angry look; screams intentionally when desired toy is not brought to him, etc.
5. Fearful behavior. Infant turns away and looks scared or cries when a stranger approaches too quickly.

6. Infant can recover from distress within 10 minutes by being involved in social interactions.

Selected Associated Motor, Sensory, Language, and Cognitive Capacities, Not Already Included in Above

1. Motor:
   a. Can sit with good balance;
   b. Can hold toy while sitting;
   c. While sitting, can reach up in air for objects;
   d. Can go from lying on back to sitting;
   e. Can go from sitting to stomach position;
   f. Creeps or crawls on stomach or hands;
   g. Holds block or toy using thumb and finger;
   h. Can scoop a Cheerio or small object into palm;
   i. Bangs hands or toy while playing;
   j. Transfers objects from hand to hand.
2. Sensory:
   a. Will feel textures and explore them;
   b. Notices when toy or object is put on different parts of body (e.g., looks at or touches textured toy);
   c. Not sensitive to loud noises like that of vacuum cleaner, toilet flushing, or dog barking;
   d. Not sensitive to bright lights;
   e. Enjoys movement in space.
3. Language:
   a. Responds to name and/or some simple requests (e.g., "No");
   b. Vocalizes different sounds from front of mouth (e.g., "Ba" or "Ma" or "Da") and can use sounds to convey intentions or emotions, such as pleasure or satisfaction;
   c. Responds to different sounds with different vocalizations of own or with selective behaviors;
   d. Can imitate a few sounds (e.g., a "raspberry" or tongue click).
4. Cognitive:
   a. Can focus on toy or person for one or more minutes;
   b. Explores and examines a new toy;
   c. Makes sounds or creates visual or tactile sensations with a toy (e.g., cause-and-effect playing);
   d. Can discriminate between different people as evidenced by different responses;

e. Looks for a toy that has fallen to floor;
f. Can pull on a part of an object (e.g., a piece of cloth) to get the object closer.

Behavioral Organization, Problem-Solving, and Internalization (A Complex Sense of Self—I)

By 13 months, the infant begins to develop a complex sense of self by organizing behavior and emotion. The toddler sequences a number of gestures together and responds consistently to caregiver's gestures, thereby forming chains of interaction (i.e., opens and closes a number of sequential circles of communication). The toddler also manifests a wide range of organized, socially meaningful behaviors and feelings dealing with warmth, pleasure, assertion, exploration, protest, and anger.

Primary Emotional

The infant strings together three or more circles of communication (interaction) as part of a complex pattern of communication. Each unit or circle of communication begins with an infant behavior and ends with the infant building on and responding to the caregiver response. For example, an infant looks and reaches for a toy (opening a circle of communication), caregiver points to the toy, gestures and vocalizes, "This one?" The infant then nods, makes a purposeful sound, and reaches further for toy (closing a circle of communication). As the infant explores the toy and exchanges vocalizations, motor gestures, or facial expressions with the caregiver, additional circles of communication are opened and closed.

Emotional Range: Sensorimotor

The infant can organize three or more circles of communication (with a responsive caregiver):
1. Using vocalization;
2. Using facial expressions;
3. Involving reciprocal touching;
4. Involving movement in space (e.g., rough-and-tumble play);
5. Using motor patterns (e.g., chase games, searching for objects; handing objects back and forth).

Emotional Range: Affective

Can organize, with caregiver support (i.e., responsive empathetic reading and responding to infant's communications), three or more circles of communication around:

1. Negotiating closeness. Gives caregiver a hug and as caregiver responds with a hug back, nuzzles and relaxes.
2. Pleasure and excitement. Infant and caregiver play together with an exciting toy or with caregiver's hair or toes or infant's toes.
3. Assertive explorations. Infant and caregiver examine new toys, explore the house.
4. Cautious or fearful behavior. Infant hides behind caregiver when in a new setting; negotiates with caregiver degrees of protection needed.
5. Angry behavior. Infant can gesture angrily back and forth.
6. Infant can recover from distress and remain organized while distressed by entering into complex gestural negotiation for what he or she wants (e.g., banging on a door to go outside and play).

Selected Associated Motor, Sensory, Language, and
Cognitive Capacities Not Already Included in Above

1. Motor:
   a. Walks on own or by holding onto furniture;
   b. Can squat while playing;
   c. Can throw a ball forward;
   d. Can feed self finger foods;
   e. Can stack two cubes;
   f. Can organize one-step motor planning sequence such as pushing or catching or throwing a ball.
2. Sensory:
   a. Infant explores and tolerates different textures with hands and mouth (e.g., willing to explore different foods);
   b. Infant is comfortable climbing and exploring off of the floor (e.g., on couch, table top);
   c. Not sensitive to bright lights;
   d. Not sensitive to loud noises (e.g., vacuum cleaner).
3. Language:
   a. Understands simple words like "shoe" or "kiss!";
   b. Uses sounds or a few words for specific objects;
   c. Jabbers.

4. Cognitive:
   a. Can focus and attend while playing on own for five or more minutes;
   b. Copies simple gestures like "bye-bye" or "No";
   c. Can find toy under caregiver's hand;
   d. Will try to imitate a scribble;
   e. Explores how toy works and figures out simple relationships like pulling a string to make a sound.

Behavioral Elaboration (Complex Sense of Self 2)

By 18 months the infant elaborates sequences of inter-reaction, which convey basic emotional themes.

Primary Emotional

1. Comprehends and communicates, via gestures, basic emotional themes as evidenced by the ability, with a responsive caregiver, to open and close 10 or more consecutive circles of communication (e.g., taking caregiver's hand and walking toward refrigerator, vocalizing, pointing, responding to caregiver's questioning gestures with more vocalizing and pointing; finally getting caregiver to refrigerator, getting caregiver to open door, and pointing to the desired food).
2. Imitates or copies another person's behavior, and then uses this newly learned behavior intentionally to convey an emotional theme (e.g., putting on daddy's hat and walking around the house with a big smile clearly waiting for an admiring laugh).

Emotional Range: Sensory and Motor

Elaborates complex interactions (i.e., 10 or more consecutive circles of communication) using:
1. Vocalizations and/or words;
2. Facial expressions;
3. Reciprocal touching and/or holding;
4. Movement in space (rough-and-tumble play);
5. Large motor activity (e.g., chase games, climbing games);

6. Communication across space (e.g., while playing with pots infant vocalizes to caregiver from across room. Caregiver vocalizes back. Infant continues playing and vocalizing without needing to come over and touch caregiver).

Emotional Range: Affective

1. Elaborates complex interactions (10 consecutive circles of communication) dealing with the emotional themes of:
   a. Closeness and dependency. Uses facial expressions, motor gestures, and vocalization to reach out for a hug, kiss, or cuddle. Can be coy and charming or even provocative, if necessary, in order to be close. Can also use imitation to feel close (e.g., talks on play telephone while mom talks on telephone with a friend).
   b. Pleasure and excitement. Can share a joke with another toddler, or with an adult. For example when the toddler drops some food accidentally and it makes a funny sound ("Splat!") or a mark on the floor, the toddler may giggle and look toward the other person to share in the pleasure. Funny faces, funny sounds, or imitating the behavior of adults or other toddlers may be a basis for giggles and pleasure.
   c. Assertiveness and exploration, including relative independence. Can now explore more independently and balance dependence with independence. Uses ability to communicate across space to feel close to caregiver while playing on own (e.g., may go into another room, or to a far corner of the same room, to look for a toy while periodically looking at or vocalizing to the caregiver). May also come over to touch base with caregiver and venture out again.
   d. Cautious or fearful behavior. Can now, via vocalizations, motor gestures, or a few words, tell caregiver exactly how to be protective in a new situation (e.g., hides behind caregiver but pushes caregiver toward the toy or toward new people as though to run interference), or says, "No," and hides behind caregiver.
   e. Anger. Can hit, pinch, yell, bang, scream, lie on floor as part of an organized pattern well under toddler's control. Can also give the angry cold shoulder to a wayward caregiver. Sometimes, can use the angry gesture, look, or vocalization instead of hitting, screaming, or pinching.

    f. Limit setting. Can, for example, respond to caregiver limits communicated through gradually louder vocal gestures, serious-looking facial expressions, and body postures, as well as to simple phrases like, "No, stop that!"; "Leave it alone!"; "Come here!" For example, with the above type limit setting, the toddler puts telephone down and returns to caregiver.

2. Can use imitation to deal with and recover from distress (i.e., toddler may bang hands on floor and yell after being yelled at).

Selected Associated Motor, Sensory, Language, and Cognitive Capacities Not Already Included in Above

1. Motor:
   a. Can plan motor pattern involving two or more steps (e.g., can bounce a balloon and try to catch it);
   b. Will try to imitate scribble or scribble on own;
   c. Holds crayon or pencil adaptively;
   d. Will put items in cup or toys in a box;
   e. Builds a tower with two or three blocks;
   f. Can put pegs in a pegboard;
   g. Can put round block in the round opening on a board;
   h. Can remove socks.
2. Sensory:
   a. Enjoys or tolerates various types of touch (e.g., cuddling, roughhousing, different types of clothing, brushing teeth or hair);
   b. Is comfortable with loud sounds;
   c. Is comfortable with bright lights;
   d. Is comfortable with movement in space.
3. Language:
   a. Comprehends some simple questions, carries out simple directions (e.g., with a ball);
   b. Imitates simple words;
   c. Uses words to make needs known.
4. Cognitive:
   a. Uses objects functionally (e.g., vocalizes on the toy telephone, combs hair with toy comb);
   b. Searches for a desired toy or hidden object in more than one place;
   c. Can play on own in focused manner for 15 or more minutes;
   d. Imitates behaviors just seen or seen a few minutes earlier;

   e. Recognizes family pictures;
   f. Can use a stick or other object to get another object.

Representational Capacity (Emotional Ideas I)

By 24 months the child creates mental representations of feelings and
ideas, which can be expressed symbolically (e.g., pretend play and words).

Primary Emotional

   1. Can construct, in collaboration with caregiver, simple pretend play
       patterns of at least one "idea" (e.g., dolls hugging or feeding the doll).
   2. Can use words or other symbolic means (e.g., selecting or drawing a
       series of pictures, creating a sequence of motor gestures) to commu-
       nicate a need, wish, intention, or feeling (e.g., "want that"; "me toy";
       "hungry!"; "mad!").

Emotional Range: Sensorimotor

Can communicate symbolically about intentions, wishes, needs, or feelings with:
   1. Words;
   2. Complex gestures and facial expressions (e.g., making angry facial ex-
       pressions in an exaggerated manner);
   3. Touching (e.g., lots of hugging or roughhousing as part of pretend
       drama where child is the "daddy");
   4. Motor movement (e.g., showing caregiver what to do).

Emotional Range: Affective

Can use pretend play or words employing at least one idea to communicate themes dealing with:
   1. Closeness or dependency (e.g., dolls feeding each other, child says,
       "Want mommy");
   2. Pleasure and excitement (e.g., makes funny faces like clown on TV and
       laughs);
   3. Assertiveness and exploration (e.g., cars racing, looking at a real car in
       wonderment and asking "car?");

4. Cautious or fearful behavior (e.g., says, "Scared");
5. Anger (e.g., dolls fighting or hitting, "Me mad");
6. Limit setting (e.g., child says to self, "No hit");
7. Can use pretend play and/or words to recover from and deal with tantrum or distress (e.g., after a few minutes, tantrumming child uses words and sounds to argue with caregiver).

Selected Associated Motor, Sensory, Language, and Cognitive Capacities Not Already Included in Above

1. Motor:
   a. Catches a large ball from a few feet away using arms and hands;
   b. Jumps with both feet off ground;
   c. Balances momentarily on one foot;
   d. Walks up stairs, two feet on each step at a time;
   e. Can run;
   f. Can stack more than four blocks;
   g. Can both scribble and make a single stroke with a crayon or pencil.
2. Sensory:
   a. Enjoys or tolerates various types of touch (e.g., cuddling, roughhousing, different types of clothing, brushing teeth or hair);
   b. Is comfortable with loud sounds;
   c. Is comfortable with bright lights;
   d. Is comfortable with movement in space.
3. Language:
   a. Understands simple questions: "Is mommy home?";
   b. Uses simple two-word sentences ("More milk"; "Go Bye-Bye");
   c. Can name some objects in a picture;
   d. Begins to use some pronouns.
4. Cognitive:
   a. Can attend or focus for 30 or more minutes;
   b. Can do pretend play on own;
   c. Can search for favorite toy where it was day before;
   d. Can do simple shape puzzles (two to three shapes);
   e. Can line up objects in design (e.g., a train of blocks);
   f. Points to parts of a doll;
   g. Puts round and square blocks in correct places on a board.

Representational Elaboration (Emotional Ideas 2)

By 30 months, the child, in both make-believe play and symbolic communication, can elaborate a number of ideas that go beyond basic needs (e.g., "want juice") and deal with more complex intentions, wishes, or feelings (e.g., themes of closeness or dependency, separation, exploration, assertiveness, anger, self-pride or showing off).

Primary Emotional

1. Creates pretend drama with two or more ideas (trucks are crashing and then they pick up rocks; or dolls are hugging and then have a tea party). Ideas need not be related or logically connected to one another.
2. Uses symbolic communication (e.g., words, pictures, motor patterns) to convey two or more ideas at a time in terms of complex intentions, wishes, or feelings (e.g., "Daddy play with car"; "No sleep, play"). Ideas need not be logically connected to one another.

Emotional Range: Sensory and Motor

Can communicate symbolically about intentions, wishes, or feelings with:
1. Words;
2. Complex gestures and facial expressions (e.g., acting tired and needy);
3. Touch (e.g., lots of hugging or roughhousing like they do on TV.);
4. Can participate in simple spatial and motor games with rules (e.g., taking turns in throwing a ball).

Emotional Range: Affective

Can use pretend play or other symbolic communication (e.g., words) to communicate themes containing two or more ideas dealing with:
1. Closeness or dependency (e.g., dolls say "Hug me," child says, "Give you kiss");
2. Pleasure and excitement (e.g., making funny words and laughing);
3. Assertiveness and exploration (e.g., pretend airplane zooms around the room);

4. Cautious or fearful behavior (e.g., pretend drama in which baby doll is scared of loud noise);
5. Anger (e.g., soldiers shoot pretend guns at one another);
6. Limit setting (e.g., dolls follow rules at tea party, "Must sit");
7. Uses pretend play to recover from and deal with distress (e.g., plays out eating the cookie he could not get in reality).

Selected Associated Motor, Sensory, Language, and Cognitive Capacities Not Already Included in Above

1. Motor:
   a. Walks up and down stairs;
   b. Throws ball;
   c. Stands on one foot.;
   d. Can walk on tip toes;
   e. Draws a line with crayon or pencil;
   f. Can turn a knob;
   g. Can remove a cap;
   h. Can fold paper;
   i. Can make a tower of eight or more blocks.
2. Sensory:
   a. Enjoys or tolerates various types of touch (e.g., cuddling, rough-housing, different types of clothing, brushing teeth or hair);
   b. Is comfortable with loud sounds;
   c. Is comfortable with bright lights;
   d. Is comfortable with movement in space.
3. Language:
   a. Understands sentences with two or more ideas (e.g., "You can have a cookie when we get home");
   b. Understands directions with two or more ideas;
   c. Organizes sentences with two or more ideas (e.g., "Want apple and banana");
   d. Refers to self using a pronoun.
4. Cognitive:
   a. Can point to some pictures from a verbal description;
   b. Can name objects in a picture;
   c. Can make a train of blocks after seeing it in a picture;
   d. Can repeat two or more numbers.

Representational Differentiation (Building Logical Bridges Between Ideas and Emotional Thinking)

By 36 months, ideas dealing with complex intentions, wishes, and feelings in pretend play or other types of symbolic communication are logically tied to one another. The child knows what is real from unreal and switches back and forth between fantasy and reality with little difficulty.

Primary Emotional

1. Pretend play, however unrealistic, involves two or more ideas that are logically tied to one another (e.g., "The car is visiting the moon" [and gets there] "by flying fast"). In addition, child can build on adult's pretend play idea (i.e., close a circle of communication). For example, child is cooking a soup and adult asks what is in it and child says, "rocks and dirt" or "ants and spiders."
2. Symbolic communication involves two or more ideas that are logically connected and grounded in reality: "No go to sleep"; "Want to watch television." "Why?" asks the adult. "Because not tired." Child can close symbolic circles of communication (e.g., child says "Want to go outside." Adult asks, "What will you do?" Child replies, "Play").

Emotional Range: Sensorimotor

Can communicate symbolically, logically connecting two or more ideas about intentions, wishes, needs, or feelings with:
1. Words;
2. Complex gestures and facial expressions (e.g., pretending to be an angry dog or cat);
3. Touch (e.g., lots of hugging or roughhousing as part of pretend drama in which child is the "daddy");
4. Can organize spatial and motor games with rules (e.g., takes turn in going up small incline or holds hands with others and goes around in a circle).

Emotional Range: Affective

Can use pretend play or words to communicate themes containing two or more logically connected ideas dealing with the following:

1. Closeness or dependency (e.g., doll gets hurt and mommy doll fixes it);
2. Pleasure and excitement (e.g., says bathroom words like "doody" and laughs);
3. Assertiveness and exploration (e.g., good soldier's search for missing princess);
4. Cautious or fearful behavior (e.g., scary monster scares baby doll);
5. Anger (e.g., good soldiers fight bad ones);
6. Limit setting (e.g., the soldiers can only hit bad guys because of the "rules");
7. Uses pretend play to recover from anger (e.g., plays out eating the cookie he could not get in reality).

Selected Associated Motor, Sensory, Language, and Cognitive Capacities Not Already Included in Above

1. Motor:
   a. Walks upstairs alternating feet;
   b. Catches big ball;
   c. Kicks big ball;
   d. Jumps forward;
   e. Hops;
   f. Copies circle;
   g. Cuts paper;
   h. Can unbutton buttons.
2. Sensory:
   a. Enjoys or tolerates various types of touch (e.g., cuddling, rough-housing, different types of clothing, brushing teeth or hair);
   b. Is comfortable with loud sounds;
   c. Is comfortable with bright lights;
   d. Is comfortable with movement in space.
3. Language:
   a. Understands and constructs logical bridges between ideas with full sentences;
   b. Uses "but" and "because";
   c. Answers "what," "who," "where," and "doing" type questions;
   d. Comprehends actions/verbs;
   e. Uses plurals;
   f. Uses two prepositions.

4. Cognitive:
   a. Pretend play has logical structure to it (i.e., pretend ideas are connected);
   b. Spatial designs are complex and interrelated (i.e., a house made of blocks has connected rooms);
   c. Identifies big and little as part of developing a quantitative perspective;
   d. Can identify objects by their function as part of developing abstract groupings.

42–48 Months

By 42 to 48 months, the child is capable of elaborate complex pretend play and symbolic communication dealing with complex intentions, wishes, or feelings. The play or direct communication is characterized by three or more ideas that are logically connected and informed by concepts involving causality, time, and space.

Primary Emotional

1. Elaborates complex, partially planned pretend play with three or more logically connected ideas dealing with intentions, wishes, or feelings. The planned quality (e.g., a special car is used) and "How," "Why," or "When" elaborations give depth to the drama (e.g., child sets up castle with an evil queen who captured the princess. Why did she capture the princess? "Because the princess was more beautiful." When did she capture her? "Yesterday." How will the princess get out? "You ask too many questions.").
2. Participates in reality-based circle closing symbolic conversation using three or more ideas dealing with intentions, wishes, or feelings. In a reality-based dialogue, the child can deal with causality. ("Why did you hit your brother?" "Because he took my toy." "Any other reason?" "He took my cookie.")
3. Distinguishes reality and fantasy (e.g., "That's only pretend"; "That's a dream. It's not real.").
4. Uses concepts of time and space to deal with intentions, wishes, and/or feelings. Caregiver: "Where should we look for the toy you can't find?" Child: "Let's look in my room. I was playing with it there."

Caregiver: "When do you want the cookies?" Child: "Now." Caregiver: "Not now; maybe in five minutes." Child: "No. Want it now!" Caregiver: "You can have the cookie in one, two, or five minutes." Child: "Okay. One minute."

Emotional Range: Sensorimotor

The child is able to use elaborate, complex, logically connected ideas (three or more) and communicates using:
1. Words;
2. Complex gestures and facial expressions (e.g., giving someone a dirty look, observing to see if they react, and giving them an even angrier look if they haven't apologized, and soon!);
3. Touch (e.g., giving caregiver a backrub, looking longingly in her eyes and smiling, and then asking for a new toy);
4. Can organize spatial and motor games with rules (e.g., can partially play baseball or basketball).

Emotional Range: Affective

The child is able to use elaborate, complex, logically connected ideas (three or more) when dealing with:
1. Closeness or dependency (e.g., doll gets hurt and mommy doll fixes it, and doll goes to party and meets the prince);
2. Pleasure and excitement (e.g., says bathroom words like doody and laughs, and then goes and says it to caregiver looking for her to laugh or get mad);
3. Assertiveness and exploration (e.g., good soldiers search for missing princess and find her, but have to battle with evil soldiers to save her);
4. Cautious or fearful behavior (e.g., scary monster scares baby doll, who hides under covers and then gets up and hits the monster);
5. Anger (e.g., good soldiers fight bad ones, and use secret bombs and rockets to defeat the enemy);
6. Limit setting: Child can now set limits for him- or herself by reasoning about consequence (e.g., using ideas causally and in time framework. "If I am bad now, I will be punished later."). Even though he doesn't always follow them, child now is able to understand rules in terms of limits. He also can form abstract principles. "You shouldn't be mean to them";

7. Separation and loss. Child can now picture mom in home while he is at school or in waiting room while he is in office, and relate some feelings of sadness and loss (e.g., "She is in waiting room. I miss her a little, but I am having fun.").

Selected Associated Motor, Sensory, Language, and Cognitive Capacities Not Already Included in Above

1. Motor:
   a. Skips;
   b. Hops;
   c. Rides tricycle;
   d. Catches ball;
   e. Bounces ball;
   f. Shows hand preference;
   g. Copies cross;
   h. Strings beads;
   i. Cuts across a line
2. Sensory:
   a. Enjoys or tolerates various types of touch (e.g., cuddling, roughhousing, different types of clothing, brushing teeth or hair);
   b. Is comfortable with loud sounds;
   c. Is comfortable with bright lights;
   d. Is comfortable with movement in space.
3. Language:
   a. Comprehends complex "why" questions such as, "Why do we need a house?";
   b. Can express ideas reflecting an understanding of relative degrees of feelings of wish or intention: "I am only a little mad";
   c. Can repeat a 5- to 10-word sentence;
   d. Can repeat four to seven numbers.
4. Cognitive:
   a. Can point to pictures that show an object with attributes that are first described verbally (e.g., "What do you eat with?"; "What makes food hot?");
   b. Can deal with concepts of quantity (e.g., which is biggest, which box has more marbles in it, etc.);
   c. Can identify similarities and differences with shapes and verbal concepts (e.g., triangle and rectangle or people and animals);
   d. Can recall and comprehend experiences from recent past.

General Infant Tendencies (Regulatory Patterns): All Ages

1. The infant is able to be calm and/or calm down and not be excessively irritable, clinging, active, or panicked.
2. The infant is able to calm down and take an interest in sights, sounds, and people and is not excessively withdrawn, apathetic, or unresponsive.
3. The infant is able to focus his or her attention and not be excessively distractible.
4. The infant enjoys a range of sounds including high and low pitch, loud and soft, and different rhythms, and is not upset or confused by sounds.
5. The infant enjoys various sights, including reasonably bright lights, visual designs, facial gestures, moving objects, and is not upset or confused by various sights.
6. The infant enjoys being touched (on face, arms, legs, stomach, trunk, and back), bathed and clothed, and is not bothered by things touching his or her skin.
7. The infant enjoys movement in space (being held and moved up and down, side to side, etc.), does not get upset with movement, and does not crave excessive movement.
8. The infant is able to maintain motor tone and carry out age-appropriate motor planning sequences (e.g., put fist in mouth, reach for object).
9. The infant enjoys a range of age-appropriate foods and is not bothered (e.g., with abdominal pains, skin rashes, irritability, or other symptoms) by any age-appropriate, healthy food as part of a balanced diet.
10. The infant is comfortable and asymptomatic around household odors and materials and is not bothered by any routine levels of household odors such as cleaning materials, paint, oil or gas fumes, pesticides, plastics, composite woods (e.g., plywood), or synthetic fabrics (e.g., polyester).

If the rating is less than four for any of the above, also rate the items below.

1. Infant tends to be hyper- or overly sensitive to:
   a. Touch (light or heavy);
   b. Sound (high pitch, low pitch, or loud);
   c. Sights (bright lights);

    d. His own movement in space (e.g., being moved horizontally or vertically);

    e. Smells (e.g., routine household odors, perfumes).

2. Infant tends to be hypo- or undersensitive (i.e., doesn't respond to sensations and may crave them) to:

    a. Touch;

    b. Sound;

    c. Sights;

    d. Movement in space;

    e. Smells.

    (Note that an infant may have a mixture of hyper- and hyposensitivities.)

3. Infant tends to have difficulty processing, organizing (making sense of), or sequencing:

    a. Sounds (e.g., 3-year-old following two simple directions such as "Take the glass and put it in the sink");

    b. Sights (e.g., 3-year-old identifying or copying a design like a circle);

    c. His or her own motor pattern (e.g., tying shoes);

    d. Spatial concepts (e.g., figuring out the geography of a new house).

General Caregiver Patterns (By History and/or Direct Observations)

In many families there are a number of caregivers. As one becomes aware of which parent or nanny or day care caregiver tends to do what, indicate the person and the amount of time he or she spends with the infant or child each day next to the rating (i.e., Father/3 hrs). You may need to draw additional lines. (Attach additional sheets as necessary.)

1. Caregiver tends to comfort the infant, especially when he or she is upset (by relaxed, gentle, firm holding; rhythmic vocal or visual contact; etc.), rather than tending to make the infant tenser (by being overly worried, tense, or anxious; or mechanical or anxiously over- or understimulating).

2. Caregiver tends to find appropriate levels of stimulation to interest the infant in the world (by being interesting, alert, and responsive, including offering appropriate levels of sound, sights, and touch— including the caregiver's face—and appropriate games and toys,

etc.), rather than being hyperstimulating and intrusive (e.g., picking at and poking or shaking the infant excessively to gain his attention).

3. Caregiver tends to pleasurably engage the infant in a relationship (by looking, vocalizing, gentle touching, etc.), rather than tending to ignore the infant (by being depressed, aloof, preoccupied, withdrawn, indifferent, etc.).

4. Caregiver tends to read and respond to the infant's emotional signals and needs in most emotional areas (e.g., responds to desire for closeness as well as need to be assertive, explorative, and independent), rather than either misreading signals or only responding to one emotional need. For example, caregiver can hug when baby reaches out, but hovers over baby and cannot encourage assertive exploration or vice versa.

5. Caregiver tends to encourage the infant to move forward in development, rather than to misread infant's developmental needs and overprotect, "hold on," infantilize, be overpressured and/or punitive, be fragmented and/or disorganized, or be overly concrete. For example:

   a. The caregiver helps the baby to crawl, vocalize, and gesture by actively responding to the infant's initiative and encouragement (rather than overanticipating the infant's needs and doing everything for him or her).

   b. The caregiver helps the toddler make the shift from proximal, physical dependency (e.g., being held) to feeling more secure while being independent (e.g., keeps in verbal and visual contact with toddler as he or she builds a tower on the other side of the room).

   c. The caregiver helps the 2- to 3-year-old child shift from motor discharge and gestural ways of relating to the use of "ideas" through encouraging pretend play (imagination) and language around emotional themes (e.g., gets down on the floor and plays out dolls hugging each other, separating from each other, or soldiers fighting with each other).

   d. The caregiver helps the 3- to 4-year-old take responsibility for behavior and deal with reality, rather than "giving in all the time," infantilizing, or being overly punitive.

The caregiver characteristics described above cover a number of developmentally based adaptive patterns. If in considering these patterns there is an impression that the caregiver patterns are less than optimal (i.e.,

ratings less than 4), it may be useful to consider the characteristics described below.

Caregiver tends to be:
1. Overly stimulating;
2. Withdrawn or unavailable;
3. Lacking pleasure, enthusiasm, or zest;
4. Random or chaotic in reading or responding to signals (e.g., vocalizes
   and interacts but without regard for infant's signals as in a pinching,
   poking, "rev-the-infant-up" type caregiver);
5. Fragmented and/or insensitive to context (e.g., responds to one part
   of an infant's communication but misses the "bigger pattern," as
   when a caregiver gets excessively upset and hugs her active toddler
   who accidentally banged his leg while trying to run and obviously
   wants to keep exploring the room);
6. Overly rigid and controlling. Trying to get the infant to conform to
   rigid agenda (e.g., making the toddler only play with a toy one way);
7. Concrete in reading or responding to communication (e.g., unable to
   tune into symbolic level in pretend play or in dialogue and instead
   keeps communication at behavioral and gestural levels. For example,
   a child is pretending with a toy telephone that he won't talk to his
   mother. Mother perceives this as a literal sign of rejection and refuses
   to "play anymore.");
8. Illogical in reading or responding to infant's communication (e.g.,
   the caregiver is so flooded with emotion that he or she misreads
   what is communicated. A 3½-year-old says, "I am scared of the monster, but I know it is just make believe." The caregiver explains,
   "Monsters will never get in the room because the door has a big
   lock on it and monsters can be nice, too, you know. You shouldn't
   play with these toys anyhow . . . and how did you get that scratch
   on your hand?").
9. Avoidant of selected emotional areas (e.g., in pretend play parent ignores the child's interest in aggression and always ignores separation
   themes). Consider the following emotional areas:
   a. Security and safety;
   b. Dependency ;
   c. Pleasure and excitement;
   d. Assertiveness and exploration;

e. Aggression;

f. Love;

g. Empathy;

h. Limit setting;

10. Unstable in the face of intense emotion (e.g., caregiver can support development only if emotions are not too intense; if emotions are strong, tends to become chaotic, unpredictable, withdrawn, or overly rigid).

Suggestions for Eliciting the Infant's Emotional and Developmental Capacities

To observe the infant's emotional and developmental capacities, observe 15 to 20 minutes or more of free interaction between infant and caregiver, followed, as needed, by free interaction between the infant and clinician. If the infant or child does not evidence age-expected patterns, the clinician or caregiver may attempt to elicit age-appropriate developmental capacities using some of the suggestions described below. These suggestions are intended only to help get things going.

The capacities to be elicited are listed in terms of the six stages of emotional development. Each set of capacities, while usually first in evidence at a certain period in infancy or early childhood, continues as the child grows. The level a child is at, as well as those he or she may have mastered, should be observed. When the suggestions only refer to the age at which a child first masters a particular capacity, the clinician should improvise a way to support that capacity in an older child (e.g., wooing an older child into a relationship with play and smiles rather than only smiles and sounds).

Self-Regulation and Interest in the World

1. To attend
2. To be calm
3. To experience sensation through each sensory modality without being hyper- or hyposensitive
4. To organize motor movements

To elicit, hold baby or put baby in infant seat with mother or father near. Offer baby opportunity to look at caregiver or clinician as one offers different types of sensations.

1. *Sights.* Beginning with a 6- to 8-foot distance, make funny faces and gradually move closer (no closer than 2 to 3 feet). Hold for 30 or more seconds at what appears to be optimal distance, moving slowly a little to the left, and then a little to the right. Then gradually move away. If baby does not clearly look at you for five or more seconds, repeat exercise while shining a light (use a flashlight) on your face; if still no response, try again putting a colorful toy in your mouth (e.g., a rattle).

2. *Sounds.* Experiment with different sounds, beginning with a soft, medium pitch and going higher and lower in pitch (while still soft). Increase loudness two times. Vary pitch at each higher sound level and note if and when baby looks at you for five or more seconds. To be sure he/she is looking at you, move a little to the left or right and see if he/she follows your voice with his/her eyes.

3. *Touch.* Stroke the baby's arms, legs, feet, hands, back, top of head, and if possible face and lips with (1) light touch (like a feathery tickle); (2) medium gentle touch; and (3) gentle firm pressure (a little squeeze or gentle rhythmic massage). Note reactions: no reaction; positive reaction (e.g., pleasure or attentiveness is increased); or negative reaction (e.g., pulling hand away, crying or making sounds suggesting discomfort).

4. *Smell.* If mother wears a cologne or perfume, you can put a little on your finger and put it under baby's nose. Alternatively, use a little lemon juice. Observe calm, pleasurable, focused, or indifferent response versus crying or pulling away.

5. *Movement in Space.* While firmly holding baby, gently and slowly move him/her up and down and side to side and then slowly spin around with him/her. Gradually increase speed and vigor of each type of movement, but stop and slow down as soon as infant gives any sign of lack of pleasure. Note what types of movement are pleasurable or aversive. Observe if he/she craves vigorous movement.

6. *Motor Patterns.* As caregiver or clinician holds infant, observe if muscle tone is loose (low) (e.g., infant doesn't cooperate in the cuddle) or tight (high) so that infant feels overly stiff. See if age-expected motor milestones are being mastered. Make up games such as holding head up, turning to voice, reaching for toy, and later on, crawling for a favorite rattle, to elicit age-appropriate movements. See if baby can plan

sequences of movements, such as putting hand in own mouth or systematically examining a new toy. Mom's, dad's, or the clinician's hair, nose, or hand can be the toy as well.

Note that many of the above capacities can be observed in the free play of the older infant, toddler, or young child.

Forming Relationships, Attachment, and Engagement

1. Taking an interest in another person through looking, listening, or moving toward them.
2. Evidencing pleasure in relating to another person through smiles, a joyful look, or just a sense of warm comfort.
3. Seeking out warmth and pleasure with another person through communicating a wish for closeness (e.g., reaching up for a cuddle or jumping into parent's lap, or snuggling warmly).

To elicit, position yourself near baby (who may be in parent's lap, in infant seat, or on floor). Begin to flirt with and woo baby with interesting facial expressions; warm, inviting sounds; and inviting motor gestures, such as moving face from side to side or back and forth. Be patient and start from 8 to 10 feet away and move in slowly. If the baby seems cautious or concerned, stop moving in and move back and forth, keeping your warm, cooing, funny face, vocalizations, and head movements going. Experiment with the different vocal tones. Also, feel free to put funny toys in your mouth or on your head. Observe if the infant is evidencing signs of relating (e.g., a smile, or vocalizations, rhythmic arm and leg movements, reaching out to you and flirting, or just being coy).

For an older child, any type of play may serve as a vehicle for wooing the child with your voice, smiles, touch, or gestural exchanges. Always move in very slowly, warmly, and sensitively.

Two-Way, Purposeful Communication

1. Initiating gestures (smiles, vocalizations, deliberate motor movements, such as pointing, reaching out to be picked up, covering face).
2. Responding to caregiver's gesture with gestures (closing or completing a circle of communication by, for example, exchanging one toy for another, or searching for the desired toy or squeezing dad's nose after it goes "toot toot").

To elicit, place yourself in front of baby on the floor with the baby up on all fours, lying on stomach, or sitting. Make sure you are three to six feet away at ground level. Create opportunities for interaction. Put a brightly colored squeezable ball in your hand and offer it to baby. If he takes it and examines it, hold your hand out and see if he will give it back. Support your action with words, "Can I have it back?" Use lots of facial gestures (nodding, etc.) and animated hand gestures, which say, "Give it to me." If he holds on to it, offer another toy in exchange. If he won't give it up, gently take it out of his hand, and slowly hide it under your hand and see if he takes it back. If he won't take the toy, try putting the toy in your mouth and move close enough for him to take it. If necessary, try over and over with different toys. While interacting, respond to baby's sounds, facial expressions, or motor gestures with sounds and gestures of your own.

You may substitute other activities for the above as long as it creates interactive opportunities (e.g., peek-a-boo game, etc.).

Behavioral Organization, Problem-Solving, and Internalization

Initiating and responding in a chain of purposeful interactions. Many circles are opened and closed in a row. Circles of communication using gestures are employed to negotiate basic emotional themes such as closeness, anger, curiosity, exploration, and independence.

To elicit, begin playing with a real or toy telephone and pretend to talk to someone else. See if toddler or child comes over and copies what you are doing or tries to babble on the telephone in his own way. If he takes phone, ask for it back, saying, "I want to talk," and see if he lets you talk for a while, and so on. If he won't give it back to you, flirt with him, offer an exchange, and, if necessary, gently take it and see if he vocalizes or gestures to get it back or just grabs it back. Pick up another phone and see if he will "talk" with you phone to phone.

If the phone won't get his attention, put on a silly hat and see if he will take it off your head and use it. Try to get it back like above.

If neither of the above works, walk around on all fours, pretending to be a horsy, and see if he rides you. If you make noises, does he?

If none of these ideas works, follow what was described under "Two-Way Purposeful Communication." Feel free to improvise and support complex interactions in other ways as well.

The goal is to see if the toddler can close a number of circles in a row.

Representational Capacity (Emotional Ideas)

1. Initiating pretend play (e.g., dolls hugging or fighting).
2. Initiating symbolic communication to convey intentions, wishes, or feelings (as compared to just labeling a picture or object).

To elicit, have toys, including dolls, action figures, cars, trucks, a house, furniture, kitchen and cooking utensils, a comb, toothbrush, two telephones, and an airplane or rocket. See what the child starts doing (e.g., pushing a car). Add a little doll to the car, saying, "He wants a ride," and see if the child builds on your gestures and words and begins a pretend drama such as the doll riding to the store. If the child opens the door to the toy house, say, "He [doll] wants to go in," and see if he/she incorporates your doll into a pretend drama.

If the child just sits still without initiating any play, try to establish some shared attention and a few simple gestural interchanges such as offering to hand him/her a doll or animal. He/She may nod or turn away and in this way begin a gestural interchange. You may put the doll in his/her lap and say, "Dolly hungry; wants to eat," and see what he/she does. Or you may begin feeding the doll, put it in the child's lap and say, "Wants more."

You may substitute other initiatives for these if they create an opportunity for the child to initiate a pretend sequence. Do not tell child what to do. Create an opportunity. To evidence this capacity, the child need not do what you expect; he/she only needs to initiate pretend play (e.g., you say, "Dolly is hungry," and child takes doll and has it hit another doll while saying, "Bad boy.").

Representational Differentiation (Building Logical Bridges Between Ideas and Emotional Thinking 2)

1. Connect pretend sequences together logically (dolls hug and get mad and fight);
2. Connecting symbolic communications together logically ("I don't like broccoli because it tastes bad");
3. Connect visual/spatial concepts together (e.g., figuring out geography of a new house, as evidenced in going upstairs and coming down and finding mom in the dining room or in knowing directions, finding things that are hidden, or building houses or farms with many interconnected parts).

To elicit, begin pretend play as described above. Only in addition to saying, "Dolly is hungry," mention other feelings ("Dolly wants a hug"; "Dolly is mad and wants to fight"). See if and how the dolly you give a voice to is incorporated (or not) into the child's play.

If Dolly is incorporated into the child's play or the child on his own initiates a pretend sequence, ask questions that create opportunities for logical reasoning (connecting ideas). They include, "Why are they hugging or fighting or exploring?" "How did that happen?" "What is this or that?" See if child connects pretend sequences or ideas. He need not respond as you want him to: "Why is the dolly hitting the dog?" Child: "Because they are from outer space and space animals like to fight" or "I don't know and stop asking questions!" Look for logical bridges between ideas, but not necessarily logical ideas.

Also discuss daily events with the child: "What do you like to play?" "Why/What do you like to eat?" etc.

To elicit the child's ability for spatial reasoning (how the child thinks nonverbally, which includes such abilities as a sense of direction, and constructing drawings of houses or farms), and reasoning about the physical properties of the world (these abilities are hard to elicit in the office), the following activities may prove useful. Hide an object the child takes an interest in, such as a little doll or car or rabbit's foot. First, hide it under a piece of paper with the child seeing you do it and see if she gets it. Next, hide the object in a box. Next hide it in a box and in turn put that box into a bigger box and see if she can find it (now that it is displaced twice). Any variation on this theme may be useful. The goal is to see how well the child figures out ever more complex spatial relations.

Another game that may get at this ability is a variation on the old shell game or three card Monte. Through speed of hand, you hide an object that the child likes, such as a key, under one of three boxes or shells. You make it look like it is in the middle one, but it is under one of the corner ones. See how many trials it takes for the child to figure it out. This can be done with cards also (i.e., find the ace or queen). If the child can look for the object in other than the middle by the third trial, he evidences a differentiated level of spatial reasoning.

Other types of activities to elicit spatial abilities might include creating a maze-like structure out of furniture, cardboard, or pillows (like the mirror room of an amusement park), and see how long it takes the child to solve the maze in order to find the new toy or keys.

This section has described only a few semistructured ways of helping a child demonstrate his emotional and developmental capacities. These suggestions should only be used if free play is unsuccessful in eliciting the child's capacities. They only start the process going. The clinician or caregiver needs to follow the child's lead and keep the action moving. A judgment can then be made about the child's various emotional and developmental capacities. The above play activities may also be useful in helping the infant or young child practice his or her emerging functional capacities. Clinicians, educators, and caregivers should consider these as examples of the types of activities that help an infant or young child explore his or her relationship with them in a way that supports developmental progress.

References

Doherty, S. C. (1991). *An investigation of depression in infancy and early childhood from a transactional, developmental structuralist perspective.* Doctoral dissertation. Saybrook Institute.

Greenspan, S. I. (1992). *Infancy and early childhood: The practice of clinical assessment and intervention with emotional and developmental challenges.* Madison, CT: International Universities Press.

Greenspan, S. I. & Lieberman, A. (1989a). A quantitative approach to the clinical assessment of representational elaboration and differentiation in children two to four. In S. I. Greenspan & G. H. Pollock (Eds.), *The Course of Life, Vol. II, Early Childhood* (pp. 387–442). Madison, CT: International Universities Press.

Greenspan, S. I. & Lieberman, A. (1989b). Infants, mothers, and their interaction: A quantitative clinical approach to developmental assessment. In S. I. Greenspan & G. H. Pollock (Eds.), *The Course of Life, Vol. I, Infancy* (pp. 503–560). Madison, CT: International Universities Press.

Hofheimer, J. A., Lieberman, A., Strauss, M., & Greenspan, S. I. (1983). Short-term temporal stability of mother-infant interactions in the first year of life. Los Angeles, CA: Paper presented at the 93rd Meeting of the American Psychological Association.

Hofheimer, J. A., Strauss, M., Poisson, S. S., & Greenspan, S. I. (1981). *The reliability, validity and generalizability of assessments of transactions between infants and their caregivers: A multi-center design.* (Working Paper). National Institute of Mental Health: Clinical Infant Development Program.

3

The FEAS Developmental Growth Chart for Observation and Developmental Monitoring

Stanley I. Greenspan, M.D.
Serena Wieder, Ph.D.

One of the most important components of a functional, developmental approach to intervention is for clinicians to initiate the interventions at the earliest possible time. Early intervention minimizes a child's ongoing functional impairments and missed opportunities for mastering critical functional skills. For example, many children who are diagnosed between ages 2½ and 4 with autistic spectrum disorders began evidencing a subtle deficit in complex preverbal interactive problem solving patterns between 12 and 18 months of age (Greenspan & Wieder, 1997). The children who are not helped to engage in complex social problem-solving interactions at this age (e.g., taking daddy by the hand to the toy area and pointing to the desired play object) miss an opportunity for mastering critical social, emotional, language, and cognitive skills.

There is mounting evidence that the absence of critical functional developmental capacities is associated with increased likelihood of severe developmental disorders. For example, Baron-Cohen, Frith, and Leslie (1988) demonstrated that by 18 months of age, a child's lack of a type of functional social pointing (which involves complex social interaction and reciprocity) and early forms of pretend play are associated with autistic spectrum disorders. Dawson, Warrenburg, and Fuller (1982) showed that a child's lack of early forms of social reciprocity at 12 months of age is also associated with autistic patterns, and Tanguay, Robertson, and Derrick (1998) isolated social reciprocity as an essential dimension of autistic spectrum disorders. Furthermore, Teitelbaum and Teitelbaum (1999) implicated early functional motor behavior patterns in developmental disorders.

Findings such as these, together with the growing road map of social, emotional, cognitive, language, and motor milestones, provide the basis for delineating essential functional developmental landmarks (Greenspan, 1992; Greenspan & Lourie, 1981).

Therefore, just as a child's physical growth can be charted, functional developmental progress should be monitored to help identify difficulties at the earliest possible age. To facilitate this goal, Figure 1 presents a functional developmental growth chart similar to the physical growth chart. The Developmental Growth Chart enables clinicians to look at the pattern of a child's growth, rather than simply at a few items at a certain age. Patterns of change over time often provide the most useful information about a child's abilities.

In Figure 1, the functional developmental stages are listed on the vertical axis. The child's age is on the horizontal axis. A 45-degree line shows the expected age range at which a child is expected to master each milestone. Historically, clinicians have approached children's development in terms of isolated areas, such as motor development, the functioning of the senses, aspects of language and cognition, spatial problem-solving, social functioning, etc. When looking at separate areas of development, a child can operate at a relatively advanced level in one area (e.g., motor development), and yet have significant challenges in another area (e.g., language development). Although specific aspects of development are very important to identify and assess, for screening purposes it is more useful to look at the full range of a child's functional capacities. These capacities represent the way in which the child uses all his/her abilities together.

The child's functional emotional capacities require a coming together of the child's motor skills, sensory processing capacities, and cognitive and language capacities under the guidance of his emotional intent and proclivities. This includes the child's ability to focus and attend; engage with others; intentionally communicate needs (such as reaching to be picked

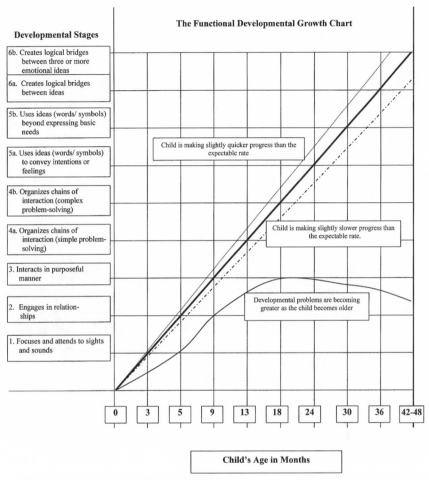

The Functional Developmental Growth Chart

Developmental Stages

6b. Creates logical bridges between three or more emotional ideas

6a. Creates logical bridges between ideas

5b. Uses ideas (words/ symbols) beyond expressing basic needs

5a. Uses ideas (words/ symbols) to convey intentions or feelings

4b. Organizes chains of interaction (complex problem-solving)

4a. Organizes chains of interaction (simple problem-solving)

3. Interacts in purposeful manner

2. Engages in relation-ships

1. Focuses and attends to sights and sounds

Child is making slightly quicker progress than the expectable rate

Child is making slightly slower progress than the expectable rate.

Developmental problems are becoming greater as the child becomes older

0 3 5 9 13 18 24 30 36 42-48

Child's Age in Months

Figure 1

up); move on to complex problem-solving interactions (such as taking the caregiver by the hand to find the desired toy); use ideas and words to communicate basic needs as well as to explore imaginative thinking (make-believe); and combine ideas together with logical bridges as a basis for rational thinking, advanced logical communication, and problem-solving involving a functional sequence.

When a child is unable to master these functional milestones, different components of development might be contributing to the child's difficulty. Simply having a mild motor delay, for example, may not derail relating, communicating, or thinking. On the other hand, a mild motor delay coupled with severe family dysfunction, or a very severe motor delay, might derail one or more functional milestones. The functional milestones are the common pathways or doors through which the child navigates. The child's ability or inability to walk through these doors provides an important picture of his/her adaptive and maladaptive development and the need for further evaluation and, possibly, intervention.

As can be observed, on the chart (Fig. 1) the child's functional developmental accomplishments can be charted in relation to the age at which the accomplishment is expected to emerge and the age at which it does emerge. When a child does not evidence the next milestone during the expected time interval, the last functional capacity mastered is recorded on the chart. The next milestone, if it occurs, is then recorded at whatever later time it is manifested. The 45-degree line indicates a typical developmental curve. A child who is precocious in a predictable manner (e.g., three months ahead of expectations) will have a functional developmental curve that parallels the typical one and is a little above it. A child who is a little behind the expected curve (e.g., three months behind on the functional developmental milestones) will have a curve that parallels the typical curve but may fall just below it. When a child's curve is below the norm, the child should be evaluated to identify what factors may be contributing to the developmental lag and what may be helpful in responding to them.

Most worrisome, and a red flag, is a curve that arcs away from the line, i.e., the distance from that line keeps growing, indicating a delay that is increasing as the child becomes older (shown as the lowest line on the chart). At the point the curve begins arcing is the point at which immediate assessment and possible intervention is indicated. It is also a red flag if the developmental curve is running parallel to the typical curve, but is significantly below it.

This developmental chart can be used by parents, educators (including daycare staff), and other childcare facilitators to monitor a child's functional capacities. In general, a child will have mastered the milestone when he can engage in the behavior associated with the milestone most of the time. Mastery is not indicated in a child who only occasionally is able to mobilize the age-appropriate milestone or requires extraordinary support to perform it. The Functional Developmental Growth Chart Questionnaire on the next few pages will help in determining the child's functional developmental level.

To further facilitate the monitoring of emotional functioning and related areas of sensory processing and motor planning, we have also included two tables (Table 3-1 and Table 3-2). These provide an additional framework for systematizing the child's functional, emotional, and developmental capacities. They also provide a framework to guide, organize, and rate clinical observations of regulatory capacities, including sensory modulation, auditory processing, visual-spatial processing, and motor planning.

Functional Developmental Growth Chart
Questionnaire

To assess if a child has achieved a new functional milestone, the answer must be "yes" to all the questions under that milestone. If the answer is "no" to even one question, the child has not yet mastered the stage. Remember, the growth chart is simply a visual tool to draw attention to those developmental areas in which a child is progressing as expected and those where he/she may be facing some challenges.

By 3 Months (Stage 1- Self-Regulation and Interest in the World):

- Does your infant usually show an interest in things around him/her by looking at sights and turning toward sounds?

By 5 Months (Stage 2 — Forming Relationships, Attachment, and Engagement):
(Ask the question from the prior category plus the new one from this category.)

- Does your baby seem happy or pleased to see favorite people: looking and smiling, making sounds or some other gesture, like moving arms, that indicates pleasure or delight?

By 9 Months (Stage 3 — Two-Way, Purposeful Communication):
(Ask the question from the prior category plus the new ones from this category.)

- Is your baby able to show what he/she wants by reaching for or pointing at something, reaching out to be picked up, or making purposeful special noises?
- Does your baby respond to people talking or playing with him/her by making sounds, faces, initiating gestures (reaching), etc.?

By 14 to 18 Months (Stage 4 — Behavioral Organization, Problem-Solving, and Internalization):
(Ask the question from the prior category plus the new ones from this category.)

- Is your toddler (by 14 months) able to show what he/she wants or needs by using actions, such as leading you by the hand to open a door or pointing to find a toy?

- Is your toddler (by 18 months) able to orchestrate more complex chains of interaction as he/she solves problems and shows you what he/she wants, including such things as getting food, for example (does he/she take your hand, lead you to the refrigerator, tug on the handle, and point to a particular food or bottle of juice or milk?)
- Is your toddler (by 18 months) able to use imitation, such as copying your sounds, words, or motor gestures, as part of a playful, ongoing interaction?

By 24 to 30 Months (Stage 5 — Representational Capacity: Uses Ideas— Words or Symbols—to Convey Intentions or Feelings):
(Ask the question from the prior category plus the new ones from this category.)

- Does your toddler (by 24 months) ever respond to people talking with or playing with him/her by using words or sequences of sounds that are clearly an attempt to convey a word?
- Is your toddler (by 24 months) able to imitate familiar pretend-like actions, such as feeding or hugging a doll?
- Is your toddler (by 24 months) able to meet some basic needs with one or a few words, such as "juice," "open," or "kiss"? (A parent may have to say the word first.)
- Is your toddler (by 24 months) able to follow simple one-step directions from a caregiver to meet some basic need, for example, "The toy is there," or "Come give mommy a kiss."
- Is your toddler (by 30 months) able to engage in interactive pretend play with an adult or another child (feeding dollies, tea parties, etc.)?
- Is your toddler (by 30 months) able to use ideas—words or symbols—to share his/her delight or interest ("See truck!")?
- Is your toddler able to use symbols—words, pictures, and organized games—while enjoying and interacting with one or more peers?

By 36 to 48 Months (Stage 6 — Representational Differentiation: Creates Logical Bridges Between Ideas and Emotional Thinking)
(Ask the question from the prior category plus the new ones from this category.)

- Is your toddler (by 36 months) able to use words or other symbols (for example, pictures) to convey likes or dislikes, such as "want that" or "no want that"?

- Is your toddler (by 36 months) able to engage in pretend play with another person in which the story or drama makes sense? (e.g., in the story, do the bears go visit grandmother and then have a big lunch)?
- Is your toddler (by 36 months) able to begin to explain wishes or needs. For example, a conversation may contain an exchange such as: "Mommy, go out." "What are you going to do outside?" "Play"? The child may need multiple-choice help from the parent, such as "What will you do, play or sleep?"
- Can your preschooler (by 48 months) explain reasons for wanting something or wanting to do something (e.g., "Why do you want the juice?.".."Because I'm thirsty")?
- Is your preschooler (by 48 months) occasionally able to use feelings as a reason for a wish or behavior (e.g., "I don't want to do that because I'm happy/excited/sad")?
- Is your preschooler (by 48 months) able to engage in interactive pretend dramas with both peers as well as adults in which there are a number of elements that logically fit together (e.g., the children go to school, do work, have lunch, and meet an elephant on the way home)?
- Is your preschooler (by 48 months) able to make a logical conversation with four or more give-and-take sequences about a variety of topics, ranging from negotiating foods and bedtimes to talking about friends or school?

Between Ages 4—7 Years:
(Ask the question from the prior category plus the new ones from this category.)

- Is your child developing friendships with peers, including play dates outside of school?
- Is your child warm and close with his parents?
- Is your child able to negotiate with two or more people at the same time (e.g., go back and forth between mom and dad to try to get a later bed time or an extra cookie or try to convince two peers to play the game his way)?
- Is your child able to compare two ideas such as explaining why he likes one friend better than another friend or one food better than another food?
- Is your child able to discuss how and why he feels a certain way?
- Is your child able to regulate his impulses and his fears and anxieties (control his behavior and calm down with a little bit of support)?
- Is he beginning to master academic challenges, such as learning to read, count, add and subtract, and write?

Table 3-1.
Levels of Organizing and/or Representing Emotions and Experiences

Developmental Level	Level of Organizing and Representing
Shared attention and regulation	Affective interest in sights, sound, touch, movement, and other sensory experiences. Also, initial experiences of modulating affects (i.e., calming down).
Engagement and relating	Pleasurable affects characterize relationships. Growing feelings of intimacy.
Two-way intentional communication	A range of affects become used in back-and-forth affective signaling to convey intentions (e.g., reading and responding to affective signals).
Complex, problem-solving gestures. Organization of presymbolic self.	Affective interactions organized into action or behavioral patterns to express wishes and needs and solve problems (showing someone what you want with a pattern of actions rather than words or pictures). a. Fragmented level (little islands of intentional problem-solving behavior). b. Polarized level (organized patterns of behavior expressing only one or another feeling states, e.g., organized aggression and impulsivity or organized clinging, needy, dependent behavior or organized fearful patterns). c. Integrated level (different emotional patterns—dependency, assertiveness, pleasure, etc.—organized into integrated, problem-solving affective interactions such as flirting, seeking closeness, and then getting help to find a needed object).
Creating representations (or ideas)	1. Words and actions used together (ideas are acted out in action, but words are also used to signify the action). 2. Somatic or physical words to convey feeling state ("My muscles are exploding," "Head is aching"). 3. Putting desires or feelings into actions (hugging, hitting, biting). 4. Using action words instead of actions to convey intent ("Hit you!"). 5. Conveying feelings as real rather than as signals ("I'm mad" or "Hungry" or "Need a hug" as compared with "I feel mad" or "I feel hungry" or "I feel like I need a hug"). In the first instance, the feeling state demands action and is very close to action, and in the second one, it's more a signal for something going on inside that leads to a consideration of many possible thoughts and/or actions. 6. Global feeling states ("I feel awful," "I feel OK," etc.). 7. Polarized feeling states (feelings tend to be characterized as all good or all bad).
Representational differentiation and emotional thinking	1. Differentiated feelings (gradually there are more and more subtle descriptions of feeling states—loneliness, sadness, annoyance, anger, delight, happiness, etc.). 2. Creating connections between differentiated feeling states ("I feel angry when you are mad at me").
Triangular Thinking	Triadic interactions among feeling states ("I feel left out when Susie likes Janet better than me").

One may use the table above, if clinically appropriate, in the following way. One may indicate:

1. Highest level achieved — emotional range of highest level —
    a. Full range (i.e., this level is achieved with regard to the full range of age-expected feelings or affects from dependency to assertiveness and pleasure).
    b. Mild constrictions (i.e., most emotions can be expressed or organized at this level, but selected emotions or very intense forms of the emotion may not be organized or represented [extreme anger or loss]).
    c. Moderate constrictions—Major feeling states cannot be represented or organized at this level (anger, assertiveness cannot be well represented or organized).
    d. Severe constrictions — A number of major emotions cannot be represented or organized at this level and only certain narrow and selected feeling states can be represented and organized at this level (superficial expressions of contentment).
2. Typical level achieved (level of organization or representation used most of the time).
3. Level used with intense feeling states, conflicts, fears, frustrations, or anxieties (the level used to cope when the going is very challenging; for example, some individuals who can reflect on feelings ordinarily will regress to an action mode and become impulsive when frustrated or very angry).

Table 3-2. Sensory Processing/Motor Planning Questionnaire-
Rating Scale[1]
Stanley I. Greenspan, M.D.

Sensory Modulation	0 = Not at all 2 = A little 4 = A medium amount 6 = A lot

Tactile

Hypersensitive
Are you sensitive to touch, for example, preferring
loose to tight clothing; smooth corduroys or velour to
scratchy wools and/or

0 . . . . . .2 . . . . . .4 6

Do you dislike getting your hands in mushy, messy
things and/or

0 . . . . . .2 . . . . . .4 6

Do you dislike light, feathery touching on your arms
and legs?

0 . . . . . .2 . . . . . .4 6

Hyposensitive
Are you relatively underreactive to different kinds of
touch, enjoying seeking out lots of tactile contact
(e.g., you like to touch everything in sight) and/or

0 . . . . . .2 . . . . .4 6

Do you enjoy getting your hands in messy things?

0 . . . . . .2 . . . . . .4 6

Pain

Hypersensitive
Are you very sensitive to pain so that any scrape or
bang tends to be very uncomfortable and even a little
scary?

0 . . . . . .2 . . . . . .4 6

Hyposensitive
Are you relatively underreactive to pain, enjoying
rough-and-tumble sports, getting over falls or bangs
pretty quickly?

0 . . . . . .2 . . . . . .4 6

Sounds

Hypersensitive
Do you tend to be very sensitive to certain frequencies
of sound, disliking, for example, low frequency sounds
such as motorized household appliances (vacuum
cleaners, blenders, etc.) or, alternatively, high-pitched
music, such as violins or piccolos or very loud noises
or loud music?

0 . . . . . .2 . . . . . .4 6

Hyposensitive
Are you relatively underreactive to sound, enjoying all
frequencies of sound, including low-pitched motor
sounds, high-pitched sounds, loud music or noise?

0 . . . . . .2 . . . . . .4 6

---

[1] This questionnaire can be used with an older child or adult or with a parent to help the parent describe their child. When these questions are asked of a parent, the "you" should be changed to "your child," e.g., "Is `your child' sensitive to touch, etc.

Continued

Table 3-2. *Continued*

Sights

Hypersensitive

Are you relatively sensitive to bright lights (preferring
dimmer lighting or not enjoying the midday sun)?   0 . . . . . .2 . . . . . .4 6

Are you sensitive and easily overloaded by lots of
bright colors in movies, TV, or pictures?   0 . . . . . .2 . . . . . .4 6

Hyposensitive

Are you relatively underreactive to sights, especially
enjoying bright lights, animated bright colors, and do
you require very vivid visual input to maintain interest?   0 . . . . . .2 . . . . . .4 6

Movement

Hypersensitive

Are you relatively sensitive to movement, tending to
be cautious, for example, rather than liking to move
around a lot?   0 . . . . . .2 . . . . . .4 6

Do you enjoy sitting or standing still rather than
running, jumping, or skipping around the room?   0 . . . . . .2 . . . . . .4 6

Hyposensitive

Are you relatively under-sensitive to movement,
enjoying moving around all the time, craving
movement, and enjoying running, jumping, spinning,
and being on the go.   0 . . . . . .2 . . . . . .4 6

Movement in space

Hypersensitive

Are you sensitive to movement in space, for example,
disliking rollercoasters or rides where you're upside
down or gymnastic type activities where you're
climbing to high places and swinging?   0 . . . . . .2 . . . . . .4 6

Hyposensitive

Are you under-sensitive to movement in space,
enjoying or craving amusement park rides, such as
rollercoasters and/or activities on the playground
where you're off the ground or upside down
(e.g., monkey bars)   0 . . . . . .2 . . . . . .4 6

Motor Planning and Sequencing — Gross Motor

Strong

Are you relatively good, for your age, at carrying out a
complex set of actions using gross motor activities, for
example, learning a new dance step or learning how to
play a new sport and/or can you negotiate your way
through an obstacle course?   0 . . . . . .2 . . . . . .4 6

Weak

Are you relatively weak at carrying out complex action
sequences, such as are involved in learning new dances,
sports, or solving obstacle courses?   0 . . . . . .2 . . . . . .4 6

Table 3-2. *Continued*

Motor Planning and Sequencing — Fine Motor

Strong
Are you relatively good for your age at copying shapes,
penmanship, and/or being able to draw pictures with
many elements to them relatively quickly?   0 . . . . . .2 . . . . . .4 6

Weak
Are you relatively weak and/or slow in penmanship or
copying shapes?   0 . . . . . .2 . . . . . .4 6

Sequencing Ideas

Strong
Are you relatively strong in sequencing ideas, as in
spontaneously arguing a point of view logically and
cohesively and/or constructing an essay in which one
point logically follows another point?   0 . . . . . .2 . . . . . .4 6

Weak
Are you relatively weak in being able to sequence ideas
in terms of constructing logical arguments or
step-by-step discussions in an essay (instead, for
example, tending to jump around from one subject to
another—intuitively and creatively, perhaps—but with
more difficulty keeping arguments tightly sequenced)?   0 . . . . . .2 . . . . . .4 6

Auditory Processing—Language

Memory — Strong
Are you able to follow multi-step verbal directions
easily and effortlessly for your age—compared to other
individuals in your age range?   0 . . . . . .2 . . . . . .4 6

Memory — Weak
Is it relatively hard for you to follow multi-step verbal
directions, for example, when a teacher or instructor is
asking you to do three or four things in a row?   0 . . . . . .2 . . . . . .4 6

Comprehension — Strong
Do you have a relatively easy time, for your age, when
hearing a lecture or story in seeing the big picture—
understanding the main point and how other points
relate to the main point?   0 . . . . . .2 . . . . . .4 6

Comprehension — Weak
Do you have a relatively difficult time seeing the big
picture, instead getting fascinated, perhaps, with some
of the specifics and having a hard time understanding
the overall point of view of the discussion?   0 . . . . . .2 . . . . . .4 6

Ideational Range — Strong
Do you tend to have a wide range of ideas about any
subject and be interested in a wide range of subjects?
In other words, could you go on and on and on, free-
associating about almost any subject under the sun and/
or have a rich and vivid imagination?   0 . . . . . .2 . . . . . .4 6

Continued

Table 3-2. *Continued*

Ideational Range — Weak
Do you tend to have more focused interests and find it
difficult to elaborate on different subjects. In other
words, if asked to talk about your ideas about any
given subject, it would be relatively hard to talk for
more than a minute or two without having first studied
the subject and/or do you tend to have a more
focused imagination, preferring the real world to the
imaginative one?   0 . . . . . .2 . . . . . .4 6

Visual-Spatial Thinking

Creating Visual Imagery — Strong
Can you easily "picture" the face of a family member
clearly and vividly in your mind?   0 . . . . . .2 . . . . . .4 6

Creating Visual Imagery — Weak
Is it hard to "picture" someone (perhaps it's easier to
think about their attributes in words)?   0 . . . . . .2 . . . . . .4 6

Constructing a Spatial Picture — Strong
Can you systematically search for lost or hidden
objects and often find what's missing and/or do you
have a hard time with a sense of direction?   0 . . . . . .2 . . . . . .4 6

Constructing a Spatial Picture — Weak
Do you tend to look in one or two places for lost or
hidden objects and give up and/or do you have a hard
time with a sense of direction?   0 . . . . . .2 . . . . . .4 6

Big-Picture Type Thinking

Strong
Do you enjoy and are you relatively gifted at broad,
theoretical explorations?   0 . . . . . .2 . . . . . .4 6

Weak
Is broad, theoretical exploration difficult for you? 0 . . . . . .2 . . . . . .4 6

Detail-Oriented Thinking

Strong
Do you prefer and are you gifted with the specifics of
a subject?   0 . . . . . .2 . . . . . .4 6

Weak
Do you find dealing with the specifics or details of a
subject difficult?   0 . . . . . .2 . . . . . .4 6

References

Baron-Cohen, S., Frith, U., & Leslie, A. M. (1988). Autistic children's understanding of seeing, knowing, and believing. *British Journal of Developmental Psychology, 4,* 315–324.

Dawson, G., Warrenburg, S., & Fuller, P. (1982). Cerebral lateralization in individuals diagnosed as autistic in early childhood. *Brain Lang, 15,* 353–368.

Greenspan, S. I. (1992). *Infancy and early childhood: The practice of clinical assessment and intervention with emotional and developmental challenges.* Madison, CT: International Universities Press.

Greenspan, S. I. & Lourie, R. S. (1981). Developmental structuralist approach to the classification of adaptive and pathologic personality organizations: Infancy and early childhood. *Am.J.Psychiatry, 138,* 725-735.

Greenspan, S. I. & Wieder, S. (1997). Developmental patterns and outcomes in infants and children with disorders in relating and communicating: A chart review of 200 cases of children with autistic spectrum diagnoses. *Journal of Developmental and Learning Disorders, 1,* 87–141.

Tanguay, P. E., Robertson, J., & Derrick, A. (1998). A dimensional classification of autism spectrum disorder by social communication domains. *J.Am.Acad.Child Adolesc.Psychiatry, 37,* 271–277.

Teitelbaum, P. & Teitelbaum, O. (1999). *Motor indicators of autism in the first year.* Paper presented at the Interdisciplinary Council on Developmental and Learning Disorders' Third Annual International Conference on Relating and Communicating. McLean, VA.

III

Research Applications of the Functional Emotional Assessment Scale

In the following four chapters, we review current assessment tools for social-emotional functioning. Psychometric evidence on the Functional Emotional Assessment Scale (FEAS) is provided and administration and scoring procedures for the FEAS are described. In addition, research studies supporting the constructs and variables used in the FEAS are described.

Chapter 4 provides a comprehensive review of current assessment tools for social and emotional functioning. Parent report measures and direct observation measures used both in research and clinical practice are described. The review shows that most assessment tools currently available focus on attainment of skills rather than in-depth observation of developmental stages underlying social-emotional functioning and dynamic parent-child interactions. A critical analysis of how the FEAS compares to available instruments is provided. This review demonstrates the uniqueness of the FEAS for assessing in-depth social-emotional functioning and parent-child interactions.

Chapter 5 describes how the research version of the FEAS was developed from Greenspan's Developmental Structuralist model and earlier clinical version (presented in Chapters 1 and 2). DeGangi operationalized and expanded test items to provide a representative sample of behaviors for each developmental stage. A complete description of behaviors that were chosen for each domain are described in Chapter 5. Validity and reliability studies were conducted on the six age-specific versions of the FEAS (e.g., 7 to 9, 10 to 12, 13 to 18, 19 to 24, and 25 to 36 months, and 3 to 4 years). Each age-specific version includes both a caregiver and a child version of the FEAS, which are used to measure the caregiver and the child's emotional capacities at each relevant developmental stage. The subjects for the validity studies include a normative sample and clinical samples including infants and children with regulatory disorders and pervasive developmental disorders. There was also a sample of children with a variety of emotional challenges, including anxiety, depression, and impulsivity from multi-problem families who were exposed to drugs in utero.

Chapter 5 describes the subjects for the validity study. Because the FEAS is a criterion-referenced instrument, relevant validity studies included construct validity (e.g., capacity of items to discriminate between normal and clinical samples), decision validity (e.g., accuracy of cutting scores for each subtest in classifying children as delayed, at risk, or typically developing), and concurrent validity of the FEAS (e.g., comparison of FEAS scores with measures of sensory processing and attention in infants). An interobserver reliability study was conducted. Supporting tables presenting the psychometric evidence of the FEAS are provided in Chapter 5. In addition, Appendix A presents the means, discrimination indices, and t-values for test items by age and caregiver or child version of the FEAS as well as means and F values for subtest and total test scores.

Administration and scoring procedures for the FEAS are described in Chapter 6. This chapter includes details about how to interpret scores for diagnosis including a case study demonstrating how the FEAS is used in the clinical assessment process. Appendix C provides copies of the protocol booklets for each of the age ranges. Protocol booklets are used for entering scores for individual items. Scores for items are summed for each subtest and interpreted using the profile form at the back of each protocol booklet. The profile form provides the ranges for interpreting test scores that are based on optimal cutting scores derived from the construct validity studies.

The reader should note that the behaviors shown in the caregiver categories are one step ahead of the behaviors shown in the child categories. This is because we observed that the caregiver is often preparing the child for the next stage of development by initiating these more advanced interactions before the child does. In a sense, the caregiver is just ahead of the child, helping the child move forward. In this way, the caregiver both engages the child at the current level and facilitates the next level. Also we observed that within the normal range, children moved forward at varying rates. Some children, for example were already engaging in reciprocal interactions by 8 to 9 months of age, while for others this capacity didn't emerge fully until 10 to 12 months (even though it was emerging in the 7 to 9 month period). In the coding, therefore, we "expected" the new behavior at the slightly older age when almost all the children without difficulties were evidencing that behavior.

The reader may also note that the behaviors in a given category may be different at different ages. For example, at 10 to 12 months of age, visual behavior is emphasized in comparison to the 13 to 18 month category where it is not.

Finally, Chapter 7 presents additional validity studies on constructs and variables used in the FEAS. Preliminary research on the developmental structuralist model is described. This model developed by Greenspan provides the framework upon which the FEAS is based. Data from two major studies are described that provide practical justification for the model. These include a study on infants, children, and their caregivers who are at high risk for psychopathology and a study on infants with regulatory disorders. These data help in understanding the connection between early developmental processes and maladaptive behaviors. Finally, research supporting early intervention and assessment is described.

4

Current Status of Assessment Tools for Social and Emotional Functioning

Georgia DeGangi, Ph.D, OTR
Stanley I. Greenspan, M.D.

Professionals are faced with numerous challenges in assessing social-emotional problems and competencies in young children. One of the key issues that they confront is finding appropriate measures that are sensitive to the way in which social-emotional problems are manifested in infants and young children. The nature and type of social-emotional problems in young children differs qualitatively from those seen in older children. Unfortunately, current assessments that are available for children under 3 years of age often do not measure the competencies and problem behaviors that are relevant to the symptoms manifested in the first years of life (Meisels, 1989). Not only is it important to accurately assess the social-emotional competencies of infants and young children to determine those who need intervention, but accurate assessment is important because interactions between the parent and child serve as a foundation for many developmental skills and provide an important context for intervention (Cicchetti, Ackerman, & Izard, 1995; Shaw, Keenan, & Vondra, 1994).

In this chapter we will review current tools for assessing emotional functioning in infants, young children, and their families. It will begin with a brief description of the challenges that must be met (e.g., assessing the many variables, including different symptoms and areas of functioning). Then we will review current assessment tools. The review will show that the majority of assessment tools that are currently available tend to focus on surface behaviors (e.g., attainment of skills) rather than in-depth observation of developmental capacities underlying social-emotional functioning and dynamic parent-child interactions. Next, the Functional Emotional Assessment Scale (FEAS) will be described along with a critical analysis of how the FEAS compares to available instruments.

There is considerable need for such a tool. Part H of Public Law 99–457 has mandated that the social-emotional needs of young children be included in the Individualized Family Service Plan, yet there is a paucity of measures that are family-centered and relevant to how children develop social-emotional competencies within the context of caregiver-child interactions. This chapter will describe how the FEAS meets this need.

The assessment process is confounded by the fact that children with social-emotional problems are often not identified early on. They also comprise a heterogeneous group. It is estimated that between 7 and 10% of children under 2 years of age and as high as 24% of 2- to 3-year olds using parent report forms have social-emotional problems (Earls, 1980; Jenkins, Bax, & Hart, 1980; Lavigne et al., 1996). In addition, there appears to be a growing incidence of children experiencing pervasive developmental disorders or other autism-spectrum problems (Ritvo et al., 1989; Sugiyama & Abe, 1989; Greenspan, et al., 2000).

Young children display problems because of constitutional variables (e.g., regulatory and processing difficulties, learning problems, difficult temperament) as well as factors in the family (e.g., maternal depression) or the parent-child relationship. Often, both are involved. For example, the presence of difficult temperament and problems of attachment are often related to risk factors in the family (e.g., maternal depression) as well as later emergence of problem behaviors (Murray, Fiori-Cowley, Hooper, & Cooper, 1996; Shaw et al., 1994; Zahn-Waxler, Iannotti, Cummings, & Denham, 1990). Infants and young children of caregivers who are depressed often evidence delays in cognitive, language, and attentional skills and show somber affect (Cogill, Caplan, Alexandra, Robson, & Kumar, 1986; Lyons-Ruth, Zoll, Connell, & Grunebaum, 1986).

Not only should an assessment of social-emotional functioning be useful in identifying existing social-emotional problems, but it should be able to identify behaviors that place a child at risk for later psychopathology. It has been hypothesized that the origins of later psychopathology can be measured in the first few years of life (Bates, 1990; Caspi & Moffitt, 1995; Cicchetti et al., 1995). The early symptoms in the first few years of life that predispose a child for later psychopathology often relate to problems of self-regulation (e.g., sleep, eating, self-calming), mood regulation (e.g., high irritability and self-calming), and sensorimotor modulation and processing, for example, hypersensitivity to sensory stimulation (DeGangi, 2000; DeGangi & Breinbauer, 1997; Greenspan & Wieder, 1993; Mattison, Handfor, & Vela-Bueno, 1987; Walker & Emory, 1983). As described earlier, infants experiencing these symptoms have recently been termed regulatory disordered (Greenspan, 1989, 1992; Zero to Three, 1994). Regulatory problems and problems with family and interactive patterns all predispose a child to later psychopathology.

Because clinical problems in infants and young children have not been adequately described by the *Diagnostic Statistical Manual-IV, ZERO TO THREE: The National Center for Infants, Toddlers, and Families* developed a diagnostic classification system—0–3—to describe typical clinical disorders for children from birth to 3 years (Zero to Three, 1994). The 0–3 diagnostic classification system is also useful in guiding clinicians on what behavioral domains should be included in the assessment process. It suggests including a range of relationship and emotional capacities in the context of constitutional and maturational variations (regulatory patterns), caregiver/child interactions, and family patterns.

Defining the behaviors that should comprise a broad-based assessment of social-emotional functioning, however, can be challenging because assessing emotional functioning often involves sampling behaviors from many areas, such as social-emotional, behavioral, adaptive skills, and play (Fewell, 1991). Unlike other developmental domains, there is less agreement among experts regarding which social-emotional milestones occur and at which ages. There are a number of issues that have been identified in assessment of infants and young children by the Division of Early Childhood (DEC) Task Force (Division for Early Childhood, 1993). These include the need to include the targeted population in the normative sample when developing social-emotional scales; the use of culturally appropriate and unbiased instruments; and inclusion of information from the family in order to optimize the validity of assessment results. Parents and caregivers are considered not only the most knowledgeable about their own children, but they have the opportunity to observe their children in different settings during different tasks. For this reason, it is important to include families in the assessment process through parent-completed rating scales or questionnaires as well as observing the child in context with the primary caregiver.

Most efforts to identify infants at risk have focused on infant temperamental dimensions through behavioral questionnaires and observational methods (Goldsmith, Rieser-Danner, & Briggs, 1991; Seifer, Sameroff, Barrett, & Krafchuk, 1994). Temperament measures have been useful because there is considerable stability of infant temperament measures and ratings in childhood (Pedlow, Sanson, & Oberklaid, 1993). In addition, ratings of infant temperament have been related to parent and teacher reports of behavior problems from 3 to 12 years of age (Guerin, Gottfried, & Thomas, 1997; Shaw et al., 1994). Temperament approaches, however, generally do not indicate the specific sensory processing capacities that are vulnerable or problematic (e.g., visual-spatial processing, motor planning, and sequencing).

What Must Be Included in a Model for Assessment

As discussed in the introduction and in Chapter 1, a model for emotional assessment needs to deal with many interrelated areas of functioning. Historically, models of assessment using typical developmental scales are often not sensitive to many important areas of functioning. For example, they do not identify qualitative problems that interfere with functional performance and emotional development such as the child's capacity to self-regulate arousal, attention, and responses to stimulation during play; to explore the environment and organize sequential interactions; or to express appropriate affect and eye contact during interactions with others. Assessments may overlook how the child functions in social relationships that matter most to the child (e.g., the parent-child relationship). Few scales examine both the child and caregiver's emotional strengths and needs using a developmental framework. Unfortunately, an infant or young child who experiences problems with attachment, relatedness, communication, play, or constricted emotional development may easily be overlooked using current developmental assessments. The professional observing the child also may not recognize how problems with sensory hypersensitivities, poor gestural communication, or a short attention span may impact the child's emotional development because current scales do not emphasize the interrelatedness of these factors. Therefore, an expanded model of evaluation is needed that assesses the important social-emotional competencies that are manifested in the early years as well as the child's capacity to organize social interactions and to regulate emotions within the context of the parent-child relationship. Not only should this assessment be sensitive to constitutional factors (e.g., activity level, sensory processing, temperament) that impact social-emotional development and caregiver-child dynamics, but as indicated earlier in Chapter 1, it should also evaluate how the child negotiates the different functional emotional and developmental stages (e.g., how the child masters such themes as intimacy and independence, curiosity and exploration, separation and individuation, and assertiveness and aggression).

Also as indicated, assessment of social-emotional competencies should also evaluate how the primary caregiver supports the child's social-emotional competencies, the parent's interactional style, and capacity to support the child's development. The quality of the parent-child interaction and parent-child relationship is an important source of information about the child's functioning (Barnard & Kelly, 1990). It is through this relationship that the child's social and cognitive development is fostered (Papousek & Papousek, 1987). Assessment of the child within the context of the parent-child relationship is important because it reflects how the infant responds to and copes with his or her primary relationship, that is, the caregiver (Stern, 1985). The parent's participation in the assessment process is crucial because it provides a valuable resource in understanding the dynamics between parent and child, the family context, cultural orientation, as well as an understanding of how the parent views his or her child's needs and what the child means to the parent and family. Therefore, it is useful to combine a variety of measures in assessing emotional development, affect regulation, behavior, and play that engage both parent and child participation.

An assessment of social-emotional development should include systematic play observations of parent-child interactions. The developmental-structuralist model developed by Greenspan (1989, 1992, 1997) provides a dynamic model that integrates current thinking about how the individual interacts with persons and objects in his or her environment. By looking at caregiver, environment, and child characteristics, it is possible to delineate those areas at which assessment and intervention should be directed. As described in Chapter 1, the developmental structuralist framework identifies six levels of emotional functioning that are important in measuring social-emotional competencies.

Barnard (1979) has described some of the important components for adaptive interactions. These are consistent with the developmental structuralist model and include the following:

1. Social engagement that includes child traits such as sootheability, attention, and developmental competence, and parent traits such as ability to read and respond to the infant's signals;
2. Contingency of responses or the capacity to respond to one another's signals appropriately;
3. Richness and flexibility of interactive content (e.g., range and content of play); and
4. Adaptability of the dyad to change over time as both the parent and child mature.

Zeanah and his colleagues (1997) have further defined the relationship domains that should be included in an assessment of parent-child interactions. Parent behaviors should include emotional availability, nurturance and empathic responses, protection, teaching, play, limit setting, and provision of structure and routines. Infant behaviors should include emotion regulation, curiosity and mastery of tasks, play behaviors, self-control, cooperation, self-regulation, and response to structure. Infant attachment status and task mastery are considered important measures of social-emotional competence (Kopp, 1989; Lieberman & Zeanah, 1995; Michnowicz, McConnell, Peterson, & Odom, 1995; Seifer, Schiller, Sameroff, Resnick, & Riordan, 1996; Zeanah, 1996). Social competence of infants may be one of the best predictors of later developmental emotional functioning (Bernstein, Hans, & Percansky, 1991). Social competence is frequently demonstrated by the quality of the parent-child relationship. For example, infants who form secure attachments in the first year of life tend to have more positive developmental outcomes later in childhood (Matas, Arend, & Sroufe, 1978).

In addition, it is important to observe the infant's capacity to regulate mood because of its impact on social-emotional development in infancy and through the lifespan (Campos, Mumme, Kermoian, & Campos, 1994; DeGangi, 2000; Fogel et al., 1992). The modulation of emotion is intimately connected with the process of "self-directed regulation" (Tronick, 1989). These self-directed regulatory behaviors involve the individual's internal capacity to shift from negative emotions to more positive ones to allow for goal-directed activity for example, self-calming when frustrated to allow child to engage in purposeful action, vocalization, or other behavioral scheme (Gianino & Tronick, 1988; Kopp, 1989). The ability of the infant and caregiver to engage in coregulated interactions may be especially important for these processes (Fogel, 1993).

Based on the literature review and the developmental structuralist model, an assessment of social-emotional problems and competencies in infants, toddlers, and young children should include the following components:

- Regulatory capacities, including:
  - *Self-regulation:* Self-soothing and mood regulation, sustained attention and activity level, and reactivity to sensory experiences
  - *Sensory processing (including auditory and visual-spatial), motor planning, and communication:* This includes the ability to tolerate, gain pleasure from, and comprehend a range of sensory experiences while interacting with persons and objects in the environment and the ability to organize facial, motor, and gestural responses for eye contact and communication.
  - *Interactive capacities:* Attachment to caregiver, social referencing, capacity to securely separate from caregiver, and ability to organize and sequence long chains of coregulated reciprocal interactions.
- The different functional emotional developmental capacities, including:
  - *Family patterns:* Especially those that influence the functional emotional developmental capacities described in Chapter 1.
  - *The ability to focus, attend, engage, reciprocate gestures, problem-solve and represent experience:* Exploration of the environment; capacity to organize play with objects in the context of an interaction with the caregiver, and represent a range of symbolic thoughts, feelings, and emotional ideas that reflect emotional meanings underlying relationships.

These processes and capacities are among the most crucial tasks of infancy and early childhood and should be included in an assessment of social-emotional functioning.

Review of Existing Tools of Social-Emotional Functioning

In reviewing existing assessment tools, we found that assessments of so-cial-emotional functioning for infants and young children fell into two main categories: parent report measures and those requiring direct obser-vation of the child. For this reason, this review includes parent report mea-sures as well as tools detailing how to conduct direct observations of par-ent-child interactions. This review is limited to scales that focus on parent-child interactions, omitting measures of peer interactions and so-cial skills because these measures are more suitable for older children. For reviews of measures of peer interactions and social skills, the reader is re-ferred to a review by Ghuman, Peebles, and Ghuman (1998). In this next section, currently available tools will be reviewed.

Parent Report Measures

Several parent questionnaires may be administered to gain the parents' perspective of their child's social-emotional functioning. The reliability and validity of parent report measures have been criticized over the years because they often reflect maternal rather than child characteristics. However, parent report measures are extremely valuable because they tap the areas that most concern parents. Parents can also provide valuable in-formation about their child's day-to-day behaviors. By combining parent report measures with reliable and valid observational techniques, one may gain a better understanding of the parent and child. In this next section, several parent report measures are described that measure the infant's reg-ulatory problems, temperament, parental behaviors and stress, home en-vironment, and child behavioral problems.

Checklists Used to Assess Self-Regulation and Emotional Functioning in Young Children

The parent's presenting concerns related to the infant's self-regulation and emotional functioning may be assessed through the use of a comprehen-sive symptom checklist, the Infant-Toddler Symptom Checklist (ITSC) (DeGangi, Poisson, Sickel, & Wiener, 1995). This checklist for infants from 7 through 30 months contains questions related to sleep, self-calming, mood regulation, feeding, sensory responses (i.e., touch, movement), listening and communication, and attachment and emotional functioning. The checklist is structured in such a way that it is possible to determine the extent of the child's regulatory problem and how different behavioral patterns occur over the course of development.

There are six versions of the ITSC, one for each age range (7 to 9, 10 to 12, 13 to 18, 19 to 24, and 25 to 30 months) and a short version for general screening purposes. The checklist may be self-administered by the parent or used in the context of an interview, particularly for parents who may be unable to complete a questionnaire without assistance because of illiteracy or cultural differences. There are a total of 58 items from which each age-specific version of the checklist was derived. All of the questions can be answered with a "yes, most times," "past," or "never or sometimes." In order to determine if a child is at risk for a regulatory disorder, the total checklist score is compared to the cutoff score derived for each version of the checklist (e.g., each age range). Infants scoring at or above a cutoff score in any category are considered "at risk" and should be referred for further testing.

The ITSC was validated on samples of infants who were typically developing and those with regulatory disorders. Cutting scores for each subtest were chosen to minimize the false normal error rate, judged to be the more serious of the two types of error from the perspective of screening and diagnostic decision making. The false delayed and false normal error rates were very low, ranging from 0 to 14% for the various age ranges. In addition, it was found that 78% of infants initially identified as having problems in the ITSC were diagnosed as having developmental or behavioral problems at 3 years using standardized measures such as the Child Behavior Checklist (Achenbach, 1989), thus showing good predictive validity. A weakness of the ITSC is that no reliability studies were conducted. In summary, the ITSC should be useful in identifying constitutional and regulatory problems that impact social-emotional development in infants and toddlers.

The Neurobehavioral Indicators of Atypical Development (NIAD) was developed as a research and clinical tool for screening children from 4 through 72 months (Bagnato, Neisworth, Salvia, & Hunt, 1992). It was specifically designed to detect neurobehavioral and self-regulatory problems in infants and preschool children. There are 154 items falling in the following nine cluster areas: (1) Temperament, (2) Attention and

Activity, (3) Attachment and Social Behavior, (4) Neurobehavioral State, (5) Play, (6) Vocal and Oral Behavior, (7) Senses and Movement, (8) Self-Stimulation/Injury, and (9) Misbehavior. The presence of behaviors is indicated with a "yes" or "no" response. The NIAD has been validated on a sample of 253 infants, toddlers, and preschoolers ranging in age from 4 to 72 months who were enrolled in early intervention programs. Initial reliability studies on the NIAD total scores show strong internal consistency (r = .94). It would be useful if further validity studies were completed on the NIAD examining the difference in performance of children with different diagnostic groupings (e.g., normal, preterm, regulatory disordered) to examine its specificity in screening and detecting children with regulatory problems. At this time, the NIAD should be useful as a general screening instrument for neurobehavioral and regulatory problems.

The Infant-Toddler Social and Emotional Assessment (ITSEA) is a newly developed parent report scale used to measure attachment, task mastery, emotion regulation, and coping behaviors (Briggs-Gowan & Carter, 1998; Carter & Briggs-Gowan, 1993; Carter, Little, Briggs-Gowan, & Kogan, 1999). The ITSEA assesses parental perceptions of infant internalizing behaviors (e.g., depression-withdrawal) and externalizing (e.g., peer aggression, activity, defiance, negative emotional reactivity) problem behaviors in addition to regulatory problems (e.g., sleep and eating problems), maladaptive problems (e.g., head banging), and competencies (e.g., attention, compliance, prosocial peer interactions, empathy, emotional positivity, task mastery, and emotional awareness). Although the ITSEA is intended for infants from 12 to 36 months, it has only been validated thus far on a sample of low-risk 12-month-olds. Items are rated on a three-point scale from *not true or rarely* to *somewhat true or sometimes* and *very true or often*. Research on the ITSEA shows an association with measures on the scale and the Infant Behavior Questionnaire (IBQ), a widely used temperament scale. In addition, the ITSEA scales were associated with attachment ratings and classifications of attachment. There was also a concordance between maternal ratings and infant behavior observed in the laboratory. Preliminary data on the ITSEA suggests that it has adequate internal consistency and test-retest reliability. With further validation on samples of high-risk infants and those with regulatory disorders, the ITSEA shows potential as a screening instrument for detection of problem behaviors in young children.

Questionnaires Used to Assess Parental Stress, Parenting Behaviors, and the Home Environment

The Parenting Stress Index (PSI) is useful in providing a measure of child characteristics (e.g., adaptability and demandingness) as well as a measure of parental stress (e.g., depression and sense of competence) (Abidin, 1986). It is a well-standardized assessment for children from birth through 19 years that measures both child characteristics and dimensions of parent stress. The 47 items within the "Child Domain" measure adaptability, acceptability, demandingness, mood, distractibility/hyperactivity, and reinforcement to parents. The 54 items in the "Parent Domain" measure depression, attachment, restrictions of role, sense of competence, social isolation, relationship with spouse, and parent health. The instrument is self-administered by the parent and can be completed within 10 to 15 minutes. For parents who are unable to read, the scale may be completed with an examiner. The PSI manual reported reliabilities ranging from .62 to .70 for the Child Domain and from .55 to .80 for the Parent Domain. The reliability for the Total Stress Score is .95. Test-retest reliability over three-week and three-month intervals was also quite high. The PSI is a useful measure of parent perception of infant temperament, adaptability, and attachment as well as parental stress and competence. It should be coupled with measures that provide more specific information about the child's regulatory and constitutional functioning (e.g., ITSC) as well as direct clinical observation measures.

The Home Observation for Measurement of the Environment (HOME) (Bradley, Caldwell, & Elardo, 1977; Caldwell & Bradley, 1978) consists of two versions—one for infants (birth to 3 years) and one for preschoolers (3 to 6 years). It is designed to measure the home environment, the mother's responsiveness to the child, organization of the physical environment, provision of appropriate play materials, and opportunities for everyday stimulation for the child. The HOME is administered in the child's home by an early intervention or mental health professional when both parent and child are present. It takes approximately one hour to administer. The items (45 in infant version; 55 in preschool version) are scored using a yes-no format. Information is collected using both observation and interview techniques. The HOME has been found to be a better predictor of performance on the Stanford-Binet at 3 years than scores from the Bayley Mental Development Index.

The HOME is useful in assessing how the home environment can support the child's development as well as the caregiver's responsivity to the child.

Measures of Infant Temperament

Measures of temperamental characteristics provided useful information regarding the child's difficultness, adaptability, demandingness, and other traits that impact the parent's response to the child as well as the child's capacity to respond to therapeutic intervention. Child temperament can be assessed using the PSI although one may wish to use a child temperament scale such as the Infant/Child Characteristics Questionnaire (ICQ) (Bates, 1984). The questionnaires are reliable and easy to administer, because they provide a good indicator of difficult temperament for 6- and 12-month-olds and preschool children through 4 years of age. The ICQ consists of 24 items, answered on a seven-point scale. As an example, the four dimensions that the 6-month questionnaire assesses are fussy/difficult, unadaptable, dull, and unpredictable. Other widely used scales of infant temperament are the Infant Behavior Questionnaire (IBQ) (Rothbart & Derryberry, 1981) and the Dimensions of Temperament Scale (Lerner, Palermo, Spiro, & Nesselroade, 1982).

It is often helpful to evaluate the child's temperament because of its impact on behavior, but if one needs to streamline the number of questionnaires that are administered to caregivers, it may be more efficient to use a scale that assesses regulatory and constitutional factors such as the ITSC.

Parent Report Measures Used in Screening
Social-Emotional Problems in Children

Once the child turns 2 years of age, the Child Behavior Checklist (CBC) may be used to assess behaviors (Achenbach, 1989). It may be either administered by an interviewer or self-administered by the parent. Separate interview forms are available for 2- to 3- (CBC), and 4- to 18-year-olds (CBCL). Scoring options are "Not true," "Somewhat or sometimes true," and "Very true or often true." There is a place on the form for parents to list concerns and their child's strengths. There are 100 items for the 2- to 3-year version. Using clinical cutoff points, problems for 2- to 3-year-olds are obtained for specific behaviors such as anxious, depressed, aggressive, or destructive. Scores are interpreted on a scoring sheet for borderline and clinical ranges for specific behaviors as well as for externalizing and internalizing behaviors. The structure of the 4-to 18-year version of the CBCL is similar to that of the 2- to 3-year version except that there are 120 items. Items are scored into externalizing and internalizing behaviors as well as eight scales including social problems, thought problems, delinquent behaviors, aggression, withdrawn, somatic complaints, anxious/depressed, and attention problems. The CBCs are reported to be reliable ($r = .85$) and valid. Both the CBC and CBCL are helpful in determining the clinical significance of problem behaviors in children.

The revised Conners' Rating Scales (CRS-R) is a comprehensive set of scales for parents, teachers, or self-report that can be used to measure psychopathology and problem behaviors in children and adolescents from ages 3 to 17 years (Conners, 1997). It has both long and short versions of each scale and can be used to assess attention-deficit/hyperactivity disorder as well other behavioral problems. Of particular value is that the CRS-R have scoring separately for males and females. The CRS-R is especially useful in measuring the child's behavioral responses in different settings (e.g., home and school) because it has equivalent versions for parents and teachers. In contrast to the CBCL, the CRS-R provide more specific data about attentional problems in children.

The Social Skills Rating Scales (SSRS) is a social skills rating scale developed to identify children in need of behavioral evaluation (Gresham & Elliott, 1990). It is also designed for use in assisting teachers and mental health professionals in developing behavioral objectives for children. Forms are completed by both parents and teachers. The preschool version has 49 questions about child behaviors that are rated as "never," "sometimes," or "very often." Parents are also asked to rate the importance of behaviors on a three-point Likert scale from *not important* to *very important.* Internal consistency through alpha coefficients and test-retest data reports that 92% of the items on the teacher rating form have alpha coefficients over .80. In contrast, only 44% of the parent forms and 20% of the child forms have alpha coefficients over .80. Test-retest data have a mean correlation of .87 for each of the behavior scales. There appears to be strong content, criterion-related, and construct validity for the SSRS. The SSRS is a useful measure in determining areas of need for interventions that focus on social skills.

Structured and Unstructured Observational Measures of Social-Emotional Functioning

In order to fully assess a child's social-emotional functioning, it is essential to use a direct observation measure, preferably one that observes the child in the context of the caregiver-child relationship. In this section, a number of scales are reviewed that provide either structured or unstructured observations for evaluating social-emotional functioning in infants and young children. The scales will be reviewed on three levels:

1. Their capacity to measure the child's social-emotional function,
2. The parent's social-emotional functioning, and
3. The caregiver-child dynamics.

One of the ways in which parent-child interactions have been evaluated over the years has been through the Strange Situation Procedure, an observational method designed to classify infant attachment among groups of infants (Lamb, Thompson, Gardner, Charnov, & Estes, 1984; Sroufe, 1988). One of the drawbacks of the Strange Situation Procedure is that it is designed for classification of infant attachment in a research setting rather than to diagnose infants within the context of a clinical setting. It is sometimes problematic to rely on separation and reunion behaviors because they comprise only one aspect of attachment relationships (Gaensbauer & Harmon, 1982). In addition, the behavior of the caregiver is often constrained in the Strange Situation. Sroufe has stated that insecure classification using the Strange Situation is not indicative of psychopathology, but rather a risk factor (Sroufe, 1988). Nonetheless, the Strange Situation Procedure is quite useful when working in a research capacity with infants as a method of classifying attachment.

Clinical observations of social relatedness may be obtained through administration of the Bayley Scales of Infant Development, Infant Behavior Record (IBR) (Bayley, 1993). This is a descriptive rating scale of behaviors for children through 3 years of age. The scale focuses on interpersonal and affective domains, motivational variables, and a child's interest in specific modes of sensory experience. Specifically, the IBR yields ratings in Social Orientation, Cooperativeness, Fearfulness, Tension, General Emotional Tone, Object Orientation, Goal Directedness, Attention Span, Endurance, Activity, Reactivity, Sensory Areas of Interest Displayed, Energy and Coordination for Age, Judgement of Test, Unusual or Deviant Behavior, and General Evaluation of Child.

The IBR provides a convenient form of recording qualitative observations and evaluations and concludes with a general evaluation of the child's overall performance. An examiner completes the IBR immediately after having administered the Mental and Motor Scales. It is completed by indicating the one statement that best describes the child's behavior. Additional space is provided for an Examiner's comments, which can broaden the base on which to make clinical judgments about a child.

Several validity studies described in the test manual have been conducted on the IBR that point to the usefulness of the various test items, capacity of the IBR in discriminating between high-risk and normal infants, and its relationship to later IQ. No reliability studies on the IBR were reported. The IBR appears to be useful as a general guide of the child's behavior that influences the child's organization and orientation toward objects and persons, however, the limited validity studies and absence of reliability studies restrict its applicability to clinical populations.

The Nursing Child Assessment Satellite Training (NCAST) Teaching and Feeding Scales was developed by Barnard (1979; NCAST, 1995a, 1995b) to provide a systematic format to observe parent and child interactive capacities. Observations are made during feeding and during two developmentally taught tasks, one at the child's level, the other slightly above the child's ability. Parent behaviors are scored for sensitivity to the child's cues, response to the child's distress, and fostering of cognitive and social-emotional growth. Child behaviors include clarity of cues and responsiveness to parents. There are 76 items in the feeding scale and 73 in the teaching scale. Scores on the scales reflect the transactional nature of the interaction between parent and infant. The NCAST Scales are intended primarily for use with mothers who have had high-risk pregnancies, for infants who are premature or exhibit failure to thrive, or for children at risk for neglect and/or abuse (Farran, Clark, & Ray, 1990).

The Teaching Scale was validated on samples of infants through 31 months and the Feeding Scale for 1- to 53-month-olds. Inter-rater reliability was found to be .79 to .83. The Teaching Scale of the NCAST has been found to be more strongly correlated with cognitive development at 3 years than the Feeding Scale (Gross, Conrad, Fogg, Willis, & Garvey, 1993). The Feeding Scales have been found to have moderate to high correlations with the HOME (Caldwell et al., 1978). The NCAST is useful in examining the interactions of high-risk dyads (e.g., preterm) or children at risk for neglect or abuse.

The Parent-Child Early Relational Assessment (PCERA) assesses the quality of parent-child relationships for children from birth through 5 years (Clark, 1985). It was developed with the primary purpose of evaluating parents and children in families at risk for or who show early relational disturbances. It consists of 65 parental, child, and dyadic variables and is designed to provide information about the affective and behavioral quality of interactions between parent and child for research and clinical purposes. The infant or child is observed for 20 minutes in interaction with each parent during four 5-minute segments that include free play, a structured activity, feeding, and a separation-reunion period. Parents are rated on amount, duration, and intensity of positive and negative affective qualities such as sensitivity to infant's cues, visual regard of baby, structuring of the environment, tone of voice, intrusiveness, and inconsistency. The infant is rated for positive and negative affects and interactive behaviors including such things as mood, attention, social initiative and responsiveness, and motor and communication skills. In addition, the dyad is rated on the quality of mutual involvement and joint attention to the task and amount of reciprocity and pleasure. Parent-child interactions are assessed across different situations to observe parental competencies (i.e., feeding, teaching, free play, and limit setting). Observations are videotaped in an office or home setting.

The PCERA was validated on 101 caregiver-infant dyads from a population of well-functioning and psychiatrically ill caregivers (Musick, Clark, & Cohler, 1981). Significant differences were found on the nonchild variables related to Maternal Consistency and Maternal Affective Involvement and Responsiveness. In addition, inter-rater reliability for the scale ranged from .83 to .98. Because of its limited validity, the PCERA is suitable for typically functioning children and caregivers with mental illness.

In addition to these scales, there is a play-based assessment, Transdisciplinary Play-Based Assessment (TPBA) (Linder, 1990). It is a naturalistic, functional assessment of the child that is developmental in nature and is based upon the observations of the transdisciplinary team consisting of both parents and professionals alike. The assessment is designed to identify service needs, to develop intervention plans, and to evaluate progress in children who are functioning between 6 months and 6 years. Observation guidelines are presented in cognitive, social-emotional, communication and language, and sensorimotor development. These guidelines may be used to observe various play and interaction skills in addition to other areas of development. The TPBA is conducted in a creative play environment (e.g., day care center, child's play room at home, preschool setting). Novel, age-appropriate toys are presented to the child that are conducive to eliciting the child's highest skill level. Qualitative observations are made, beginning with whatever level the child is currently functioning at. The entire assessment takes approximately 60 to 90 minutes.

There are no reliability or validity studies of the TPBA, therefore, it has limited applicability for clinical use, but may be helpful in guiding naturalistic observations during a transdisciplinary team assessment.

The Functional Emotional Assessment Scale

In this section, the research version of the Functional Emotional Assessment Scale (FEAS) will be described. It is a unique scale that provides a method to assess infants, toddlers, and young children from 7 months through 4 years and their caregivers who are at risk or have problems in development of social engagement, attachment, play interactions, and emotional functioning. It was specifically designed for infants and young children who experience problems in self-regulation, attachment, communication, attention, and behavioral control. The FEAS is useful in detecting problems in children who have regulatory disorders who experience disturbances in sensory processing, sleep, feeding, state control, self-calming, and mood regulation as well as children with more serious relational disturbances such as pervasive developmental disorder, autism, or multi-system developmental disorder. In addition, the FEAS is useful in observing the play interactions of children who are challenged by complicated family situations or have caregivers who are less able to provide a nurturing environment for them because of factors such as maternal depression, mental illness, substance abuse, and other socio-environmental problems such as poverty. The FEAS includes both a caregiver and child scale, and for this reason, it provides useful information not only about the child's emotional capacities, but about the caregiver's capacity to support the child's emotional development and play interactions. Administration and scoring of the FEAS appears in Chapter 6 of this book. Details of the psychometric properties of the FEAS are presented in Chapter 5.

Items from the FEAS are based upon an ego psychology developmental framework developed by Stanley Greenspan (1979, 1989, 1992). Unlike other instruments focusing on parent-child interactions, the FEAS provides a formal system of coding the infant and caregiver's behaviors using six levels of emotional development that include the following:

1. Regulation and interest in the world,
2. Forming relationships (attachment),

3. Intentional two-way communication,
4. Complex sense of self
   a. Behavioral organization of sequential circles of communication
   b. Behavioral elaboration of feelings dealing with warmth, pleasure, assertion, exploration, protest, and anger,
5. Emotional ideas: Representational capacity and elaboration of feelings and ideas that are expressed symbolically,
6. Emotional thinking connecting symbols together logically to represent communication and reflection.

These areas were included because of their clinical significance in the identification of children with a variety of disturbances. The same domains of behavior are measured for the caregiver and the child.

There are six different age-specific versions of the FEAS with items in each domain that are valid and reliable for each age level. In addition to these six levels of emotional development, items on the FEAS measure the infant or child's regulatory patterns and caregiver's responsivity. The FEAS is versatile because it is useful for children with regulatory disorders, pervasive developmental disorders, and emotional and behavioral problems such as oppositional behaviors or social withdrawal, as well as children who have experienced physical or emotional abuse or neglect. Because each level of emotional development contains at least eight items, the scale also lends itself to measuring progress and developing treatment goals.

The FEAS is based on the assumption that stages of emotional development can be observed through play interactions between the parent and child and that clinically relevant behaviors can be included within each stage. The FEAS focuses on constitutional and maturational patterns of the child, the parent's capacity to sustain and support the child's interactions, and the dynamic interaction between parent and child. The caregiver is asked to play with the child as he/she might at home for 15 minutes. It is useful to ask the parent to play with his/her child in several different play situations to observe the child's varying play skills, interaction abilities, and the parent's capacity to facilitate the child's play skills. For this reason, it is suggested to observe the parent and child as they play with three different types of toys: symbolic toys, textured toys, and movement equipment.

The FEAS was designed as both a research and clinical tool that can be used in screening and diagnosis. Clinicians are faced with the dilemma of determining which infants and their caregivers are at risk for emotional problems and, therefore, must rely on clinical judgment to determine whether, and to what extent, deficits exist. The FEAS provides a comprehensive cost-effective and efficient way to determine which infants or children and their caregivers require intervention. It is unique because it integrates current conceptual thinking about how problems with self-regulation, attention, sensory processing, and communication impact the child's emotional development. In addition, it includes observations that help the clinician in observing caregiver responses to their child. Problems in play behaviors are often reported as concerns by parents to pediatricians, educators, and health professionals. Since these behaviors are not tapped by traditional developmental tests, a child with needs in these areas may not be identified until more serious emotional or behavioral problems develop in later years.

The FEAS consists of six versions. Each version is age specific (e.g., 7 to 9, 10 to 12, 13 to 18, 19 to 24, and 25 to 35 months, and 3 to 4 years). The checklist focuses on the child and caregiver's responses in the following domains:

1. Regulation and interest in the world,
2. Forming relationships or attachment,
3. Intentional two-way communication,
4. Development of a complex sense of self (e.g., behavioral organization and elaboration),
5. Representational capacity and elaboration of symbolic thinking, and
6. Emotional thinking or the development of logical thematic play.

The FEAS should be administered to a caregiver and child in the context of a comprehensive evaluation of the child and family. Family concerns should be identified through an interview process. Information about the child's regulatory functions may be obtained through administration of the ITSC (DeGangi et al., 1995). Other diagnostic tests examining sensory processing (i.e., the Test of Sensory Functions in Infants; DeGangi & Greenspan, 1989), attention (i.e., the Test of Attention in Infants; DeGangi et al., 1995), movement, communication, cognition (i.e., Mental and Motor Bayley Scales of Infant Development; Bayley, 1993), and child behaviors (i.e., CBC; Achenbach, 1989) are useful in completing the child's diagnostic profile. When it is possible to administer parent report measures to the family, more information may be obtained through questionnaires such as the PSI (Abidin, 1986).

Comparison of Social-Emotional Scales and Recommendations for Use

A comprehensive assessment of social-emotional development in infants and young children should include both parent report measures and systematic observations of parent-child interactive capacities. In this section, recommendations for selection and use of parent report and direct observation measures will be made.

Professionals in early intervention programs and clinical settings are often faced with the dilemma of selecting parent report measures that provide them with the maximum amount of information without running the risk of overwhelming caregivers with numerous forms to fill out. When possible, it is useful to select a comprehensive measure that provides an index of how the parent views the child's social-emotional functioning, that screens the child for constitutional factors, and that identifies problem behaviors. Exploration of these dimensions should be made while focusing on the caregiver and child's strengths, and the family's resources in supporting the child's development. A major risk of focusing on problem behaviors is that the professional team and caregivers may become overly focused on deficits and consequently overlook the child's, caregiver's, and family's strengths and resources. Keeping this in mind, the following recommendations are being made in selecting a parent report measure.

In reviewing the parent report measures described in this chapter, the scales seem to fall into three main categories: those that measure

1. Child characteristics such as self-regulation and temperament,
2. Parent characteristics, and
3. The home environment.

Because differing symptoms are exhibited at different ages for infants and children with social-emotional problems, most of the parent report measures are targeted for certain ages. Table 4-1 summarizes the various parent report measures and the areas of social-emotional functioning that they measure.

As can be seen from Table 4-1, the three parent report measures that show the most promise in evaluating more components of social-emotional functioning are the Infant-Toddler Symptom Checklist (ITSC), the Infant-Toddler Social and Emotional Assessment (ITSEA), and the Neurobehavioral Indicators of Atypical Development (NIAD). The only

Table 4-1.

Parent Report Measures Pertaining to Assessment of Social-Emotional Interaction

		CHILD BEHAVIORS					
Name of Scale	Age Range	Self-Regulation Temperament	Sensory Processing and Attention	Engagement and Affect	Attachment	Reciprocity, Contingency	Representational Capacities
Infant-Toddler Symptom Checklist (ITSC)	7 to 30 mo.	X	X	X	X	X	
Neurobehavioral Indicators of Atypical Development (NIAD)	4 to 72 mo.	X	X	X	X	X	
Infant-Toddler Social and Emotional Assessment (ITSEA)	12 to 36 mo.	X	X	X	X	X	
Parenting Stress Index (PSI)	Birth to 19 yrs.	X	X		X		
Home Observation for Measurement of the Environment (HOME)	Birth to 3 yrs 3 to 6 yrs.					X	

area that these scales fall short in assessing is the representational capacities of the child. In selecting which of these parent report measures to use, it is important to keep in mind their psychometric soundness.

Of the three scales mentioned above, the ITSC seems to have the strongest validity because it has been validated on infants and toddlers with regulatory disorders and it shows good predictive validity; however, no reliability studies have been conducted on the ITSC to date. The NIAD has both reliability and validity but the validation sample is a general population of children from early intervention programs, therefore, the scale may lack specificity. The ITSEA remains a newly developed tool and has thus far been validated only on a sample of low risk 12-month-olds; however, it has adequate reliability and with further validation shows promise. These parent report measures are useful in complimenting direct observational measures of social-emotional functioning.

In reviewing the direct observation scales described in this chapter, it is striking how few scales are available that measure social-emotional development in children as well as parent-child interactions. The ability of the direct observation measures to evaluate both the child and parent's emotional capacities was evaluated using the stages of emotional development described by the developmental structuralist model. Using these stages, Table 4-2 presents scales that measure child behaviors through direct observation and Table 4-3 presents those that measure parent behaviors through observation. Only those scales that contain key elements of the model of social-emotional development are included in these tables.

As shown in Tables 4-2 and 4-3, the only observational measure that evaluates all of the components necessary for a comprehensive evaluation of social-emotional functioning for both parent and child is the FEAS. The Parent-Child Early Relational Assessment (PCERA) also shows promise; however, it is not as comprehensive as the FEAS, measuring only four of the six areas of social-emotional development for the child and three of the five areas for the caregiver scale. Since the PCERA is validated only on populations of psychiatrically ill and typically functioning caregivers and children, its usefulness for clinical assessment is limited. Further validation is needed on the PCERA on clinical populations of infants and children before it can be recommended as a clinical measure for social-emotional functioning.

The NCAST is widely used because it captures the transactional nature of the parent-child relationship as well as pertinent social-emotional levels in children. It is well suited for high-risk populations (e.g., preterm

Table 4-2.
Observational Measures Pertaining to Assessment of Social-Emotional Interaction: Child Behaviors

Name of Scale	Age Range	CHILD BEHAVIORS					
		Self-Regulation Temperament	Sensory Processing and Attention	Engagement and Affect	Attachment	Reciprocity, Contingency	Representational Capacities
Bayley Scales of Infant Development, Infant Behavior Record	Birth to 3 yrs.	X	X	X			
Nursing Child Assessment Satellite Training Teaching Scales (NCAST)	Birth to 31 mos.	X				X	
Parent-Child Early Relational Assessment (PCERA)	Birth to 5 yrs.	X	X	X		X	
Transdisciplinary Play-Based Assessment (TPBA)	6 mos. to 6 yrs.		X	X		X	
Functional Emotional Assessment Scale (FEAS)	6 mos. to 4 yrs.	X	X	X	X	X	X

Table 4-3.
Observational Measures Pertaining to Assessment of
Social-Emotional Interaction: Parent Behaviors

Name of Scale	PARENT BEHAVIORS				
	Capacity to Regulate Child	Engagement and Affect	Attachment	Reciprocity Contingency	Representational Capacities
Nursing Child Assessment Satellite Training Teaching Scales (NCAST)	X	X		X	
Parent-Child Early Relational Assessment (PCERA)	X	X		X	
Functional Emotional Assessment Scale (FEAS)	X	X	X	X	X

infants and children at risk for abuse and neglect as well as caregivers who are at-risk), but when we compare it to the FEAS, it is not as comprehensive. Tables 4-4 and 4-5 present recommendations for selection of parent report and direct observation measures as summarized in this section.

As can be seen, the FEAS compares very favorably to the other instruments described in this chapter. It integrates constitutional variables that impact emotional development, incorporates the critical levels of social-emotional development for both caregiver and child, and addresses the parent-child interactive dynamics. When used in combination with other developmental measures and parent report scales, it is, at this time, the most comprehensive approach to social-emotional functioning for infants and young children. In addition, reliability and validity studies on the FEAS (see Chapter 5) show that it is a psychometrically sound instrument.

Table 4-4.
Recommended Parent Report Measures to Evaluate
Social-Emotional Functioning

Age Range	Child Characteristics	Parent Characteristics
Infant: **0 to 24 months**	Infant-Toddler Symptom Checklist (ITSC)	Parenting Stress Index (PSI)
	Neurobehavioral Indicators of Atypical Development (NIAD)	HOME
	Parenting Stress Index (PSI)	
Toddler: **24 to 36 months**	Infant-Toddler Symptom Checklist (ITSC)	Parenting Stress Index (PSI)
	Neurobehavioral Indicators of Atypical Development (NIAD)	HOME
	Parenting Stress Index (PSI)	
	Child Behavior Checklist (CBC)	
Preschool: **36 to 60 months**	Neurobehavioral Indicators of Atypical Development (NIAD)	Parenting Stress Index (PSI)
	Parenting Stress Index (PSI)	HOME
	Child Behavior Checklist (CBC of CBCL)	
	Connors' Parent Rating Scale	
	Social Skills Rating Scale (SSRS)	

Table 4-5.
Recommended Direct Observation Measures to Evaluate
Social-Emotional Functioning

Scale	Recommended Populations
NCAST Teaching and Feeding Scales	High risk infants and toddlers who are at risk for abuse or neglect; infants with prematurity
	Teaching Scales valid through 31 months
Parent-Child Early Relational Assessment (PCERA)	Typically developing children and parents at risk for mental illness
Functional Emotional Assessment Scale (FEAS)	Infants and children with regulatory disorders, pervasive developmental disorders, and high-risk infants and caregivers

Summary

The importance of identifying infants who experience difficulties in social-emotional functioning is crucial in light of research suggesting that infants with constitutional difficulties or who come from high-risk family environments are at high risk for later learning and emotional/behavioral difficulties in the preschool and school-aged years (DeGangi, 2000; DeGangi, Porges, Sickel, & Greenspan, 1993). During infancy, these infants may appear normal in developmental skills, but show difficulties in behavioral organization, attachment to their caregiver, and interactive capacities. A comprehensive assessment should include the infant's regulatory profile, functional emotional developmental capacities, and measures of parent-child interactions in the context of the caregiver-child and family relationships. Parent characteristics (e.g., personality dimensions, interactional styles) and the caregiver's availability to be involved in the assessment and treatment process should also be assessed.

Based on the review of current scales for social-emotional development, it appears that there are several good parent report measures that can be used in conjunction with a direct observation measure of caregiver-child interactions to provide a comprehensive assessment of social-emotional functioning. At this time, the FEAS is the most comprehensive observational measure of parent-child interaction patterns and related emotional capacities. It should be used in combination with one of the suggested parent report measures in a formal research or clinical assessment of social-emotional functioning as well as a clinical interview of parent and child. By using the FEAS in conjunction with other developmental measures, a relatively more complete profile of the child's overall social-emotional and developmental capacities may be obtained.

References

Abidin, R. R. (1986). *Parenting stress index.* Charlottesville, VA: Pediatric Psychology Press.

Achenbach, T. M. (1989). *Child behavior checklist.* Burlington, VT: University of Vermont.

Bagnato, S. J., Neisworth, J. T., Salvia, J., & Hunt, F. M. (1992). *Neurobehavioral indicators of atypical development (NIAD).* Pittsburgh, PA: University of Pittsburgh.

Barnard, K. E. (1979). *Instructor's learning resource manual.* Seattle: NCAST Publications, University of Washington.

Barnard, K. E. & Kelly, J. (1990). Assessment of parent-child interaction. In S.J. Meisels & J.P. Shonkoff (Eds.), *Handbook of Early Childhood Intervention* (pp. 278–302). New York: Cambridge University Press.

Bates, J. E. (1984). *Infant characteristics questionnaire, revised.* Bloomington: Indiana University.

Bates, J. E. (1990). Conceptual and empirical linkages between temperament and behavior problems: A commentary on the Sanson, Prior, and Kyrios study. *Merrill-Palmer Quarterly, 36,* 193–199.

Bayley, N. (1993). *Bayley scales of infant development.* New York: Psychological Corporation.

Bernstein, V. J., Hans, S. L., & Percansky, C. (1991). Advocating for the young child in need through strengthening the parent-child relationship. *Journal of Clinical Child Psychology, 20,* 28–41.

Bradley, R., Caldwell, B., & Elardo, R. (1977). Home environment, social status, and mental test performance. *Journal of Educational Psychology, 69,* 697–701.

Briggs-Gowan, M. & Carter, A. S. (1998). Preliminary acceptance and psychometrics of the Infant-Toddler Social and Emotional Assessment (ITSEA). *Infant Mental Health Journal, 19,* 422–445.

Caldwell, B. & Bradley, R. (1978). *Manual for the home observation for measurement of the environment.* Little Rock: University of Arkansas.

Campos, J. J., Mumme, D. L., Kermoian, R., & Campos, R. G. (1994). A functionalist perspective on the nature of emotion. In N. A. Fox. The development of emotion regulation: Biological and behavioral considerations. *Monographs of the Society for Research in Child Development, 59* (2–3), 284–303.

Carter, A. S. & Briggs-Gowan, M. (1993). *The infant-toddler social and emotional assessment (ITSEA).* Unpublished measure.

Carter, A. S., Little, C., Briggs-Gowan, M., & Kogan, N. (1999). The Infant-Toddler Social and Emotional Assessment (ITSEA): Comparing parent ratings to laboratory observations of task mastery, emotion regulation, coping behaviors, and attachment status. *Infant Mental Health Journal, 20,* 375–392.

Caspi, A. & Moffitt, T. E. (1995). The continuity of maladaptive behavior: From description to understanding in the study of antisocial behavior. In D. Cicchetti & D. Cohen (Eds.), *Developmental Psychopathology: Risk Disorder and Adaptation* (pp. 472–511). New York: John Wiley & Sons.

Cicchetti, D., Ackerman, B. P., & Izard, C. E. (1995). Emotions and emotion regulation in developmental psychopathology. *Development and Psychopathology, 7,* 1–10.

Clark, R. (1985). *The parent-child early relational assessment.* Madison: University of Wisconsin Medical School, Department of Psychiatry.

Cogill, S. R., Caplan, H. L., Alexandra, H., Robson, K. M., & Kumar, R. (1986). Impact of maternal postnatal depression on cognitive development of young children. *Br.Med.J.(Clin.Res.Ed), 292,* 1165–1167.

Conners, C. K. (1997). *Conners' Rating Scales-Revised.* North Tonawanda, NY: Multi-Health Systems.

DeGangi, G. A. (2000). *Pediatric disorders of regulation in affect and behavior: A therapist's guide to assessment and treatment.* New York: Academic Press.

DeGangi, G. A. & Breinbauer, C. (1997). The symptomatology of infants and toddlers with regulatory disorders. *Journal of Developmental and Learning Disorders, 1,* 183–215.

DeGangi, G. A. & Greenspan, S. I. (1989). *The test of sensory functions in infants.* Los Angeles: Western Psychological Services.

DeGangi, G. A., Poisson, S., Sickel, R. Z., & Wiener, A. S. (1995). *Infant-toddler symptom checklist.* Tucson, AZ: Therapy Skill Builders.

DeGangi, G. A., Porges, S. W., Sickel, R. Z., & Greenspan, S. I. (1993). Four-year follow-up of a sample of regulatory disordered infants. *Infant Mental Health Journal, 14,* 330–343.

Division for Early Childhood (1993). *DEC recommended practices: Indicators of quality in programs for infants and young children with special needs and their families.* Reston, VA: The Council for Exceptional Children.

Earls, F. (1980). Prevalence of behavior problems in 3-year-old children. A cross-national replication. *Arch.Gen.Psychiatry, 37,* 1153–1157.

Farran, D., Clark, K., & Ray, A. (1990). Measures of parent-child interaction. In E. D. Gills & D. Teti (Eds.), *Interdisciplinary assessment of infants: A guide for early intervention professionals* (pp. 227–248). Baltimore: Paul H. Brookes.

Fewell, R. R. (1991). Trends in the assessment of infants and toddlers with disabilities. *Except.Child, 58,* 166–173.

Fogel, A. (1993). *Developing through relationships.* Chicago: University of Chicago Press.

Fogel, A., Nwokah, E., Dedo, J. Y., Messinger, D., Dickson, K. L., Matusov, E., & Holt, S. A. (1992). Social process theory of emotion: A dynamic systems approach. *Social Development, 1,* (pp. 122–142).

Gaensbauer, T. J. & Harmon, R. J. (1982). Attachment in abused/neglected and premature infants. In R. N. Emde & R. J. Harmon (Eds.), *The Development of Attachment and AffiliativeSystems* (pp. 263–280). New York: Plenum Press.

Ghuman, J. K., Peebles, C. D., & Ghuman, H. S. (1998). Review of social interaction measures in infants and preschool children. *Infants and Young Children, 11,* 21–44.

Gianino, A. & Tronick, E. (1988). The mutual regulation model: The infant's self and interactive regulation coping and defense. In T. Field, P .McCabe, & N. Schneiderman (Eds.), *Stress and coping* (pp. 47–68). Hillsdale, NJ: Lawrence Erlbaum & Associates.

Goldsmith, H. H., Rieser-Danner, L. A., & Briggs, S. (1991). Evaluating convergent and discriminant validity of temperament questionnaires for preschoolers, toddlers, and infants. *Developmental Psychology, 27,* 566-579.

Greenspan, S. I. (1979). Psychopathology and adaptation in infancy and early childhood: Principles of clinical diagnosis and preventive intervention. *Clinical Infant Reports, No. 1.* New York, International Universities Press.

Greenspan, S. I. (1989). *The development of the ego: Implications for personality theory, psychopathology, and the psychotherapeutic process.* Madison, CT: International Universities Press.

Greenspan, S. I. (1992). *Infancy and early childhood: The practice of clinical assessment and intervention with emotional and developmental challenges.* Madison, CT: International Universities Press.

Greenspan, S. I. (1997). *Developmentally based psychotherapy.* Madison, CT: International Universities Press.

Greenspan, S.I., et al. (2000). Panel on Autism: The causes and increase in cases. Papers presented at the Fourth International Conference on Autism and Disorders of Relating and Communicating of the Interdisciplinary Council on Developmental and Learning Disorders. Bethesda, MD.

Greenspan, S. I. & Wieder, S. W. (1993). Regulatory disorders. In C. H. Zeanah (Ed.), *Handbook of Infant Mental Health* (pp. 280–290). New York: The Guilford Press.

Gresham, F. & Elliott, S. N. (1990). *Social Skills Rating System (SSRS).* Circle Pines, MN: American Guidance Services.

Gross, D., Conrad, B., Fogg, L., Willis, L., & Garvey, C. (1993). What does the NCATS (Nursing Child Assessment Teaching Scale) measure? *Nurs.Res., 42,* 260–265.

Guerin, D. W., Gottfried, A. W., & Thomas, C. W. (1997). Difficult temperament and behaviour problems: A longitudinal study from 1.5 to 12 years. *International Journal of Behavioral Development, 21,* 71–90.

Jenkins, S., Bax, M., & Hart, H. (1980). Behavior problems in pre-school children. *J Child Psychol Psychiatry, 21,* 5–17.

Kopp, C. (1989). Regulation of distress and negative emotions: A developmental view. *Developmental Psychology, 25,* 343–354.

Lamb, M., Thompson, R. A., Gardner, W. P., Charnov, E. L., & Estes, D. (1984). Security of infantile attachment as assessed in the "strange situation": Its study and biological interpretation. *The Behavioral and Brain Sciences, 7,* 127–171.

Lavigne, J. V., Gibbons, R. D., Christoffel, K. K., Arend, R., Rosenbaum, D., Binns, H., et al. (1996). Prevalence rates and correlates of psychiatric disorders among preschool children. *Journal of the American Academy of Child & Adolescent Psychiatry, 35,* 204–214.

Lerner, R. M., Palermo, M., Spiro, A., & Nesselroade, J. (1982). Assessing the dimensions of temperamental individuality across the life-span: The Dimensions of Temperament Survey (DOTS). *Child Dev., 53,* 149–159.

Lieberman, A. F. & Zeanah, C. R. (1995). Disorders of attachment in infancy. *Child Adolest Psychiatr Clin North Am, 4,* 571–588.

Linder, T. W. (1990). *Transdisciplinary Play-Based Assessment.* Baltimore, MD: Paul H. Brookes Publishing Co.

Lyons-Ruth, K., Zoll, D., Connell, D., & Grunebaum, H. (1986). The depressed mother and her one-year-old infant: Environment, interaction, attachment, and infant development. In E. Tronick & T. Field (Eds.), *Maternal Depression and Infant Disturbance: New Directions for Child Development* (pp. 61–82). San Francisco: Jossey-Bass.

Matas, L., Arend, R. A., & Sroufe, L. A. (1978). Continuity of adaptation in the second year: The relationship between quality of attachment and later competence. *Child Dev., 49,* 547–556.

Mattison, R. E., Handfor, H. A., & Vela-Bueno, A. (1987). Sleep disorders in children. *Psychiatric Medicine, 4,* 149–164.

Meisels, S. J. (1989). Can developmental screening tests identify children who are developmentally at risk? *Pediatrics, 83,* 578–585.

Michnowicz, L. L., McConnell, S. R., Peterson, C. A., & Odom, S. L. (1995). Social goals and objectives of preschool IEPs: A content analysis. *Journal of Early Intervention, 19,* 373–382.

Murray, L., Fiori-Cowley, A., Hooper, R., & Cooper, P. (1996). The impact of postnatal depression and associated adversity on early mother-infant interactions and later infant outcome. *Child Dev., 67,* 2512-2526.

Musick, S. J., Clark, R., & Cohler, B. (1981). The Mother's Project: A program for mentally ill mothers of young children. In B. Weissbourd & J. S. Musick (Eds.), *Infants: Their Social Environments* (pp. 111–127). Washington, DC: National Association for the Education of Young Children.

NCAST (1995a). *Caregiver/parent-child interaction feeding manual.* Seattle: NCAST Publications, University of Washington, School of Nursing.

NCAST (1995b). *Caregiver/parent-child interaction teaching manual.* Seattle: NCAST Publications, University of Washington, School of Nursing.

Papousek, H. & Papousek, M. (1987). Intuitive parenting: A dialectic counterpart to the infant's integrative competence. In J. D. Osofsky (Ed.), *Handbook of Infant Development* (2nd ed., pp. 669–720). New York: John Wiley & Sons.

Pedlow, R., Sanson, A. M., & Oberklaid, F. (1993). Stability of maternally reported temperament from infancy to 8 years. *Developmental Psychology, 29,* 998–1007.

Ritvo, E. R., Freeman, B. J., Pingree, C., Mason-Brothers, A., Jorde, L., Jenson, W. R., McMahon, W. M., Petersen, P. B., Mo, A., & Ritvo, A. (1989). The

UCLA-University of Utah epidemiologic survey of autism: prevalence. *Am.J.Psychiatry, 146,* 194–199.

Rothbart, M. & Derryberry, D. (1981). Development of individual differences in temperament. In M. E. Lamb, A. L. Brown, & B. Rogoff (Eds.), *Advances in Developmental Psychology* (pp. 37–86). Hillsdale, NJ: Lawrence Erlbaum & Associates.

Seifer, R., Sameroff, A. J., Barrett, L. C., & Krafchuk, E. (1994). Infant temperament measured by multiple observations and mother report. *Child Dev., 65,* 1478–1490.

Seifer, R., Schiller, M., Sameroff, A. J., Resnick, S., & Riordan, K. (1996). Attachment, maternal sensitivity, and infant temperament during the first year of life. *Developmental Psychology, 32,* 12–25.

Shaw, D. S., Keenan, K., & Vondra, J. I. (1994). Developmental precursors of externalizing behavior: Ages 1 to 3. *Developmental Psychology, 30,* 355–364.

Sroufe, L. A. (1988). The role of infant-caregiver attachment in development. In J. Belsky & T. Nezworski (Eds.), *Clinical Implications of Attachment* (pp. 18–40). Hillsdale, NJ: Lawrence Erlbaum.

Stern, D. (1985). *The interpersonal world of the infant: A view from psychoanalysis and developmental psychology.* New York: Basic Books.

Sugiyama, T. & Abe, T. (1989). The prevalence of autism in Nagoya, Japan: A total population study. *J.Autism Dev.Disord., 19,* 87–96.

Tronick, E. (1989). Emotions and emotional communication in infants. *American Psychologist, 44,* 112–119.

Walker, E. & Emory, E. (1983). Infants at risk for psychopathology: Offspring of schizophrenic parents. *Child Dev., 54,* 1269–1285.

Zahn-Waxler, C., Iannotti, R. J., Cummings, E. M., & Denham, S. (1990). Antecedents of problem behaviors in children of depressed mothers. *Development and Psychopathology, 2,* 271–291.

Zeanah, C. H. (1996). Beyond insecurity: A reconceptualization of attachment disorders of infancy. *J.Consult Clin Psychol., 64,* 42–52.

Zeanah, C. H., Boris, N. W., Heller, S. S., Hinshaw-Fuselier, S., Larrieu, J. A., Lewis, M., Palomino, R., Rovaris, M., & Valliere, J. (1997). Relationship assessment in infant mental health. *Infant Mental Health Journal, 18,* 182–197.

Zero to Three (1994). *Diagnostic classification of mental health and developmental disorders of infancy and early childhood.* Arlington, VA.

5

Research on the FEAS:
Test Development, Reliability,
and Validity Studies

Georgia A. DeGangi, Ph.D., OTR
Stanley I. Greenspan, M.D.

Test Development

The Functional Emotional Assessment Scale (FEAS) was developed as a criterion-referenced instrument for children ranging in age from 7 months through 4 years. It was designed to measure emotional functioning in children with constitutional- and maturation-based problems (e.g., regulatory disorders), children with interactional problems leading to a variety of symptoms such as anxiety, impulsivity, depression, etc., and children with pervasive developmental difficulties. This includes children who experience constitutional or developmental maturational problems, such as those with regulatory disorders or pervasive developmental disorder, as well as caregivers and children with relational problems, such as attachment disorders, or children from multi-problem families with a variety of interactional difficulties (e.g., anxiety, depression, impulsivity, etc.). The FEAS provides a systematic assessment of the child and caregiver's functional emotional capacities. For infants and young children, these capacities include the child's ability to organize play interactions with objects and persons, to self-regulate mood and organize attention, to form an attachment with the caregiver, to engage in reciprocal emotional in-teractions and communications, and to represent feelings and ideas and engage in emotional thinking through play interactions. Caregiver behav-iors are evaluated in relation to their capacity to support their child's de-velopment in each of these areas.

The FEAS is intended for use to profile social-emotional functioning in infants and young children. As will be seen in this chapter, it distin-guishes between the child with a high-risk profile of emotional function-ing and those without problems, as well as between different types of prob-lems. When used in conjunction with other instruments as part of a comprehensive evaluation, the FEAS provides data on the child and care-giver's social and emotional capacities using a developmental framework that integrates observations of a number of variables. These include con-stitutional variables, such as self-regulatory, sensory, and attentional ca-pacities. They also include developmental levels of emotional functioning as well as interactive components that form the basis for attachment, mood regulation, emotional functioning, and social communication. Findings from the FEAS do not lead to a formal diagnosis of specific dis-orders, such as autism, anxiety disorder, attachment disorder, or regula-tory disorder; however, data from the FEAS, combined with other diag-nostic information (e.g., clinical interview of parent and child, parent report measures, and other formal testing) may help to provide a profile of emotional functioning. (See Chapters 8 and 9 for further discussions of a comprehensive clinical evaluation.)

A collection of 46 items for the caregiver version and 79 items for the child version of the FEAS were generated systematically from a list of do-main specifications. These are presented in Table 5-1. This strategy assures that the items are representative of each domain. Several items were con-structed for each of the functions to be measured. The first version of the FEAS was developed in 1992 by Stanley I. Greenspan, M.D. and was pi-loted by Georgia A. DeGangi, Ph.D. on a sample of 45 infants, 30 of whom were typically developing and 15 with regulatory disorders. In collabora-tion with Dr. Greenspan, Dr. DeGangi revised test items then collected data over the course of five years. The research version of the FEAS ap-pears in Appendix B. This was the version from which the specific age-ver-sions of the FEAS were derived.

Observable behaviors were selected and operationalized for test items within each domain. Below is a description of behaviors that were chosen for each domain. These behaviors cover both the child and parents'

Table 5-1.
Domain Specifications for the FEAS

Domain	Description of Domain
Regulation and interest in the world (0 to 3 months)	Internal regulation (harmony and balanced interest in the world)
Forming relationships or attachment (2 to 7 months)	Rich, deep, multisensory emotional investment in animate world (especially with primary caregivers)
Intentional two-way communication (3 to 10 months)	Flexible, wide-ranging, affective, multisystem contingent (reciprocal interactions [especially with primary] caregivers)
Development of a complex sense of self (e.g., behavioral organization and elaboration) (9 to 24 months)	Complex, organized, assertive, innovative, integrated behavioral and emotional patterns
Representational capacity and elaboration of symbolic thinking (1½ to 4 years)	Formation and elaboration of internal representations (imagery); organization and differentiation of imagery pertaining to self and nonself, emergence of cognitive insight; stabilization of mood and gradual emergence of basic personality functions
Emotional thinking or the development and expression of thematic play (3 to 5 years)	Enhanced and eventually optimal flexibility to conserve and transform complex and organized representations or experience in the context of expanded relationship patterns and phase-expected developmental tasks

capacities. In the actual scoring protocol in Appendix C, the parent and child behaviors will be presented separately. In addition, each age range will have a separate protocol covering the relevant items for that age range.

Self-Regulation and Interest In the World

Test items were developed to depict the various ways in which a parent and child self-regulate and show a balanced interest in the world. Specific behaviors tapped by this domain include the following:

- Both parent and child show interest in toys through facial or verbal expressions of interest or by handling and touching toys, but are not so absorbed by the toys that, for the caregivers, they play with toys by themselves, ignoring the child.

- The caregiver shows sustained interest in the child, focusing on child's signals (gestures, vocalizations), keeping child involved in play while the child explores objects freely without caution.
- Parent and child show their capacity to self-regulate by remaining calm and focused. The parent interacts calmly with the child, able to wait for the child's responses and the child remains calm for the play period with no signs of distress (crying or whining), showing only appropriate frustration.
- Affective display is measured by the type of expression shown (e.g., pleasant or animated, happy affect throughout play; neutral and content; somber or depressed).
- Comfort at exploring textured toys or in touching one another in appropriate ways (e.g., pat on back or hug) are observed by the parent's sensitivity and responsiveness to the child's need for touch by stroking or touching the child in pleasurable ways and/or encouraging the child to explore textured toys while noting the child's comfort at touching textured toys or in being touched by his/her caregiver.
- Ease in using movement in play is measured by the caregiver's ability to provide pleasurable movement experiences to the child or encouraging movement exploration and the child's pleasure at moving on equipment or engaging in rough-house play.
- Vigilant behavior in the child is noted which may reflect sensory defensiveness, attentional problems, or trauma and neglect.
- The child's activity level, whether underreactive (e.g., sluggish or withdrawn) or overreactive (e.g., overaroused by toys and environment), is observed.

Forming Relationships, Attachment, and Engagement

Items within this domain focus on the parent and child's ability to show an emotional investment in the animate world. Specific behaviors measured include the following:

- The caregiver is relaxed during the interchange with the child, not overly attentive to the child's every action as might be seen in an anxious parent.
- The parent looks at the child with affection, showing a warm connection.

- The parent and child clearly enjoy being with one another, playing together, showing their warmth through smiles, vocalizing, or a joyful look or by each emoting a sense of warmth by providing inviting gestures to one another. It is important to keep in mind cultural differences in how this may be expressed.
- Anxious attachment of the parent to the child is observed by the parent overwhelming the child with affectionate touching; ambivalent attachment is further observed by the parent's appearing uncomfortable in showing feelings or relating warmly and intimately with the child, appearing overly vigilant towards the child.
- The caregiver maintains a verbal or visual connection with his/her child, showing clear availability and interest in the child. The child may move away from the caregiver to explore the room, yet the caregiver maintains connected to the child across space through gestures, vocalizations, and facial expressions. Different levels of connectedness are observed in the child. The child may anticipate with curiosity or excitement when the caregiver presents an interesting object or game. The child may initiate physical closeness to the caregiver by moving close but without becoming clingy. If the child is active and moves away from the caregiver, he/she maintains a visual or verbal connection with the caregiver through glances, gestures, or vocalizations.
- Disorganized, ambivalent, or anxious attachment in the child can be observed in the child's turning away his/her head, averting gaze, moving away, or sitting facing away from the caregiver without social referencing the caregiver. The child may appear indifferent, aloof, withdrawn, or avoidant of the caregiver. It is important to recognize, however, that these same behaviors may reflect a child who is unable to organize face-to-face interactions because of the challenge it presents (e.g., organizing affective, gestural and vocal cues with another person while organizing intentional actions with objects).
- Security of attachment may be observed in the child's general sense of security and/or comfort when near the caregiver. The child may initiate physical closeness to the caregiver but is not clingy. If the child is active and moves away from caregiver, he/she references the caregiver from across space, maintaining a connection with him or her through looking, gestures, or vocalizations.

- Lastly, attachment behaviors in the child may be observed in the child's display of signs of discomfort, displeasure, or sadness during interactive play if the caregiver should become unresponsive or engage in anticontingent behaviors.

Two-Way, Purposeful Communication (Somatopsychological Differentiation)

This domain reflects the parent and child's capacity to engage in flexible, contingent interactions with one another. This is measured in a variety of ways:

- The parent and child's capacity to "open circles of communication," that is, to initiate interactions with one another through vocalizations or gestures to create interactive opportunities with one another, is observed.
- Contingent responses are measured by the parent responding to the child's wishes, intentions, and actions, building on how the child wishes to play and by the child responding to the parent's actions or requests. For example, the child may hand a toy to the parent, and the parent responds by taking it and saying something about the toy, then gives the child an opportunity to respond to what he/she just did. Scoring reflects problems that may arise in organizing contingent responses including anticontingent responses (e.g., opposite to what child seeks), misreading the child's cues, or changing the activity from what the child wants to do to something else. In our studies of regulatory disordered children and their parents, we found that anticontingent responses were commonly observed.
- Noncontingent responses are noted when the parent plays with the toys in a parallel play fashion, removing attention from playing with the child, a behavior that was frequently observed in the sample of multi-problem children.
- The parent's capacity to plays with the child at a developmentally appropriate level is observed (e.g., caregiver plays slightly above child's level of skill, modeling new ways to do things or labeling what child does or describing the functions of objects).
- The parent's capacity to stimulate the child at a pace that allows the child to respond, waiting for the child's responses. Many parents of

regulatory disordered children tend to overstimulate their child with language or actions, not allowing their child the time to process information or organize interactions.

- The parent's capacity to relinquish control and allow the child to decide on the play topic, to initiate play and explore toys in ways that the child seeks or needs is also observed.
- The child's ability to motor-plan, organize, or execute play interactions by initiating purposeful and intentional actions in play with objects is observed. Scoring includes observations of children who engage in stereotypic actions; i.e., lining toys up, mouthing toys for long periods of time, banging toys without engaging in any other actions with the same toy or initiates play but actions appear aimless or disorganized, behaviors that are common in children with developmental dyspraxia (e.g., motor planning problems) and pervasive developmental delay.
- Disorganized behaviors in the child may be observed by them showing anger, frustration, aggression, or protest repeatedly. This behavior reflects not only the child's difficulties in sustaining reciprocal interactions, but also how he or she deregulates in the process.
- The child's use of language is also observed since language emerges as the child learns to organize reciprocal interactions (e.g., sounds, words, and/or gestures).

Behavioral Organization, Problem-Solving, and Internalization (A Complex Sense of Self)

Items in this domain demonstrate complex, organized, and integrated behavioral and emotional patterns and include the following:

- The parent and child respond and initiate reciprocal back and forth chains of interactions with one another, stringing together connected circles of communication or units of interaction. For example, caregiver introduces baby doll, child touches doll's face, mother touches doll's hair, child pats the doll, mother says "baby," and child glances between mother and doll. The caregiver may imitate the child (i.e., pushing car alongside child), then interject her turn by an action or verbalization related to the child's actions (i.e., "Oh, a bump!" then bumps her car into child's car).

- The various ways in which the caregiver organizes circles of communication with the child are coded (e.g., through gestures and facial expressions; touch or rough-house play) because of the importance of using different modalities in organizing the child's behaviors.
- The caregiver's ability to sustain multiple circles of communication while also showing pleasure and excitement in playing with the child in whatever way the child wishes to play is coded.
- One of the items measures the parent's ability to set appropriate limits on the child (e.g., redirecting child not to leave room, or not throw toy).
- The parent's ability to elaborate on and add complexity into the child's play behaviors while engaged in interactive sequences between one another is observed. The parent expands on what the child is doing, thus creating a problem solving opportunity for the child, while remaining on the child's play topic (e.g., the parent does not introduce a completely new play idea). At the same time, the child's ability to imitate or copy something new that the caregiver introduces, then incorporate the idea into his or her own play is observed (i.e., caregiver feeds doll; child copies this).
- The parent's capacity to support behavioral organization in the child is observed through the parent's allowing the child to assert him- or herself in play and supporting the child's needs for dependency and closeness, assertiveness and curiosity, aggression, autonomy, or pleasure and excitement by admiring, showing interest, and/or by joining the child's play in whatever way the child seeks. Problems that may interfere with the caregiver's capacity to support this area might be intrusiveness, withdrawal, overprotectiveness, or playing at a level far above the child's level of competence.

Representational Capacity and Elaboration of Symbolic Thinking

The formation and elaboration of internal representations (e.g., symbolic thinking) are measured by the following:

- The caregiver encourages the child to engage in symbolic play by modeling or combining materials in ways that facilitate representational actions (i.e., mother holds spoon near baby doll's mouth and says, "Feed baby?").

- The caregiver elaborates on the child's pretend play idea by building on the child's ideas and adding some complexity to them.
- The caregiver allows the child to express different pretend play themes involving closeness or dependency, pleasure and excitement, and assertiveness.
- The child engages in symbolic play with the various toys or equipment, going beyond simple concrete actions.
- The child engages in pretend play patterns of at least one idea in collaboration with the caregiver.
- The child uses language or pretend play (e.g., playing out with doll figures) to communicate needs, wishes, intentions, or feelings.
- The child constructs pretend play to express themes around closeness or dependency, pleasure and excitement, and assertiveness.
- The child creates pretend drama with two or more ideas that are not related or logically connected.

Emotional Thinking or Development and Expression of Thematic Play

Within this domain, the parent and child's capacity to organize representational concepts and emotional ideas within elaborated play sequences are demonstrated. Test items focus on the following:

- The caregiver elaborates on the child's pretend play, creating opportunities to logically connect ideas in play. The caregiver accomplishes this by asking questions to give depth to the drama such as "how," "why," or "when." If the child strays off the topic, the caregiver asks questions to bridge the circle of communication back to the pretend play theme.
- The caregiver incorporates causality into pretend play by helping the child to logically connect three or more ideas into a reality-based story sequence.
- The caregiver helps child to elaborate on a wide range of emotional themes, whatever they might be—assertiveness, pleasure and excitement, fearfulness, anger, or separation and loss. The caregiver is accepting of the child's expressions of different feelings and themes through play and shows no discomfort at the expression of different ideas from the child.

- The child constructs pretend play, however unrealistic, involving two or more ideas that are logically tied to one another.
- The child elaborates on a pretend play sequence of two or more ideas that are logically connected and grounded in reality. There is a planned quality and the child can elaborate to "how," "why," or "when" questions, giving depth to the drama.
- The child uses pretend play or language to communicate themes containing two or more ideas dealing with closeness or dependency, pleasure and excitement, or assertiveness.

Validity Studies

The FEAS was validated on four samples of infants and children ranging in age from 7 to 48 months (197 normal, 190 infants and children with regulatory disorders, 41 children with pervasive developmental disorders, and 40 children from multi-problem families and with drug exposure in utero). The children in this study participated in a larger validation study of qualitative measures of sustained attention, parent-child interactions, and sensory processing. The sample sizes and characteristics of the subjects within each sample are shown in Table 5-2. The majority of the infants were white, middle class, with only 6% from Hispanic, Black, or Asian populations. All subjects except those with pervasive developmental disorders fell within normal limits on developmental testing (e.g., Bayley Scales of Infant Development, Mental Scales [Bayley, 1969]). Statistical analyses yielded no differences in the normal and regulatory disordered samples in their performance on the Mental Bayley.

The criteria for selection of infants in the regulatory disordered sample was based on symptomatology. The infants had to have at least two of the following difficulties:

- Sleep disturbance consisting of repeated awakenings in the night and taking over 20 minutes to fall asleep.
- Difficulties self-consoling with an inability to self-calm, and requiring extensive help from the parent to console (e.g., parents spend from two to four hours a day attempting to console the infant).

- Distress around feeding with regurgitation, refusal to eat, and other feeding problems not related to allergies or food intolerance.
- Hyperarousal with high distractibility.

The diagnostic criteria presented in DSM-IV (American Psychiatric Association, 1994) were used to classify children with pervasive developmental disorders. In general, children had to show qualitative impairments in social interactions, communication, and symbolic or imaginative play, and had to show restricted repetitive and stereotypic behaviors such as ritualistic or perseverative behaviors.

Children in the multi-problem family group came from single-parent families with low socio-economic status. All of the children in the sample had been exposed to drugs in utero. At the time of testing, mothers of children in this sample were participating in a residential drug treatment program.

Table 5-2 presents the characteristics and sample size of the subjects for the validity study.

Table 5-2.
Characteristics of Subjects for the Validity Study

Variable	Normal (N = 197)	Regulatory Disorder (N = 190)	Pervasive Developmental Disorder (N = 41)	Multi-problem (N = 40)
Sex:				
Male	116	116	31	29
Female	81	74	10	11
Age:				
7 to 9 mos.	36	19	0	6
10 to 12 mos.	28	21	0	2
13 to 18 mos.	36	35	0	9
19 to 24 mos.	44	41	2	4
25 to 35 mos.	19	16	20	3
36 to 48 mos.	34	58	19	16

Construct Validity Study

A criterion-group validation model was used to investigate the validity of the FEAS. In this model, evidence of construct validity was obtained at three levels—item, subscale, and total for the caregiver and child scale. The effectiveness or validity of each item was determined by computing its mean score for the normal and clinical groups for each age range (e.g., 7 to 9, 10 to 12, 13 to 18, 19 to 24, 25 to 30 months, and 3 to 4 years). Mean scores were only computed for the 25 to 30 month and 3 year level for the PDD group and at the 3 to 4 year level for children in the multi-problem group. Because there were fewer subjects in the different age categories for the children in the multi-problem sample under 3 years, the mean scores for individual items and subscales are not reported, but were used as a guide in determining which items may have particular relevance for that population.

A discrimination index reflecting the difference between group item performance was calculated for normal and regulatory disorder (RD) and for normal and PDD groups. The magnitude of the discrimination index was computed and the effect size of this index estimated (Cohen, 1977, 1985). The effect sizes for items ranged from small (.2 to .39) to medium (.4 to .59) and large differences (.60+) in means. Tables A-1 through A-6 in Appendix A provide information on the item means and mean differences (e.g., discrimination index) for each of the age ranges.

A t-test analysis was conducted to determine if differences in the two samples reached the level of significance for items at the various age ranges. The means and standard deviations were computed for the collection of items comprising each category. Of special interest was the statistical significance of the difference between means for the normal and regulatory disordered infants. This was assessed with the t-test between samples drawn from independent populations. Results from these analyses are presented in Appendix A, Tables A-1 through A-6. In addition, analyses of variance were conducted on subtest and total test scores for each of the age ranges. These results are presented in Appendix A, Tables B-1 through B-6. The vast majority of the subtests discriminated between the normative and clinical samples for each of the age ranges.

Optimal cutting scores were located to determine the best points of group discrimination for each category (Berk, 1976). Infants scoring at or above a cutoff score in any category would be considered "at risk" and should be referred for further testing. The cutoff scores are presented in Tables 5-3 through 5-8.

Table 5-3.
Cutoff Scores, Total Accuracy, and Error Rates for Various Classification Decisions for 7 to 9 Month-Olds

Subtest	Cutoff Score[a]	Performance[b] Standard	Total Accuracy Normal & Delayed	Error Rates		Specificity[c] (Normal)	Sensitivity[d] (Delayed)
				False Delayed	False Normal		
Caregiver:							
Regulation	6/10	60%	64%	79%	3%	21%	97%
Attachment	6/6	100%	69%	42%	19%	58%	81%
Two-way communication	8/10	80%	60%	53%	25%	47%	75%
Total Caregiver	20/26	77%	69%	74%	8%	26%	94%
Child:							
Regulation	14/16	87.5%	69%	37%	28%	53%	72%
Attachment	8/10	80%	69%	42%	19%	58%	81%
Total Child	22/26	85%	71%	31%	17%	69%	83%
Total Scale	**41/52**	**79%**	**76%**	**37%**	**17%**	**63%**	**83%**

[a] The number to the left of the slash mark represents the actual cutoff score for that subtest or total test; the number to the right of the slash mark represents the total number of points available on the subtest or total test.

[b] Percentage of items that the child must perform correctly to have mastered that domain.

[c] Probability of correctly identifying a normal child in a sample of actual normal children.

[d] Probability of correctly identifying a delayed child in a sample of actual delayed children.

179

Table 5-4.
Cutoff Scores, Total Accuracy, and Error Rates for Various Classification Decisions for 10 to 12 Month-Olds

Subtest	Cutoff Score[e]	Performance[f] Standard	Total Accuracy Normal & Delayed	Error Rates			
				False Delayed	False Normal	Specificity[g] (Normal)	Sensitivity[h] (Delayed)
Caregiver:							
Regulation	8/10	80%	55%	61%	25%	39%	75%
Attachment	8/8	100%	69%	52%	14%	48%	86%
Two-way communication	9/10	90%	59%	61%	25%	39%	75%
Behavioral organization	4/6	66.6%	61%	61%	21%	39%	79%
Total Caregiver	*27/34*	*79%*	*67%*	*52%*	*18%*	*48%*	*82%*
Child:							
Regulation	14/16	87.5%	67%	52%	18%	48%	82%
Attachment	10/10	100%	58%	61%	25%	39%	75%
Two-way communication	7/8	87.5%	69%	35%	28%	65%	72%
Total Child	*31/34*	*91%*	*73%*	*19%*	*32%*	*81%*	*68%*
Total Scale	**61/68**	**90%**	**74%**	**26%**	**25%**	**74%**	**75%**

[e] The number to the left of the slash mark represents the actual cutoff score for that subtest or total test; the number to the right of the slash mark represents the total number of points available on the subtest or total test.

[f] Percentage of items that the child must perform correctly to have mastered that domain.

[g] Probability of correctly identifying a normal child in a sample of actual normal children.

[h] Probability of correctly identifying a delayed child in a sample of actual delayed children.

Table 5-5.
Cutoff Scores, Total Accuracy, and Error Rates for Various Classification Decisions for 13 to 18 Month-Olds

Subtest	Cutoff Score[i]	Performance[j] Standard	Total Accuracy Normal & Delayed	False Delayed	False Normal R.D.	False Normal Multi-Problem	Specificity[k] (Normal)	Sensitivity[l] (Delayed)
Caregiver:								
Regulation	6/8	75%	60%	74%	0%	17%	36%	83–100%
Attachment	7/8	87.5%	59%	68%	67%	8%	32%	33–92%
Two-way communication	9/10	90%	64%	66%	22%	11%	34%	78–89%
Behavioral organization	7/10	70%	63%	51%	22%	22%	49%	78%
Total caregiver	*30/36*	83%	66%	54%	11%	19%	46%	81–89%
Child:								
Regulation	13/14	93%	73%	26%	66%	28%	98%	34–72%
Attachment	9/10	90%	73%	26%	11%	25%	74%	75–89%
Two-way communication	7/8	87.5%	83%	17%	33%	14%	83%	67–86%
Total Child	*29/32*	91%	73%	37%	11%	25%	63%	75–89%
Total Scale	**60/68**	**88%**	**68%**	**43%**	**11%**	**28%**	**57%**	**74–89%**

[i] The number to the left of the slash mark represents the actual cutoff score for that subtest or total test; the number to the right of the slash mark represents the total number of points available on the subtest or total test.

[j] Percentage of items that the child must perform correctly to have mastered that domain.

[k] Probability of correctly identifying a normal child in a sample of actual normal children.

[l] Probability of correctly identifying a delayed child in a sample of actual delayed children.

Table 5-6.
Cutoff Scores, Total Accuracy, and Error Rates for Various Classification Decisions for 19 to 24 Month-Olds

Subtest	Cutoff Score[m]	Performance[n] Standard	Total Accuracy Normal & Delayed	Error Rates			
				False Delayed	False Normal	Specificity[o] (Normal)	Sensitivity[p] (Delayed)
Caregiver:							
Regulation	3/6	50%	56%	62%	25%	38%	75%
Attachment	6/6	100%	58%	72%	9%	38%	91%
Two-way communication	9/10	90%	53%	70%	23%	30%	77%
Behavioral organization	11/14	78.5%	50%	60%	39%	40%	61%
Total caregiver	28/36	78%	56%	62%	25%	38%	75%
Child:							
Regulation	13/16	87.5%	64%	51%	20%	49%	80%
Attachment	12/14	86%	60%	60%	18%	40%	82%
Two-way communication	9/10	90%	60%	57%	20%	43%	80%
Behavioral organization	3/4	75%	61%	45%	32%	55%	68%
Total Child	36/44	82%	64%	53%	16%	47%	84%
Total Scale	**64/80**	**82.5%**	**65%**	**51%**	**18%**	**49%**	**82%**

[m]The number to the left of the slash mark represents the actual cutoff score for that subtest or total test; the number to the right of the slash mark represents the total number of points available on the subtest or total test.

[n] Percentage of items that the child must perform correctly to have mastered that domain.

[o] Probability of correctly identifying a normal child in a sample of actual normal children.

[p] Probability of correctly identifying a delayed child in a sample of actual delayed children.

Table 5-7.
Cutoff Scores, Total Accuracy, and Error Rates for Various Classification Decisions for 25 to 35 Month-Olds

| Subtest | Cutoff Score[q] | Performance[r] Standard | Total Accuracy Normal & Delayed | Error Rates | | | Specificity[s] (Normal) | Sensitivity[t] (Delayed) |
| | | | | False Delayed | False Normal | | | |
					R.D.	Multi-Problem		
Caregiver:								
Regulation	6/8	75%	52%	69%	45%	26%	31%	55–74%
Attachment	7/8	87.5%	55%	75%	50%	5%	25%	40–95%
Two-way communication	9/10	90%	55%	62.5%	60%	10.5%	37.5%	40–89%
Behavioral organization	12/14	86%	67%	44%	25%	21%	56%	75–79%
Representational elaboration	4/12	33%	65.5%	69%	5%	26%	31%	74–95%
Total caregiver	*38/51*	*73%*	*67%*	*62.5%*	*15%*	*16%*	*37.5%*	*84–85%*
Child:								
Regulation	15/18	83%	58%	81%	30%	11%	39%	70–89%
Attachment	14/18	78%	60%	75%	25%	16%	25%	75–84%
Two-way communication	8/10	80%	57%	81%	30%	16%	19%	70–84%
Behavioral organization	2/4	50%	57%	75%	25%	21%	25%	75–79%
Representational elaboration	2/8	25%	64%	81%	10%	16%	39%	84–90%
Total Child	*42/58*	*70%*	*64%*	*69%*	*10%*	*16%*	*31%*	*84–90%*
Total Scale	**77/110**	**70%**	**67%**	**63%**	**20%**	**11%**	**37%**	**80–89%**

q The number to the left of the slash mark represents the actual cutoff score for that subtest or total test; the number to the right of the slash mark represents the total number of points available on the subtest or total test.

r Percentage of items that the child must perform correctly to have mastered that domain.

s Probability of correctly identifying a normal child in a sample of actual normal children.

t Probability of correctly identifying a delayed child in a sample of actual delayed children.

Table 5-8.
Cutoff Scores, Total Accuracy, and Error Rates for Various Classification Decisions for 3 to 4 Year Olds

Subtest	Cutoff Score[u]	Performance[v] Standard	Total Accuracy Normal & Delayed	False Delayed	False Normal		Specificity[w] (Normal)	Sensitivity[x] (Delayed)
					R.D.	Multi-Problem		
Caregiver:								
Regulation	4/6	66%	50%	66%	79%	6%	34%	21–94%
Attachment	7/8	87.5%	50%	71%	58%	3%	39%	42–97%
Two-way communication	9/10	90%	50%	72%	47%	12%	38%	63–88%
Behavioral organization	12/14	86%	51%	53%	32%	12%	47%	68–88%
Representational elaboration	6/10	60%	57%	66%	16%	15%	34%	84–85%
Emotional thinking	2/6	33%	65%	43%	16%	25%	57%	75–84%
Total Caregiver	42/54	78%	65%	48%	5%	21%	52%	79–95%
Child:								
Regulation	12/14	86%	53%	76%	53%	3%	24%	47–97%
Attachment	14/16	87.5%	66%	48%	5%	18%	52%	84–95%
Two-way communication	8/8	100%	44%	81%	37%	6%	19%	63–94%
Behavioral organization	2/4	50%	50%	81%	11%	3%	19%	89–97%
Representational elaboration	8/14	57%	65%	48%	5%	21%	52%	79–85%
Emotional thinking	2/10	20%	66%	57%	5%	6%	43%	94–95%
Total Child	48/66	73%	68%	50%	5%	15%	50%	85–95%
Total Scale	**93/120**	**77.5%**	**72%**	**38%**	**5%**	**18%**	**62%**	**82–95%**

[u] The number to the left of the slash mark represents the actual cutoff score for that subtest or total test; the number to the right of the slash mark represents the total number of points available on the subtest or total test.

[v] Percentage of items that the child must perform correctly to have mastered that domain.

[w] Probability of correctly identifying a normal child in a sample of actual normal children.

[x] Probability of correctly identifying a delayed child in a sample of actual delayed children.

Decision Validity

False normal and false delayed error rates were calculated in the decision validity study. The cutting scores for each subtest were chosen to minimize the false normal error rate, judged to be the more serious of the two types of error from the perspective of screening and diagnostic decision making. As presented in Tables 5-3 through 5-8 , the false normal error rates ranged from 5 to 28% for the total scale for the various age ranges, between 5 and 32% for the child scale, and between 5 and 25% for the caregiver's scale. The false delayed error rates were substantially higher, ranging from 26 to 63% for the total scale. Thus, this test had a lower error rate (i.e., fewer misclassifications) for delayed children than for normal children. However, given the serious consequences of false normal errors, the error rates for false delayed are tolerable.

The overall classification accuracy for delayed and normal children for the caregiver scale, child scale, and total test ranged from 56 to 76%. These figures are deflated because the test is much better at discriminating delayed children with social emotional problems than normal children. Because the FEAS is designed for children who are at risk for problems in social emotional functioning, it is recommended that results from the FEAS be combined with other clinical information obtained through a comprehensive intake interview and other diagnostic information as described in this book.

From the standpoint of diagnostic decision making, the FEAS shows better sensitivity (probability of correctly identifying a delayed child in a sample of delayed children) for the majority of subscales at the different age ranges. Specificity rates (probability of correctly identifying a normal child in a sample of normal children) were quite low for most of the subscales at the different age ranges. However, between 7 and 18 months, specificity for the child scales ranged from 63 to 81% suggesting that the FEAS is more useful in screening normal children at these ages.

Based upon the sensitivity calculations, the FEAS appears to be well suited for children with regulatory disorders, particularly between 7 and 24 months. At 25 to 35 months and at 3 to 4 years, there appear to be certain subscales that are better for children with regulatory disorders, although the total caregiver and child scale scores show good discrimination for this group of children. For example, at 3 to 4 years, only 2 of the 6 caregiver subscales and 4 of the 6 child subscales showed good discrimination for the RD sample. It appears that the FEAS is effective in screening and diagnosing children from multi-problem families at 13 to 18 months, however, conclusions cannot be drawn about the general applicability of the FEAS on children from multi-problem families until more data are obtained. The FEAS appears to be very effective in assessing children with pervasive developmental disorders at the 2 to 4 year age ranges.

Concurrent Validity

Intercorrelations between FEAS scores during symbolic and tactile play situations, the Test of Sensory Functions in Infants (DeGangi & Greenspan, 1989), and the Test of Attention in Infants (DeGangi, Poisson, Sickel, & Wiener, 1995) were examined for a subsample of 84 children with regulatory disorders evaluated between 7 and 18 months of age. None of the intercorrelations were significant for the regulatory disordered sample. These findings suggest that, for the most part, the FEAS provides information that is distinct from that obtained by diagnostic measures (e.g., sensory processing, attention).

Reliability Study

An interobserver reliability study was conducted on 46 children among five different observers. The subjects for the study are presented in Table 5-9. Videotaped observations of subjects were used for this study. The raters for this study included three psychologists, one of whom was also an occupational therapist, and a nurse practitioner. Observers 1 and 2 coded all 46 children. Observers 3 through 4 coded 20 videotapes and observer 5 coded only 15 videotapes. Alpha reliability coefficients were cal-

Table 5-9.
Characteristics of Subjects for the Reliability Study

Variable (Age)	Normal (N = 26)	RD (N = 27)	PDD (N = 8)
7 to 9 months	5	5	
10 to 12 months	5	5	
13 to 18 months	5	5	
19 to 24 months	5	4	
25 to 35 months	3	4	4
36 to 48 months	3	4	4

culated between observers. Results of the reliability study showed that for the caregiver scale, reliability ranged from .8961 to .9196 for the total caregiver score. Reliability coefficients ranged from .9119 to .9786 for the total child scores. In addition to the above reliability studies, reliability was calculated for 15 subjects between two observers, one coding the play interaction live, the other coding the videotape. The two observers were two of the psychologists listed above, one of whom was also the occupational therapist. This reliability coefficient was .83 for the caregiver scale, .89 for the child scale, and .88 for the total child scores. Results of the reliability study are presented in Table 5-10.

The results from the reliability studies suggest that the FEAS can be administered using either videotapes or observations of live interactions. The FEAS can be administered under either condition (e.g., videotape or live observation), however, it is strongly recommended that professionals scoring the FEAS under either circumstance practice scoring with another rater and obtain at least an 80% inter-observer agreement before considering their scores reliable and valid.

Table 5-10.
Results of Interobserver Reliability Study

Observers	Reliability Coefficients		
	Caregiver Scale	Child Scale	Subjects
Videotape Observations:			
I and 2	.907	.9254	46
I and 3	.919	.9369	20
I and 4	.9137	.9319	20
I and 5	.9003	.9791	15
2 and 3	.9099	.9040	20
2 and 4	.9087	.9119	20
2 and 5	.8961	.9784	15
3 and 4	.9165	.9245	20
3 and 5	.9040	.9786	15
4 and 5	.9119	.9786	15
Live Recording and Videotape Observation:			
I and 3	.8321	.8942	15

Summary of Psychometric Evidence

The FEAS is designed as an assessment tool of emotional functioning in children from 7 months through 4 years who are at risk for developing emotional and behavioral problems. These include children experiencing regulatory disorders, pervasive developmental disorders, or who are at risk for relational disturbances, including children from multi-problem families and other types of emotional challenges. There are six versions of the checklist that are age specific (e.g., 7 to 9, 10 to 12, 13 to 18, 19 to 24, 25 to 35 months, and 3 to 4 years). The versions of the FEAS presented in this manual are the product of extensive revisions over a period of 5 years.

The FEAS is intended for use in creating a profile of social-emotional functioning in infants and young children and their caregivers. Test items and subtests were developed to provide information about the child and caregiver's social and emotional capacities using a developmental framework that integrates information and a number of variables. These include observations of constitutional variables, such as self-regulatory, sensory, and attentional capacities. It also includes specific data regarding developmental levels of emotional functioning for both the child and caregiver. It also integrates information about interactive components that form the basis for attachment, mood regulation, emotional functioning, and social communication.

Although the FEAS is designed as an observational tool, it is important to note that findings from the FEAS alone do not lead to a formal diagnosis of specific disorders, such as autism, anxiety disorder, attachment disorder, or regulatory disorder. However, data from the FEAS, when combined with other diagnostic information (e.g., clinical interview of parent and child, parent report measures, and other formal testing) may help to profile emotional functioning in a variety of problems. Also, the FEAS should be helpful in distinguishing between children with disorders of regulation, pervasive developmental disorder, and children from multi-problem families with a variety of symptoms because the FEAS was validated on these samples. Further research is needed on children with other mental health disorders, such as problems related to attachment, anxiety, depression, or conduct disorders. In the following section, the psychometric properties of the FEAS will be summarized.

The FEAS was validated on 197 normal infants, 190 infants with regulatory disorders, 41 with pervasive developmental disorders, and 40 children from multi-problem families. Evidence pertaining to construct validity was obtained from an analysis of item discrimination indexes. Items with small to large discrimination indices were included in the final version of the FEAS. Some items were included because of their face validity or to provide a developmental continuum across ages. From the standpoint of diagnosis, the FEAS is accurate in differentiating the performance of children who are from clinical samples including regulatory disordered and pervasive developmental delay. The FEAS also appears to have promise for children from multi-problem families. The false normal error rate, deemed to be a more serious type of error, ranged from 5 to 32%.

Conceptually the FEAS measures the dimensions of behavior that we and other researchers (see Chapters 4 and 7) have described as important in the assessment of social-emotional functioning in young children. The items are sensitive and discriminate behaviors in the following areas: regulatory components of emotional development (e.g., self-regulation), relational aspects (e.g., attachment), social communication including preverbal communication, representational capacities, emotional thinking, and social interactions between parent and child.

Concurrent validity studies examining intercorrelations between the FEAS and other diagnostic tests (e.g., Test of Sensory Functions in Infants and the Test of Attention in Infants) showed that there was no relationship between performance on the FEAS and sensory processing and attention skills for children with regulatory disorders between the ages of 7 and 18 months. This evidence suggests that the FEAS is examining behaviors that are uniquely different than those tested by available diagnostic tools.

An interobserver reliability study was conducted among five different observers on 53 subjects from the normal, regulatory disorder, and pervasive developmental disorder samples. Reliability coefficients ranged from .896 to .919 for the caregiver scale and .911 to .978 for the child scale for videotape recordings and from .83 to .89 between live and videotape observations. The high level of reliability of the FEAS shows that it can be reliably administered by trained early intervention and mental health professionals.

Overall, this psychometric evidence on the quality of the FEAS suggests that the score can be used validly and reliably for diagnostic decisions. When coupled with other test information (e.g., observations of sensory processing, attention, and cognitive development), the FEAS is a valid and reliable tool for assessingchildren, including children at risk for relational, social-emotional, regulatory, and communication problems. Table 5-11 presents the strengths and weaknesses of the FEAS.

Table 5-11.
Strengths and Weaknesses of the FEAS

Strengths	Weaknesses
The FEAS is a systematic and comprehensive observational scale that is useful in documenting emotional functioning of children and their caregivers.	
It is theoretically grounded and reflects domains of behaviors that are viewed as important in the measurement of social-emotional functioning in infants and young children.	
It is useful for children ranging in age from 7 months through 4 years have regulatory disorders, pervasive developmental disorders, or are at risk for relational disturbances and their caregivers.	The FEAS may not be useful in assessing children with specific emotional problems such as generalized anxiety disorder, depression, or oppositional defiant disorder. Validation studies are needed to determine if the FEAS is effective in assessment of these populations.
The FEAS has been validated on typically developing children and children with regulatory disorders, pervasive developmental disorders, and children from multi-problem families.	More cross-validation studies are needed on more diverse ethnic populations. The current validation samples are predominately Caucasian.
The FEAS has good construct validity including item discrimination. It is accurate in differentiating the performance of children who are from regulatory disordered and PDD samples.	The FEAS is more useful in detecting children with atypical social-emotional development than typically developing children.
The FEAS is useful in screening normal children between 7 and 18 months of age.	The false delayed error rates are high, therefore, the FEAS may inadvertently rate a typically developing child as having social-emotional problems when they are, in fact, normal.
Concurrent validity studies show that the FEAS is unique in what it measures in relation to other developmental scales.	Concurrent validity is needed with other parent report scales measuring emotional/behavioral problems (e.g., CBC).
Interobserver reliability between five observers was high for ratings on both typically developing and clinical samples. The FEAS can also be administered reliably with live or videotaped observations.	
The FEAS is best at assessing children with regulatory disorders from 7 to 24 months. Certain subscales are better for regulatory disorders from 25 to 48 months than others.	It is important to cross-validate observations from the FEAS with other rating scales such as the Infant-Toddler Symptom Checklist and a comprehensive intake interview to assure accuracy and relevance in diagnosis.
The FEAS is useful for children with pervasive developmental disorders from 2 to 4 years of age.	Because of the difficulties in diagnosing children with PDD under 2 years of age, it may not be possible to expand the usefulness of the FEAS for children with PDD under 2 years of age.
The FEAS is useful in assessing children and their caregivers from multi-problem families from 13 to 18 months of age.	A more expanded sample is clearly needed on multi-problem families.

Directions for Future Research

These recommendations are couched in the context of a need for cross-validation studies. We welcome collaborators who are interested in conducting research on the FEAS. Further research with more extended samples of delayed infants must be conducted before use of the instrument with a variety of populations is justified. In particular, further validation is needed on children with a range of emotional problems (e.g., anxiety, depression) and with children from multiproblem families. Differential performance in terms of ethnicity should be explored, particularly because the sample was predominately Caucasian. Additional research is needed to determine how the FEAS correlates with parent report scales such as the Child Behavior Checklist.

Social-emotional scales are difficult to develop because of the problems in operationalizing reliable and valid behaviors relevant to dynamic interactions and emotional development. The research is time consuming, expensive, and challenging, however, considering the limited funding available for the development of the FEAS, the validity and reliability studies are impressive. The information this kind of assessment approach can provide will contribute toward identifying infants with regulatory disorders and relational disturbances, including pervasive developmental disorders, as early as possible and promoting the use of appropriate intervention programs for those infants.

References

American Psychiatric Association (1994). *DSM-IV: Diagnostic and statistical manual of mental disorders.* Washington, DC: American Psychiatric Press.

Bayley, N. (1969). *Bayley Scales of Infant Development.* New York: Psychological Corp.

Berk, R. A. (1976). Determination of optimal cutting scores in criterion-referenced measurement. *Journal of Experimental Education, 45,* 4–9.

Cohen, J. (1977). *Statistical power analysis for the behavioral sciences.* (Revised edition) New York: Academic Press.

DeGangi, G. A. & Greenspan, S. I. (1989). *The test of sensory functions in infants.* Los Angeles: Western Psychological Services.

DeGangi, G. A., Poisson, S., Sickel, R. Z., & Wiener, A. S. (1995). *Infant-toddler symptom checklist.* Tucson, AZ: Therapy Skill Builders.

6

Administration and Scoring of the Functional Emotional Assessment Scale

Georgia A. DeGangi, Ph.D., OTR
Stanley I. Greenspan, M.D.

As indicated earlier, the FEAS is a criterion-referenced instrument designed for children from 7 months through 4 years of age to assess emotional functioning. This chapter will present the administrative procedures and scoring for the Functional Emotional Assessment Scale.

Administration Procedures

The FEAS consists of six versions that are intended to be used for diagnostic and screening purposes: the 7 to 9 month, 10 to 12 month, 13 to 18 month, 19 to 24 month, 25 to 35 month, and 3 to 4 year versions. The six versions of the FEAS are displayed in Figures 6-1 through 6-6. Administration of the FEAS takes approximately 15 to 30 minutes. The FEAS may be administered in the home environment, school, or clinic setting. It may be useful to observe the child in multiple situations (i.e., playground, home, clinic).

The examiner should ask the caregiver to play with the child for 15 minutes as they normally would at home. The examiner should stress that there is no right or wrong way to play with the child. Should the caregiver

193

appear uncertain about his/her play skills or mention that he/she normally does not play with his/her child at home, the examiner should encourage the caregiver to do his/her best. Depending upon the purpose of the evaluation, it may be useful to observe the child with different caregivers (e.g., mother and father; foster mother and biological mother).

After the caregiver has had the opportunity to play with the child, the examiner may wish to facilitate play interactions with the child to facilitate the child's play repertoire. This is especially useful when testing children who fall on the pervasive developmental disorder spectrum who may need a special approach to elicit interactions. The examiner should attempt to elicit play behaviors that may not have been observed during play with the caregiver. When different behaviors are elicited with the examiner, indicate that in the column for play with the examiner (EXAM). Depending upon the purpose of the evaluation, it may be useful to observe the child with different caregivers (e.g., foster mother and biological mother; mother and father). Indicate who played with the child in the last column and enter responses accordingly.

A variety of developmentally appropriate toys should be provided. In order to observe the child in different play contexts, it is often useful to present the child with three different sets of toys to explore. Each set may be made available for five minutes, then removed. The first set of toys should be symbolic because most children and caregivers are more familiar with these types of toys. The second set of toys should be tactile, and the last set should involve large movement activities. The toys used in our validation study were as follows:

Symbolic Play Materials:

- *Infants and toddlers:* Toy telephone, large baby doll, bottle, toy cars, toy boat, and plastic tableware, cups, and plates.
- *Preschoolers:* Large supermarket structure, puppets, crates with pretend food, and doll house with people, furniture, and cars.

Tactile Play Materials:

- *Infants and toddlers:* Plastic porcupine toys, textured balls, furry puppets, paint brush, heavy musical toy with balls on spokes, and furry blanket.

- *Preschoolers:* Large plastic bin filled with dried beans and action figures, furry puppets, and textured balls.

Movement Play Materials:

- *Infants and toddlers:* Large inflatable bolster, large plastic dome, and rotating spinning board.
- *Preschoolers:* Trampoline, scooter board, and suspended swing.

We found it useful to place all the toys except for the large equipment in a laundry basket for each play situation. This way we were able to see how the caregiver and child organized themselves (i.e., dumping out all the toys versus systematically playing with each toy). The basket also helped for quick clean up. By presenting each set of toys for five minutes, we were also able to examine how well the child was able to attend and to elaborate on play ideas. Preschool children will need a longer amount of time to develop their play ideas, therefore, we suggest that a 15-minute observation for symbolic play be used.

When entering scores on the score sheet, responses for symbolic (SYM) and sensory (SENS) play may be entered in different columns. This information is particularly useful in planning intervention because different responses may occur depending upon the play context. For example, we have found that children with regulatory disorders show better play capacities during symbolic play (DeGangi & Breinbauer, 1997) whereas children with pervasive developmental disorders are more available for social interactions during sensory play.

Examiners administering the FEAS should be knowledgeable in the theoretical framework underlying the sub-domains of the FEAS. It is suggested that examiners administer the instrument to at least five normal children in each of the age categories before attempting to score the FEAS on children with problems. Knowledge of how play behaviors will differ in children who experience problems in self-regulation, sensory processing, emotion regulation, and attention is critical for interpretation of findings on clinical samples. The examiner should also be well versed in understanding the problems experienced by children and caregivers from multi-problem families (e.g., child abuse and neglect, maternal depression).

These free, unstructured, and, if necessary, semi-structured interactions are close to the infant's natural way of interacting with his world.

They can be done both in the office and at home and can be repeated as many times as necessary in order to gain a true picture of the infant/young child and caregiver's capacities. It is often very helpful to see the infant/young child and his caregiver(s) interacting at least on two or more separate occasions; however, if there are time limitations or other constraints on the assessment process, the FEAS may be scored from one play observation. In fact, the children who participated in the validation samples for the FEAS were observed only once for a 15- to 20-minute play observation in addition to other developmental testing.

Scoring

For accurate scoring, the play observations should be videotaped. Play observations may be scored while observing live play interactions; however, considerable experience is needed on the part of the examiner for reliable scoring. Live scoring should not be attempted until the observer has practiced scoring on at least 10 videotapes and has obtained reliability of at least 80% in scoring live and videotaped play observations.

There are two parts of the FEAS—one for the caregiver, the other for the child. The purpose of scoring the caregiver's play is to observe the caregiver's skill in supporting the child's play and emotional development and to identify needs that the caregiver might have for intervention. The child's play behaviors should be evaluated for play interactions and the depth and range of capacities for each level of emotional development. The scale may be used descriptively to profile the infant and young child's emotional, social, and related developmental capacities. It can also be used in a quantitative manner by rating each capacity on the 0 to 2 rating scale.

All of the test items are scored except when indicated on a two-point scale. Scoring is as follows:

0 = behavior not seen at all or observed only briefly; skill not mastered
1 = behavior present some of the time or observed several times; skill partially mastered
2 = behavior is consistently present or observed many times; skill mastered.

Indicate N/O for behaviors that are not observed because there was no opportunity to observe the presence or absence of the behavior.

Where it is indicated to convert a score, transform the scoring as follows:

0 becomes a 2, 1 = 1, 2 becomes a 0.

These ratings can then be added together for subtest scores for caregiver and child as well as a total test score. The points are tallied for each category as well as for all responses in the caregiver and child scales. In order to determine if a child or caregiver is at risk for relational problems, the total child and caregiver scores are compared to the cutoff scores derived for the age-level version of the scale.

Interpretation of Scores

Scores should be totaled and entered at the bottom of the scale. Scores falling at or below the cutoff score for a given scale are considered at risk or indicative of relational problems. The results of the FEAS should be incorporated with the results of a comprehensive evaluation examining family functioning, sensory processing, attention, self-regulation, and developmental functions. Appropriate cutoff scores are provided in Tables 6-1 through 6-6 and also appear on the individual profile forms for ages 7 to 9, 10 to 12, 13 to 18, 19 to 24, 25 to 35 months, and 3 to 4 years. Refer to the section, "Construct Validity" in Chapter 4, for an explanation of how cutoff scores were determined.

Table 6-1.
Interpretive Ranges for Scores for 7- to 9-Month-Olds

Subtest	Normal	At Risk	Deficient
Caregiver:			
Regulation	6–10	5	0–4
Attachment	6	5	0–4
Two-way communication	20–26	18–19	0–17
Total Caregiver	20–26	18–19	0–17
Child:			
Regulation	14–16	13	0–12
Attachment	8–10	7	0–6
Total Child	22–26	20–21	0–19
Total Scale	**41–52**	**38–40**	**0–37**

Table 6-2.
Interpretive Ranges for Scores for 10- to 12-Month-Olds

Subtest	Normal	At Risk	Deficient
Caregiver:			
Regulation	8–10	7	0–6
Attachment	8	7	0–6
Two-way communication	9–10	8	0–7
Behavioral organization	4–6	3	0–2
Total Caregiver	*27–34*	*25–26*	*0–24*
Child:			
Regulation	14–16	13	0–12
Attachment	10	9	0–8
Two-way communication	7–8	6	0–5
Total Child	*31–34*	*29–30*	*0–28*
Total Scale	**61–68**	**54–56**	**0–53**

Table 6-3.
Interpretive Ranges for Scores for 13- to 18-Month-Olds

Subtest	Normal	At Risk	Deficient
Caregiver:			
Regulation	6–8	5	0–4
Attachment	7–8	6	0–5
Two-way communication	9–10	8	0–7
Behavioral organization	7–10	6	0–5
Total Caregiver	*30–36*	*28–29*	*0–27*
Child:			
Regulation	13–14	12	0–11
Attachment	9–10	8	0–7
Two-way communication	7–8	6	0–5
Total Child	*28–32*	*27–28*	*0–26*
Total Scale	**60–68**	**55–59**	**0–54**

Table 6-4.
Interpretive Ranges for Scores for 19- to 24-Month-Olds

Subtest	Normal	At Risk	Deficient
Caregiver:			
Regulation	3–6		0–2
Attachment	6	5	0–4
Two-way communication	9–10	8	0–7
Behavioral organization	11–14	10	0–9
Total Caregiver	*28–36*	*26–27*	*0–25*
Child:			
Regulation	13–16	12	0–11
Attachment	12–14	11	0–10
Two-way communication	9–10	8	0–7
Behavioral organization	3–4		0–2
Total Child	*36–44*	*34–35*	*0–33*
Total Scale	**64–80**	**60–63**	**0–59**

Table 6–5.
Interpretive Ranges for Scores for 25- to 35-Month-Olds

Subtest	Normal	At Risk	Deficient
Caregiver:			
Regulation	6–9	5	0–4
Attachment	7–8	6	0–5
Two-way communication	9–10	8	0–7
Behavioral organization	12–14	11	0–10
Representational elaboration	4–12		0–3
Total Caregiver	*38–52*	*36–37*	*0–35*
Child:			
Regulation	15–18	14	0–13
Attachment	14–18	13	0–12
Two-way communication	8–10	7	0–6
Behavioral organization	2–4		0–1
Representational elaboration	2–8		0–1
Total Child	*42–58*	*40–41*	*0–39*
Total Scale	**77–110**	**75–76**	**0–74**

Table 6-6.
Interpretative Ranges for Scores for 3- to 4-Year-Olds

Subtest	Normal	At Risk	Deficient
Caregiver:			
Regulation	4–6		0–3
Attachment	7–8	6	0–5
Two-way communication	9–10	8	0–7
Behavioral organization	12–14	11	0–10
Representational elaboration	6–10	5	0–4
Emotional thinking	2–6		0–1
Total Caregiver	*42–54*	*40–41*	*0–39*
Child:			
Regulation	12–14	11	0–10
Attachment	14–16	13	0–12
Two-way communication	8	7	0–6
Behavioral organization	2–4		0–1
Representational elaboration	8–14	7	0–6
Emotional thinking	2–10		0–1
Total Child	*48–66*	*46–47*	*0–45*
Total Scale	**93–120**	**86–92**	**0–85**

Case Study

Background

Mr. and Mrs. F. attended the intake interview to discuss their presenting concerns and background history for their 2-year-old son, Steven. They described Steven as an easy baby who was calm and slept well. At 1 year of age, they became concerned that Steven did not seem connected to them. He would not respond to his name when called and he often ignored them when they attempted to interact with him. He engaged in repetitive play with toys and seemed content to entertain himself for long periods of time. At 15 months, they discussed their concerns with their pediatrician, who urged them to wait another three months. By 18 months, Steven had not progressed. Mr. and Mrs. F. noted that Steven was not pointing, using gestures or words, and continued to be detached. Steven did not show eye contact and seemed to treat people as objects. Mrs. F. noticed that when she picked Steven up from day care, he did not show pleasure or excitement to see her. To engage Steven's attention, Mrs. F. began using firm deep-pressure and massage. Steven has responded well to this input and now enjoys being near his mother.

At 19 months, Steven was evaluated by the County Infants and Toddlers Program, who found him to have delays in language, play, and fine motor skills. They reported that Steven seemed more responsive to interactions when provided with proprioceptive and vestibular input. Steven was described as being hyporeactive to touch. He also showed oral-motor problems, including drooling and a high need to mouth objects. Steven had difficulty producing sounds but could vocalize vowel sounds. Hearing and vision were tested and were found to be normal. Neurological testing was also conducted without any positive findings. The parents recently tried using Tegritol but Steven began to bang his head and it was discontinued. Mr. and Mrs. F. used dietary supplements with Steven and planned to consult with a nutritionist to determine if diet should be adjusted in any way. As a result of the various diagnostic evaluations, Steven was diagnosed as having pervasive developmental disorder.

In addition to the occupational therapy and speech and language therapy provided by the county, Steven had been seen by Stanley Greenspan, M.D. He guided Mr. and Mrs. F. in how to do "floor time," which is a developmentally based play therapy that fosters social engagement, reciprocity, and communication skills.

Mr. and Mrs. F. described Steven as a very affectionate child. They were successful in eliciting eye contact by engaging Steven in rough and tumble types of games. Steven's favorite activities included watching videos, pushing trains back and forth, bath time, and running outside along a driveway or sidewalk in a repetitive manner. Mr. and Mrs. F. noticed that Steven held his head looking sideways as he ran along a wall. If they attempted to interfere with his activity, Steven became distressed.

Steven has made some gains in the past few months. He is starting to anticipate certain activities and he will lead his parents to things that he wants. He is able to make a choice when offered two options. Although he does not point to indicate wishes, Steven has pointed occasionally for things such as juice. Steven likes to run with his 6-year-old brother, Kevin, but does not interact directly with him or other children. Recently Mr. and

Mrs. F. noted that Steven imitated Kevin when he jumped on the bed, then ran to touch the wall.

Steven is a large child who currently weighs 36 pounds (90th percentile for weight). He prefers drinking juices and milk instead of eating solids, however, he will eat some baby foods, crackers, rice, raisins, and rye cereal or pudding with a spoon. He sits in the high chair for breakfast and dinner although it is sometimes a struggle to keep him seated. He will arch his back or become floppy if he doesn't want to sit in the chair. Steven sleeps well and falls asleep by himself after a nighttime routine.

There is no significant family history for learning disabilities. Both parents reported a family history of depression. On the father's side there are several persons who have experienced mood swings as well.

Tests Administered

The Test of Attention in Infants was used to evaluate sustained attention. Parent-child play observations were conducted and coded using the FEAS. Some items from the Bayley Scales of Infant Development, Mental Scale, were also administered.

General Observations

Steven was an adorable 2-year-old boy who was accompanied to the testing by both parents. When transitioning from the waiting room, Steven had difficulty following his parents and needed to have his hand held to direct him to go to the play room. He was readily interested in the toys in the playroom and showed good focused attention in play with both parents for 20 minutes. Steven was somewhat reticent to play with me and sought out his mother's side for assurance. Ultimately, despite his obvious awareness that I was a stranger, he was willing to engage in play with me. The play interactions were followed by structured attentional and cognitive testing to observe Steven's responses to structured learning activities. During the Test of Attention in Infants, he sat on his mother's lap and was able to attend to most of the test items. He also showed interest in a few of the items from the Mental Bayley.

Results

Attentional Behaviors

The Test of Attention in Infants (TAI) includes four subtests that measure visual, auditory, tactile, and multi-sensory attention. This test has been validated on children from 7 through 30 months of age. The results from these subtests provide useful information about the child's learning styles and capacity to process input from different sensory channels. In addition, the test provides an overall index of the child's capacity to sustain attention and understand concepts of cause and effect. The TAI uses a series of switch-activated battery-operated toys that require the child to press a switch plate to cause an interesting toy to operate (e.g., record player, musical light box, drumming panda bear).

During this test, Steven showed high visual interest for many of the test items, however, he had difficulty organizing looking while engaged in a motor response. For example, he pressed the switch to activate the toy when his hand was placed on the switch but without this help; he could not look and press the switch at the same time. Although it appeared that he understood the cause-effect that pressing the switch would activate the toy, he seemed to have motor planning problems in organizing this response. Although Steven seemed very visually oriented during the TAI, he was also responsive to the auditory and tactile items suggesting that he is responsive to different types of sensory input.

The results from the TAI concur with naturalistic observations of Steven's attentional abilities. In the play room, Steven appeared highly distractible, going from one toy to the next, but he could organize his attention around visual events such as pushing the trains back and forth. He was most attentive when engaged in intense sensory play (i.e., riding on his father's shoulders). Shifting attention from repetitive tasks such as pushing the trains back and forth or running along the driveway was difficult for Steven unless his play was interrupted by games that forced him to engage in a more adaptive response. Based on these results, it appeared that Steven had difficulties organizing attention for purposeful activity, but he was available and responsive to sensory and interactive activities that helped him focus. He had a tendency to become overly fixated on repetitive actions, which caused him to have difficulty shifting attention. Problems with motor planning could have impacted his capacity to organize attention as well.

Sensory Processing Functions

Sensory processing was evaluated through play observations. During Steven's play, he showed a clear preference for play that involved movement (i.e., riding on his father's shoulders), proprioceptive input (i.e., father shaking Steven's hands on his face while making a funny sound), and tactile contact (i.e., massage and touch provided by mother). These sensory activities seemed to have a strong organizing effect for Steven and seemed to help him to become more available for interactive exchanges and functional play. Observations of Steven's movement and posture suggested that he had low muscle tone (i.e., toes in as he walked, and open-mouth posture with drooling). He appeared to be underreactive to sensory input and seemed to need high intensity sensory stimulation to help him perceive and make use of the input.

Play Interactional Behaviors

Steven's play interactions were observed in a series of play situations with his parents using the FEAS appropriate to Steven's age (the 24- to 35-month version). The materials provided for play included a range of developmentally appropriate toys. Steven's play and interaction skills were analyzed in terms of the first four areas of emotional functioning using the FEAS. Figure 6-1 reproduces the FEAS scores that were used in the following interpretation.

Self-Regulation and Interest In the World

The first area has to do with a child's ability to regulate attention and behavior while being interested in a range of sensations (sounds, sights, movement). Steven was interested and motivated to play with the various toys. He explored the objects freely without caution but seemed to like being near either his mother or father. He remained calm, showing no signs of distress, however, his attention span was brief except when he engaged in repetitive played with trains or rough house play. When provided sensory and interactive support, Steven was able to sustain play activities for several minutes at a time (i.e., peek-a-boo at mirror). It was important for him to learn how to organize attention during a range of play experiences.

Forming Relationships, Attachment, and Engagement

The second area has to do with the child's ability to engage in relationships, including the depth and range of pleasure and warmth and related feelings such as assertiveness. Steven tended to engage in isolated play, but if his parents engaged him in high intensity sensory play, he would look at them briefly and give them a radiant smile. He appeared excited and animated when engaged in this sensory play. His best social engagement was when he sat on his father's shoulders and played different games initiated by Mr. F. using the mirror (i.e., peek-a-boo, vibrating Steven's hands on his face, looking in the mirror then moving down to the floor). Steven struggled with the task of organizing eye contact in face-to-face interactions. He also did not use social referencing in play. Despite this difficulty, Steven showed a clear attachment for his parents. He showed a definitive reaction to me when I began to play with him and immediately sought his mother's side. Overall, it appeared that Steven was well attached to his parents but was disorganized in his ability to organize social approach. He needed to learn how to make use of social cues by referencing others and signaling interest. He also needed to initiate interactions from others and become less interested in solitary play activities.

Two-Way, Purposeful Communication (Somatopsychological Differentiation)

The third area has to do with a child's ability to enter into two-way, purposeful communication. At its most basic level, this involves helping the child open and close circles of communication. A circle of communication is opened and closed when a child evidences some interest or behavior; for example, the child looks at a toy, the parent or caregiver follows the child's lead by picking up the toy or showing it to the child, and the child closes the circle by reaching for the toy, nodding with a smile, etc.

Steven was able to initiate intentional interactions through object play. He was particularly interested in pushing trucks and trains at eye level (e.g., on a table surface or by lying down on the floor with them). His play with objects tended to be repetitive with little variety of actions. During his play, he initiated some sound play (i.e., doh, aah). Unless engaged in intense sensory play, Steven had difficulty noticing and responding to his parents' cues. He did not point or use gestures in his interactions with his parents. However, when his father engaged him in play at the mirror, Steven became highly animated and initiated lifting his arms and clapping in an interactive game. In order to determine if Steven could initiate and organize two-way communication in play that did not have movement and touch. I engaged Steven in play with a doll, making simple sounds such as "Waah" while moving the baby under a blanket in a game of peek-a-boo. He became interested in this game and sustained his attention for several minutes. He was also able to organize simple gestures during this activity (i.e., reaching for baby's face, removing blanket).

In summary, Steven needed to develop better signal reading, to organize gestures and language during interactions, and to respond contingently to others. High intensity sensory play seemed to help organize his attention for interactions. Because he showed elements of sensory underreactivity, he needed sensory input to increase arousal for interactions, but once this occurred it was important to broaden his capacity to respond to a range of sensory, cognitive, and language cues during interactions.

Behavioral Organization, Problem-Solving, and Internalization (A Complex Sense of Self)

The fourth level involves stringing together many circles of communication into interactive sequences. One sees this when a child can take a parent or caregiver by the hand, walk her to the door, point that he wants to go out, and perhaps vocalize the sounds or words to further the caregiver's understanding of his intentions. This level is very important because many children who have command of a number of words are still unable to maintain a flow of two-way communication, which is necessary for negotiating many of the most important emotional needs of life (e.g., being close to others, exploring and being assertive, limiting aggression, negotiating safety, etc).

Steven was able to assert what he wanted in play, but he could not engage in complex patterns of communication. Only occasionally could he string together two or three circles of communication in play. He was not yet organizing symbolic play (e.g., taking people for a ride in the train), however, Steven was able to imitate feeding the doll after he was shown how to do this. Steven needed to develop the capacity to organize and sequence interactions in play without becoming ritualistic or repetitive (i.e., pushing trains back and forth, running along a wall).

Cognitive and Language Skills

Portions of the Mental Bayley were used to assess Steven's cognitive and language abilities. Steven was able to sit on his father's lap during administration of some of the test items. Because Steven had difficulty understanding language and sustaining attention for more complex tasks, a developmental index could not be obtained; however, enough items were administered to obtain a general level of functioning. Most of the skills that he was able to do fell at the 10- to 12-month level, which represented a significant delay in his development. Steven could place pegs in a peg-board, look at pictures in a book, and place a circle in the form-board. He could not build a tower of two cubes, a task that requires imitation and visual-motor skill. He would not put cubes in a cup, however, it appeared that lack of interest and inattention to the task affected his performance on this and other similar items. Steven said a variety of bi-syllabic sounds (doh, gah, diddle) but these were not used to indicate wants. Although he had a high interest in looking at pictures in books, he did not point to pictures on request. Steven's performance on the Bayley reflected his difficulties in processing language, organizing purposeful communication, solving problems, and imitating routines and gestures. Until he learns how to use these skills in the context of social interactions and everyday activities, his true cognitive potential will not be completely understood.

Summary

Steven is a 2-year-old child who shows difficulties organizing his attention during novel or unfamiliar play activities, but who has a good capacity for visual attention during activities that provide him with strong visual feedback (i.e., looking in the mirror, pushing trains). Steven seems to be underreactive to sensory input and tends to be self-absorbed in his own world. However, if he is provided intense sensory play that incorporates movement, touch, and auditory and visual stimulation, he becomes more attentive, animated, and interactive.

Steven has a warm attachment towards his parents, but he does not use social referencing and has difficulty reading their signals because of difficulties organizing eye contact and social engagement. He tends to engage in repetitive play, but if provided with strong sensory feedback, he can be drawn into social interactions. Once engaged in the social interchange, Steven is dependent upon others to keep the interaction going. He needs to build the capacity to respond to other persons' cues in a contingent fashion and to organize gestures, actions, and vocal cues.

Steven is not yet using gestures or sounds for communicative intent. Although he does not readily imitate others, he has the capacity to learn this skill. He needs to broaden his repertoire of interactive capacities so that he can initiate, organize, and sustain interactions in a variety of contexts. He also needs to develop the capacity to sustain eye contact, to organize gestures and words in communication, as well as to organize sequential reciprocal interactions. Problems in these areas seem to have a strong impact on Steven's functional performance in cognitive and language skills.

FEAS-based Intervention Options to be Considered

Steven needs an intensive therapeutic and educational program that includes the following components:

- A home-based program using the DIR (floor time) model, focusing on enhancing Steven's functional emotional developmental and processing capacities (see the ICDL *Clinical Practice Guidelines* for further discussion). Peer play opportunities four or more times a week.
- Occupational therapy two or more time a week for hourly sessions to address Steven's sensory, attentional, and motor planning needs.
- Speech and language therapy two or more time a week for hourly sessions to improve gestural and vocal communication and reciprocity during play interactions. Steven may benefit from joint occupational therapy and speech and language therapy sessions whereby sensory integration activities are provided in conjunction with communication.
- An educational program that integrates Steven's needs in social-emotional, cognitive, language, attention, and sensory processing several times per week.
- Steven needs developmentally based intervention provided at least twice/week by a clinician trained in using the DIR model and in integrating emotional, communication, attention, cognitive, and sensory processing needs in play interactions (e.g., "floor time"). A parent consulatiuon or a parent training component should be used so that Mr. and Mrs. F. can learn how to integrate developmental interactions into everyday interactions and functional routines. The therapy should focus on improving social engagement (e.g., social referencing), organized two-way gestural and vocal communication, sequenced interactions, and regulatory capacities (e.g., attention).

Figure 6-1. Example of FEAS on a 2-year-old: 19-24 Month
Protocol Booklet

Stanley I. Greenspan, M.D. and Georgia A DeGangi, Ph.D., OTR
Interdisciplinary Council on Developmental and Learning Disorders, Bethesda, MD

The Functional Emotional Assessment Scale Administration and Scoring Form

Age: **19-24 Months**

Behaviors: **Caregiver**

Name of Child: <u>Steven</u>   Date of Testing: _____

Age of Child: <u>24 months</u>

Person Playing
With Child: Mother: <u>X</u>   Father: <u>X</u>
                Caregiver: ___   Examiner: ___

Key: SYM = Symbolic; SENS = Sensory; EXAM = Examiner

	SYM	SENS	EXAM
SELF-REGULATION AND INTEREST IN THE WORLD			

1. Shows pleasant or animated, happy affect throughout play
  Scoring:
  0 = flat, somber, or depressed affect
  1 = content, but neutral
  2 = happy and animated with warm and engaging smiles
	2	2	

2. Is sensitive and responsive to child's need for touch by stroking or touching baby in pleasurable ways and/or encourages child to explore textured toys.	2	2	
3. Provides pleasurable movement experiences to the child or encourages movement exploration.	2	2	
Total for Self-Regulation and Interest in the World	6	6	
FORMING RELATIONSHIPS, ATTACHMENT, AND ENGAGEMENT			
4. Is relaxed during interchange with child, not overly attentive to child's every action.	2	2	
5. Looks at child with affection, showing a warm connection.	2	2	
6. Enjoys being with and playing with the child through smiles or a joyful look and emits a sense of warmth and inviting gestures. Keep in mind cultural differences in how this may be expressed.	2	2	
Total for Forming Relationships, Attachment, and Engagement	6	6	

Age: **19-24 Months** Child's Name: <u> Steven </u>
Behaviors: **Caregiver**

	SYM	SENS	EXAM
TWO-WAY, PURPOSEFUL COMMUNICATION			
7. Allows child to decide on the play topic, to initiate play and explore toys in ways that the child seeks or needs in play.	2	2	
8. Responds to child's wishes, intentions, and actions in a contingent way, building on how the child wishes to play. For example, child may hand toy to parent, and parent responds by taking it and saying something about the toy, then gives the child an opportunity to respond to what they just did. *Scoring:* 0 = Consistently does opposite to what baby seeks, misreads child's cues, changing activity from what child wants to do. 1 = Misreads child's signals about 25 to 50% of time changing activity or toy while at other times reads child's signals accurately. 2 = Responds to child's signals in appropriate way most of time (up to 75% time responsive to child), staying on the activity that the child has chosen.	2	2	
9. Predominately handles toys, engaging in parallel play and removing attention from playing with child. *Converted Score:** Score of 0, converts to 2	2	2	
10. Plays with child at developmentally appropriate level. Caregiver may play slightly above child's level of skill, modeling new ways to do things or labeling what child does or describing the functions of objects.	2	2	
11. Stimulates child at pace that allows child to respond, waiting for child's responses. Avoids overstimulating child with language or actions.	2	2	
Total for Two-Way, Purposeful Communication	10	10	
BEHAVIORAL ORGANIZATION, PROBLEM-SOLVING, AND INTERNALIZATION (A Complex Sense of Self)			
12. Responds and initiates reciprocal back and forth chains of interactions with child, stringing together connected circles of communication or units of interaction. For example, caregiver introduces baby doll, child touches doll's face, mother touches doll's hair, child pats the doll, mother says "baby", and child glances between mother and doll). The caregiver may imitate child (i.e., pushing car alongside child), then interject her turn by an action or verbalization related to the child's actions (i.e., "Oh, a bump!", then bumps her car into child's car). *Scoring:* 0 = 0 to 2 circles 1 = 3 to 5 circles 2 = 6 or more circles	0*	0*	
13. Uses gestures and facial expressions as a modality to promote circles of communication.	2	2	
14. Uses touch or rough house play as a modality to promote circles of communication.	2	2	

Age: **19-24 Months**   Child's Name: ___Steven___

Behaviors: **Caregiver**

	SYM	SENS	EXAM
15. Elaborates on and builds complexity into the child's play behaviors while engaged in interactive sequences between parent and child. The parent expands on what the child does while remaining on the child's play topic (e.g., the parent does not introduce a completely new play idea). The parent provides a small challenge or interesting twist to the play that requires the child to respond slightly differently than before, thus creating a problem solving opportunity for the child. For example, the parent and child are pushing a car back and forth towards each other. The parent expands on this by creating a wall with her leg to prevent the car from rolling, then waits to see how the child will solve this situation.	1	1	
16. Allows child to assert self in play, exploring with confidence what he or she wishes (i.e., child expresses strong wish to play in a certain way such as banging toys, being silly, holding a doll, or running around room.) Parent supports the child's needs for dependency and closeness, assertiveness and curiosity, aggression, autonomy, or pleasure and excitement by admiring, showing interest, and/or by joining in to the child's play in whatever way the child seeks. Problems that may interfere with caregiver's capacity to support this area might be intrusiveness, withdrawal, overprotectiveness, or playing at level far above child's level of competence.	2	2	
17. Shows pleasure and excitement in playing with child in whatever way the child wishes to play. *Scoring:* 0 = little pleasure and excitement shown by caregiver. 1 = pleasure and excitement sustained by parent over the course of several (3 to 5) circles of communication. 2 = pleasure and excitement sustained for many (6 or more) circles of communication.	1	1	
Note here if child is unable to sustain circles of communication if it affects caregiver's score: Child can sustain circles: _____ Child cannot: ___X___	/////	/////	/////
18. Expresses appropriate limits on baby. The caregiver may redirect child not to leave room, not to hit her, or not throw toy. If no need for limits arise during play, mark N/O and give 2 points.	N/O 2	N/O 2	
Total for Behavioral Organization, Problem-Solving, and Internalization (Note: Scores are deflated for parent scale because child cannot sustain interactions.)	**11**	**11**	
TOTAL CAREGIVER SCORE FOR SCALE	*33*	*33*	

Stanley I. Greenspan, M.D. and Georgia A DeGangi, Ph.D., OTR
Interdisciplinary Council on Developmental and Learning Disorders, Bethesda, MD

The Functional Emotional Assessment Scale Administration and Scoring Form

Age: **19-24 Months**

Behaviors: **Child**

Name of Child: _Steven_   Date of Testing: _____

Age of Child: _24 months_

Person Playing
With Child: Mother: _X_   Father: _X_
                Caregiver: ___   Examiner: ___

Key: SYM = Symbolic; SENS = Sensory; EXAM = Examiner

	SYM	SENS	EXAM
SELF-REGULATION AND INTEREST IN THE WORLD			
1. Is interested and attentive to play with toys.	2	2	
2. Explores objects freely without caution.	1	2	
3. Remains calm for play period with no signs of distress (crying or whining), showing appropriate frustration.	2	2	
4. Is comfortable touching textured toys and in being touched by caregiver.	2	2	
5. Enjoys moving on equipment or engaging in rough house play.	2	2	

6. Shows happy, content affect
  Scoring:
  0 = flat, somber, or depressed affect
  1 = content but neutral
  2 = happy and content, robust smiles, warm and engaging affect
	0	2	

7. Remains focused on objects or caregiver without being distracted by sights or sounds.
  Scoring:
  0 = distracted frequently, no focused play for more than a few seconds at a time
  1 = distracted some of time with brief periods of focused play
  2 = remains focused in play most of time with only brief distractibility
	0	2	

Age: **19-24 Months** Child's Name: __Steven__
Behaviors: **Child**

	SYM	SENS	EXAM
Note: Score one item only, either item 8 or 9, whichever applies			

8. Underreactivity: Appears sluggish or withdrawn
    Scoring:
    0 = withdrawn, difficult to engage
    1 = sluggish or slow-paced in actions but can eventually be aroused or engaged
    2 = shows a bright, alert state with focused play throughout
	0	2	

9. Overreactivity: Appears overaroused by toys and environment.
    Scoring:
    0 = Very active, moves quickly from one toy to the next or wanders away from caregiver and toys constantly
    1= Moderately active, occasional bursts of changing activity quickly or wandering away, then settles into play with one toy for short period
    2 = Well-modulated in pace and activity level, focusing on a toy or caregiver for long periods before changing activity.			

Total for Self-Regulation and Interest in the World	**9**	**16**	
FORMING RELATIONSHIPS, ATTACHMENT, AND ENGAGEMENT			
10. Shows emotional interest and connection with caregiver by vocalizing and smiling at her.	0	2	
11. Evidences a relaxed sense of security and/or comfort when near caregiver. If child is active and moves away from caregiver, he references her from across space and shows relaxed security in distal space.	2	2	
12. Anticipates with curiosity or excitement when caregiver presents an interesting object or game.	0	2	
13. Initiates physical closeness to caregiver but is not clingy; If child is active and moves away from caregiver, child maintains a visual or verbal connection with caregiver.	2	2	

14. Turns head away, averts gaze, moves away, or sits facing away from caregiver without social referencing caregiver. Appears indifferent, aloof, withdrawn, or avoidant of caregiver.
    *Converted Score:**
    For symbolic play, score of 2 , converted to 0.
    For sensory play, score of 1.
	0	1	

15. Social references caregiver while looking at toys.	0	0	
16. After moving away, communicates to caregiver from across space by looking, gestures, or vocalizations.	0	0	
Total for Forming Relationships, Attachment, and Engagement	**4**	**9**	

Age: **19-24 Months**   Child's Name: Steven
Behaviors: **Child**

	SYM	SENS	EXAM
TWO-WAY, PURPOSEFUL COMMUNICATION			
17. Opens circles of communication: Initiates intentional actions with objects while also engaged in interactions with caregiver (i.e., manipulates object then looks at mother and smiles or vocalizes).	2	2	

18. Gives signals: Initiates purposeful and intentional actions in play with objects.
  Scoring:
  0 = Needs considerable help to get started in play or to engage in purposeful actions; no clear gestures or organized intent
  1 = Initiates play but engages in stereotypic actions; i.e., lining toys up, mouthing toys for long periods of time, banging toys without engaging in any other actions with the same toy OR initiates play but actions appear aimless or disorganized.
  2 = Play shows intentionality and variety, engaging in two or more different behaviors with a given toy or activity. Gestures are specific and activity is functionally tied to objects.
	1	1	

19. Closes circles: Responds to caregiver's cues in contingent manner (i.e., mother offers toy, baby takes it and puts it in a container).
  Scoring:
  0 = Does not notice caregiver's response
  1 = Notices caregiver's response and looks, but does not respond contingently through actions; instead does something that has nothing to do with what caregiver did (i.e., mother holds toy out for child; child looks at mother and toy, then returns to what he was doing before)
  2 = Notices caregiver's response, then responds contingently by elaborating on what caregiver did, by taking toy held by caregiver and examining it, by imitating her, or some other response that is clearly linked to what caregiver did.
	0	1	

20. Shows anger, frustration, aggressive behavior (e.g., hitting), or protest repeatedly. *Converted Score:* *	2	2	
21. Uses language (e.g., sounds, words, and/or gestures) during interactions. Circle which ones were used.	0	0	
Total Two-Way, Purposeful Communication	5	6	

Age: **19-24 Months**   Child's Name: ___Steven___

Behaviors: **Child**

	SYM	SENS	EXAM
BEHAVIORAL ORGANIZATION, PROBLEM-SOLVING, AND INTERNALIZATION (Complex Sense of Self)	/////	/////	/////

22. Engages in complex patterns of communication stringing together several circles of communication with caregiver (initiated and elaborated on by child) using gestures, vocalizations, and/or words.
    Scoring:
    0 = 0 to 2 circles
    1 = 3 to 5 circles
    2 = 6 or more circles
	0	0	

23. Imitates or copies something new that the caregiver introduces, then incorporates idea into play (i.e., caregiver feeds doll; toddler copies this)	0	0	
Total Behavioral Organization, Problem-Solving, and Internalization	**0**	**0**	
TOTAL CHILD SCORE FOR SCALE	*18*	*31*	
TOTAL FEAS SCALE SCORE (add Caregiver and Child scores)	*51*	*64*	

Profile Form
For 19 to 24 Months Olds

	Score				
Subtest	SYM	SENS	Normal	At Risk	Deficient
Caregiver:					
Regulation	6	6	3-6		0-2
Attachment	6	6	6	5	0-4
Two-way communication	10	10	9-10	8	0-7
Behavioral organization	11	11	11-14	10	0-9
Total Caregiver	*33*	*33*	*28-36*	*26-27*	*0-25*
Child:					
Regulation	9	16	13-16 (sens)	12	0-11 (sym)
Attachment	4	9	12-14	11	0-10
Two-way communication	5	6	9-10	8	0-7
Behavioral organization	0	0	3-4		0-2
Total Child	*18*	*31*	*36-44*	*34-35*	*0-33*
Total Scale	51	64	64-80 (sens)	60-63	0-59 (sym)

References

Bayley, N. (1993). *Bayley scales of infant development.* New York: Psychological Corporation.

DeGangi, G. A. & Breinbauer, C. (1997). The symptomatology of infants and toddlers with regulatory disorders. *Journal of Developmental and Learning Disorders, 1,* 183–215.

DeGangi, G. A. & Greenspan, S. I. (1989). *The test of sensory functions in infants.* Los Angeles: Western Psychological Services.

DeGangi, G. A., Poisson, S., Sickel, R. Z., & Wiener, A. S. (1995). *Infant-toddler symptom checklist.* Tucson, AZ: Therapy Skill Builders.

7

Additional Validity Studies on Constructs and Variables Used in the FEAS

Georgia A. DeGangi, Ph.D., OTR
Suzanne C. Doherty, Ph.D.

The developmental structuralist model (Greenspan, 1979, 1989a, 1992; Greenspan & Lourie, 1981) developed by Greenspan (Greenspan, 1981) and described in Chapter 1 provides a comprehensive framework for assessment of psychosocial functioning in the parent and child. The model focuses on age-related organizational behaviors associated with adaptive functioning as well as maladaptive behaviors manifested along the developmental continuum (Greenspan et al., 1987; Greenspan 1981, 1989a, 1992). This is the model upon which the Functional Emotional Assessment Scale (FEAS) is based. Validation of the developmental structuralist model is important to provide justification, not only for the constructs underlying the basic model, but to lend empirical support for use of the FEAS.

This chapter describes preliminary research on the developmental structuralist model. This is followed by research from two major studies that support the developmental structuralist model as a framework for assessment of psychosocial development. Data from these studies provide practical justification for the developmental structural model from which the FEAS is derived. First, a research study on infants, children, and their caregivers who are at high-risk for psychopathology is described. Second, a research study on infants with regulatory disorders is presented. These research studies focus on validation of the first three developmental levels of the developmental structuralist model: regulation and interest in the world (homeostasis), attachment, and purposeful two-way communication (somatopsychological differentiation). Finally, research supporting early intervention and assessment is described.

Preliminary Research and Supporting Studies

Research using the developmental structuralist model was carried out over the course of several years in the Clinical Infant Development Program (CIDP) on a sample of 47 at-risk mothers in multirisk families (Wieder, Jasnow, Greenspan, & Strauss, 1989). This research confirmed the importance of focusing on the child's physiological and constitutional vulnerabilities as well as environmental, parent, and family problems as they impact the parent-child relationship. Specific variables were identified in the CIDP that may impair optimal development at different points in the developmental continuum. These variables are useful in guiding the assessment process as one explores the caregiver and child's psychosocial functioning. The variables found to be important include the following:

- Constitutional and developmental status of the infant including prenatal variables, pregnancy history, and sensorimotor, cognitive, motor, language, and self-regulatory capacities of the infant;
- Parent, family, and environmental variables such as the caregiver's mental health status and personality development, the caregiver's child-rearing capacities, family interaction patterns, support systems, and the home environment; and
- The caregiver-infant/child relationship, including the nature of the attachment between parent and child, the capacity for joint pleasure, rhythmicity and contingency in interactions, flexibility in tolerating tension and frustration, the capacity for intimacy and to experience differentiation in the dyad, and the ability to form complex emotional and behavioral interactive patterns (Greenspan, 1989a).

Child-caregiver interactions are considered an important avenue through which to influence developmental outcomes (McCollum & Hemmeter, 1997). Other researchers have also examined areas that should be included in an assessment of social-emotional functioning. Their results show that the following should be included as well: reciprocity (Dawson & Galpert, 1990; Lewy & Dawson, 1992); shared attention (Mundy, Sigman, & Kasari, 1990); development of empathy, social problems solving, and "theory of mind" or the ability to take in and integrate another's perspective (Baron-Cohen, 1997); and functional use of language within the context of interactions (Prizant & Wetherby, 1993). In addition to examining the dynamics of play interactions between parent and child, it is also important to observe the child's play in different contexts (e.g., symbolic play, play with sensory mediums) to observe the interplay among developmental, sensory integration, and interactional components (DeGangi, Sickel, Kaplan, & Wiener, 1997b).

Research With At-Risk Mother/Infant Behavior Patterns Using the Greenspan Lieberman Observation Scale-Revised

Research on caregivers from multirisk families and the nature of their relationship with their infants was conducted as part of the process in validating the developmental structuralist model. Several dimensions were identified as relevant in the process of investigating the relationship between developmental processes described in the developmental structuralist model (Greenspan, 1979, 1989a, 1992) and the manifestation of maladaptive emotional functioning in children aged 4 months to 36 months (Doherty, 1997). The subjects comprised 33 mother/child dyads from multi-problem families and 30 more typically functioning mother/child dyads ranging in age from 4 months to 36 months. The children were matched for age and gender as closely as possible. Six child/mother dyads were selected from each of six different age groups representing the six domains of the developmental structuralist model:

1. Attachment (2 to 4 months)
2. Homeostasis (4 to 6 months)
3. Two-way, purposeful communication (somatopsychological differentiation) (7 to 10 months)
4. Behavioral organization (11 to 15 months)
5. Representational capacity (18 to 27 months)
6. Representational differentiation (27 to 36 months)

The objective was to test the ability of the developmental structuralist model using the Greenspan Lieberman Observation Scale-Revised (GLOS-R) (Greenspan & Lieberman, 1980) to differentiate children from multi-problem families and a low-risk, normative sample.

Description of the Methodology: GLOS-R

The Greenspan Lieberman Observation Scale-Revised (GLOS-R) (Greenspan et al., 1980) used in this study is a research tool specifically developed to operationalize and measure the developmental domains of Greenspan's model of personality development. The GLOS was developed for use with multi-problem families whose children are at high risk for developmental, psychological, and educational dysfunction (Adnopoz, Grigsby, & Nagler, 1991; Bernstein, Jeremy, & Marcus, 1986; Cohn & Tronick, 1989). It provides a systematic method to characterize and rate behaviors related to adaptive vs. maladaptive emotional functioning at each of the functional emotional developmental stages conceptualized in the developmental structuralist model for infancy and early childhood. The FEAS is conceptually based on the GLOS but there are major differences in behavioral observations and scoring methods for the two scales. The FEAS provides a more accessible and efficient system of scoring based on operationally defined behaviors. The GLOS requires extensive training and uses highly detailed observations measured at 15-second intervals using videotaped behaviors.

An interobserver reliability study of the original GLOS (Poisson, Hofheimer, Strauss, & Greenspan, 1983) resulted in the revised version that was used in this study. Interobserver reliability of the GLOS-R ranged from .90 to .99 with two independent raters who were blind to the purpose of the study. The raters used a checklist to note the behaviors within each of 15-second intervals for the duration of the videotape (15 minutes).

Overall Study Findings

In this study, data from videotapes of the interaction between parents and children were examined. There were strong significant differences in the overall functioning of the at-risk and the non-clinical groups with differences for mothers and children in four of the seven variables associated with the developmental structuralist model. These variables included reciprocal interactions, negative affect, control, and non-involvement. The findings suggest that the developmental structuralist model as measured by the GLOS-R may be useful in exploring maladaptive functioning in infants and young children.

Specific Findings Related to the Stages in the Developmental Structuralist Model

The items in the GLOS-R were operationalized to depict adaptive and maladaptive behaviors underlying the stages of the developmental structuralist model. Each of the developmental domains in the developmental structuralist model were subdivided into "conceptual clusters," which included the following:

- *Positive Affect:* This conceptual cluster represents behaviors on the part of the parent associated with physical contact with the child and, on the part of the child, seeking proximity or physical contact with the parent and expression of pleasure.
- *Reciprocity:* Included in this cluster are behaviors that are contingent to the parent's or child's initiation of social interaction and exploration of the environment. It also included contingent responses to pleasure or distress by either parent or child. Among children, reciprocity included the child's contingent response to parental command and/or to the parent's attempt to soothe or console the child when distressed.
- *Promotion of Social Behavior:* The behaviors included the parent's and the child's initiating and engaging in social interaction.
- *Developmental Initiative:* This cluster was comprised of all parental behaviors associated with providing developmental assistance and facilitating the child's exploration and manipulation of the environment, language usage, and representational play.
- *Negative Affect:* The behaviors included anticontingent responses, that is, responses that were directly opposed to the signaled need, desire, or interest of either member of the dyad; abrupt handling and direct physical punishment by the parent; and distress, withdrawal, or expression of fear by the child.

- *Control:* Included were instances of intrusive or undermining be-havior on the part of the parent and any parental commands that were not related to protecting the child's safety. Child behaviors in-cluded acts of aggression against the parent, avoidance of contact with the parent, and physical over-stimulation and consequent lack of control.
- *Non-Involvement:* This cluster comprised noncontingent responses by parent and/or child; parental behaviors reflecting withdrawal or nonparticipation in the child's activities and any behaviors associ-ated with maternal depression such as flat affect; undirected, unfo-cused activity on the part of the child; behaviors associated with lack of interest in interaction with the parent and/or the environment; and flat affect of the child.

Each data set included an analysis of the language and behaviors ob-served in the videotapes according to developmental structural concepts of adaptive/maladaptive organizational processes measured by the GLOS-R. A total of 23 maternal behaviors and 23 infant behaviors associated with the conceptual clusters were included for coding on the GLOS-R obser-vation record (Table 7-1).

Analysis of the data revealed a significant difference between the par-ent-child dyads in the at-risk and control groups in four conceptual clus-ters of the GLOS-R: reciprocity, negative affect, control, and non-in-volvement. In addition, significant interaction of age and parent/child, clinical/non-clinical effects emerged in five of the conceptual clusters: pos-itive affect, reciprocity, promotion of social behavior, developmental ini-tiative, and negative affect. Important trends by age for each of these be-haviors will be described.

Positive Affect

Four-month-old babies in the at-risk group exhibited more positive affect behaviors than their control group peers, in part because they were more often observed in direct physical contact with their mothers. Parents in the control group, on the other hand, appeared to have encouraged more ex-ploratory behavior by the infant from an infant seat or in floor play. The fact that all the mothers of the 4-month-old babies engaged in more pos-itive affect behaviors than their infants is consistent with the general need, at this age, for parents to initiate caregiving activity to meet infant needs.

Table 7-1.
Variables Used in Study of Mother-Infant Interactions in High-Risk Families

Cluster	Caregiver Behaviors	Child Behaviors
Positive Affect	Physical contact: Affectionate Physical contact: Kiss/cuddle Physical contact: Caregiving	Seeks proximity Seeks physical contact Affectionate behavior Pleasure, joy
Reciprocity	Contingent responses: • Social, exploration • At age level • Below age level Contingent chains: • Social, exploration, pleasure	Contingent responses • Social, exploration Contingent chains: • Exploration, pleasure
Promotion of Social Involvement	Engagement in social interactions Pleasure Rough and tumble	Initiates social interaction Engaged in social interactions
Developmental Initiative	Developmental assistance: • Physical • Language Facilitation of inanimate: • Verbal and nonverbal • Basic • Functional • Representational Nonparticipating (available)	Exploratory manipulation: • Functional • Representational • Representational social Exploratory roaming Use of language: • Basic (recognition) • Functional • Representational • Monologic • Social
Negative Affect	Direct physical punishment Abrupt handling Anticontingent response: • Social • Exploration Anticontingent chains: • Social • Exploration • Pleasure	Distress Anticontingent: • Exploration Anticontingent chains: • Social • Exploration • Pleasure Withdrawal/fear
Controlling	Command (not safety related) Intrusive Undermining Physical overstimulation (escalating aversive behavior)	Aggressive behavior Avoids physical contact Resists physical contact Physically overstimulated
Non-Involvement	Flat affect Noncontingent response Nonparticipating (withdrawn)	Flat affect Aimless movement Noncontingent responses Reckless/self-harm

At 8 months, children engaged in more positive affect behaviors than their mothers. This may be related to the babies' interest in object exploration and more autonomous activity that necessitates less parental caregiving in a play observation.

Babies in the 8- and 12-month-old non-clinical group demonstrated an increasing frequency of behaviors associated with positive affect. Proximity-seeking, for example, is expected as babies become more mobile. One would expect them to engage in more exploratory activity with frequent moves back to mother's "circle" of safety. The decline in positive affect behaviors among the children at 24 months in the non-clinical group is consistent with the development of autonomy at this age. The fact that at 36 months children in the non-clinical group exhibit another increase in positive affect behaviors appears associated with more expression of pleasure in interaction with their mothers and objects in the play room.

Children in the clinical group showed a pattern of positive affect behaviors exactly opposite to their control group peers. The behaviors of the children in the at-risk group reflect dynamics that are counter to developmental expectations across the age groups. Mothers in the at-risk and control groups exhibited nearly identical patterns of positive affect behaviors. They showed high levels at 4 months with a downward progression across the age groups due to declining need for direct caregiving as the babies grew older.

Reciprocity

The difference in group means for reciprocity showed a deficit in the at-risk dyads in the area of reciprocal interaction. They were less likely to accurately read and follow with contingent responses each other's cues for social interaction, exploratory activity, or expression of pleasure/distress. The matched decrease in reciprocity in the at-risk dyads and the matched increase in the control dyads began with the 12-month age group. This suggests an association between the characteristics of reciprocity and the way in which infants develop an attached relationship to their mothers. A continuing difference in reciprocity and quality of dyadic relationship is reflected in the higher levels of reciprocity in the more typically functioning dyads at 24 and 36 months. The possible connection between the development of reciprocity and other conceptual clusters will be discussed later.

Promotion of Social Behaviors

Mothers of 4-month-old babies in the at-risk group exhibited a higher frequency of promotion of social behaviors than did the parents in the more typically functioning group. Given that these infants exhibited considerable negative affect, this higher frequency may reflect how mothers in the multi-problem group had difficulty following their infants' cues. The very low frequency of promotion of social behaviors in the at-risk dyads of the 12-month-old group seems to coincide with low reciprocity. Although parent/child dyads in the at-risk group showed increases of promotion of social behaviors at 24 months and 36 months, the frequency was below that of the parent/child dyads in the non-clinical group. These dyads showed steady increases in promotion of social behavior from 4 to 36 months, a trend that one might normally expect.

Developmental Initiative

As would be expected, behaviors associated with development initiative increased in frequency with the increasing age of the babies. Also expected is that developmental initiative is more a function of the child's development with the parent participating in a facilitative role. The differences between the at-risk and control groups was not significant.

Negative Affect

Parents in the more typically functioning group exhibited relatively few negative affect behaviors. The babies in this group showed a general decline in negative affect from 4 to 36 months, which suggests that they learned effective self-soothing strategies and/or to find comfort in their interactions with their mothers who, in turn, were able to respond appropriately.

The children in the 4-month-old at-risk group exhibited the highest frequency of negative affect behaviors, which may reflect, in part, a physiologically based tendency toward "fussiness." The infants in this group may also have had difficulty making use of their mothers' attempts to comfort or soothe them. Another possibility is that the caregiver had difficulty adjusting her responses to the infant's needs, which might have been reflected in the frequency of behaviors related to promoting social engagement.

That the 8-month-old children in both the at-risk and control groups showed less negative affect than those at 4 months was most likely due to maturational factors. The frequency of negative affect behaviors in the at-risk group, however, remained approximately twice that of the non-clinical group, which suggests a pattern of emotional distress at this age as well. This pattern is repeated for the children in the 24 and 36 month at-risk groups, which may be of particular clinical relevance in identifying early signs of developmental psychopathology.

There was considerable variability in negative affect expressed by parents in the at-risk group. "Peaks" of negative affect behaviors were noted among parents in the 8- and 24-month clinical groups. These ages entail both periods associated with increased autonomy in the child that may provoke negative responses from a mother who is stressed and struggles with the task of parenting.

Negative affect may be linked to impaired reciprocal interaction between mother and baby. Irritable, "fussy babies," or babies who are difficult to read or impossible to comfort, are often unable to effectively elicit appropriate responses from their mothers. A mother may be vulnerable to the effects of parenting a difficult baby and may be unable to experiment and adjust responses to better "fit" the infant's need. The baby may be, in turn, sensitive to the mother's expression of distress and react with heightened negative affect behaviors.

Control

Controlling behavior on the part of parents in the at-risk group may reflect overly intrusive behaviors. The frequency of control behaviors may also mean that these mothers were responding to children who were difficult to control. The marked elevation in frequency of control behaviors by mothers of 24-month-old children in the at-risk group may reflect the mother's inability to incorporate the child's emerging autonomy into her scheme of her child's developmental needs.

Non-Involvement

The frequency of non-involvement behaviors for the at-risk parent group may reflect the mother's tendency to withdraw from interaction or to withhold attention, possibly because of depression or other emotional problems. The results may also indicate feelings of inadequacy in parenting difficult babies. The transactional nature of this domain is seen in the way the parent/child scores are paired beginning with the 8-month-old group. The 4-month-old infants in both the at-risk and control groups showed high levels of non-involvement behaviors as might be expected of socially inexperienced infants. The differences in parenting behaviors between the mothers in the at-risk and control groups at this age may have a strong influence on the quality of infant/parent involvement in later stages. This domain is also closely linked to the development of reciprocity.

The development of reciprocal interactions between mother and baby begins in the earliest stage of infancy and is critical to the development of attachment. Impaired reciprocal interaction and negative affect in both parent and child appears associated with maladaptive functioning across the ages of the children in the at-risk group. The pattern of behaviors in the 12-month at-risk group offers evidence that this is a "critical period" in infant development. That the infant/mother dyads in this group showed low reciprocity and high non-involvement suggests a combination of maladaptive behaviors early in the parent/child relationship. The fact that negative affect was lowest in this group may be linked to withdrawal (non-involvement) and the possibility that "detachment," rather than attachment, has occurred. The children and mother in the 24- and 36-month at-risk groups appear linked in a pattern of mutual maladaptation. The 3-year-old children in the at-risk group exhibited a troubling pattern of behaviors (fewer positive affect, reciprocal, and less promotion of social behaviors; higher frequencies of negative affect and non-involvement behaviors), which seems to represent developmental failure of the kind associated with psychopathology in early childhood.

Early assessment and intervention to help mothers be more effectively involved with difficult infants would facilitate development of reciprocity in the mother/infant dyad. This, in turn, might facilitate appropriate completion, within the first and subsequent years, of other developmental tasks described in the developmental structuralist model and contribute to more optimal functioning in later childhood.

Limitations of the Research

One of the limitations of this research was the small sample size. Although 30 dyads within the at-risk and control groups were sufficient for the analyses that were conducted, the GLOS-R comparisons of the groups across five age ranges were based on samples of six. These comparisons yielded interesting results; however, they will need to be further substantiated with a larger, more representative sample.

Another limitation of this research project was that, despite every effort to recruit participants of diverse racial and socioeconomic backgrounds, the control, or non-clinical, group was relatively homogeneous in its racial and socioeconomic composition. These results offer practical evidence of the validity of the precepts of the developmental structuralist model as a conceptual framework within which to further explore adaptive-maladaptive functioning in infancy and early childhood.

How the FEAS Incorporates These Research Findings

This research is very useful in understanding the behaviors manifested in high-risk clinical groups. Although the research was conducted using the GLOS-R, the FEAS was originally based upon the theoretical framework used in developing the GLOS-R. In her research, Doherty found that the variables that distinguished at-risk and non-clinical groups included difficulties organizing reciprocal interactions, expression of negative affect, controlling, intrusive, or undermining behavior on the part of the parent, and non-involvement (e.g., withdrawal, flat affect, or noncontingent behaviors) on the part of the infant (Doherty, 1997).

Items on the FEAS within the sub-domains of regulation and interest in the world, attachment, and intentional two-way communication incorporate specific behaviors that are useful in measuring problems that may arise in at-risk clinical groups. In the subdomains of regulation and interest in the world and attachment, the FEAS has items that measure proximity seeking or avoidant behavior, positive or negative affect, exploration, affectionate behavior, intrusive, overstimulating, or hypervigilant behavior on the part of the caregiver, and pleasure in the dyad. Items on the intentional two-way communication subscale focus on contingent responses and capacity to sustain reciprocal interactions, caregiver facilitation of child's behaviors and play, use of language, and intentional exploratory manipulation of objects. Our research in using the FEAS with at-risk clinical samples further validates the usefulness of including these items on the scale.

Regulatory Problems in Infants and Their Impact on the Parent-Child Relationship

The research that follows in this section provides validation for the first stage of the developmental structuralist model: self-regulation and interest in the world (homeostasis). The developmental structuralist model supports that adaptive behaviors at this stage provide an important foundation for subsequent stages and their associated adaptive behaviors. The ability for self-regulation and taking an interest in the world supports the infant's ability to engage with others, be purposeful, problem solve, and eventually create and connect ideas. On the other hand, the developmental structuralist model suggests that problems in the capacities associated with this stage are associated with maladaptive behaviors at this and subsequent stages and therefore can constitute a regulatory disorder.

In this section, studies that support the above hypotheses are presented on infants with regulatory disorders. The symptoms of regulatory disordered children are discussed in relation to the child's functional developmental capacities and their impact on the caregiver-child relationship. The evolution of symptoms over time and how they interfere with development are discussed. Finally, the use of the FEAS in evaluation of regulatory problems and their impact on parent-child interactions is discussed.

What Is a Regulatory Disorder?

Although some constitutionally based traits are transient in nature and resolve once the child develops internal self-organizational mechanisms (Thelen, 1989), others are not. For example, infants frequently display sleep disturbances and/or colic, which resolve spontaneously by five or six months of age. If, however, early signs of irritability do not resolve by six months, the fussiness experienced by the infant persists and is coupled with other symptoms such as poor self-calming, intolerance for change, and a hyper-alert state of arousal. Using Greenspan's original definition of regulatory disorder and his clinical constructs (Greenspan, 1992), these infants recently have become recognized as regulatory disordered in the *Diagnostic Classification of Mental Health and Developmental Disorders of Infancy and Early Childhood* (Diagnostic Classification Task Force, 1994).

A regulatory disorder is one in which problems exist both at the physiologic level of regulation and in the presence of maladaptive behaviors. Typically, the regulatory disordered infant displays problems in sleep, self-consoling, feeding, attention and arousal, mood regulation, behavior control, or transitions. Often these infants are hyper- or hyposensitive to sensory stimuli including auditory, tactile, visual, and vestibular and/or evidence of other sensory processing or motor planning difficulties (DeGangi & Greenspan, 1988).

Research on Symptoms of Infants With Regulatory Disorders

It has been suggested that disorders of regulation involve maladaptive responses to early organization of sensory and interactional experiences (Greenspan, 1989b, 1992; Greenspan & Porges, 1984). Regulatory disordered infants exhibit deficits in psychological processes (e.g., sustained attention) and physiological organization (DeGangi, 1991, 2000). Our preliminary studies of this population reveal that they are often hypersensitive to sensory stimuli including auditory, tactile, visual, and vestibular stimulation (DeGangi et al., 1988). Moreover, psychophysiological research has identified a pattern of autonomic hyperreactivity in regulatory disordered infants (DeGangi, DiPietro, Greenspan, & Porges, 1991). Heart period and cardiac vagal tone were measured during baseline and during sensory and cognitive challenges to examine psychophysiological responses in normal and regulatory disordered infants (8 to 11 months). The regulatory disordered infants tended to have higher baseline vagal tone. Across groups there was a significant suppression of vagal tone during cognitive processing. Baseline vagal tone was correlated with the suppression of vagal tone during the cognitive task only for the normal infants. In contrast, the responses of the infants with regulatory disorders were heterogeneous. The results provided preliminary support for the hypothesized relationship between vagal tone and the regulatory disorder.

   In the past, research has focused on the trait of difficult temperament, which is shared by many infants with regulatory disorders. Difficult infants have been described as irritable with high intensity, low adaptability, and high activity level (Chess, Thomas, & Hassibi, 1983). Difficult infants have been reported to react negatively to social interactions, to demonstrate a heightened reactivity to negative environmental overstimulation such as noise confusion (Wachs & Gandour, 1983), and, as preschoolers, to display problem behaviors such as tantrums, aggression, refusals, attention seeking, and being difficult to manage (Barron & Earls, 1984; Lee & Bates, 1985; Stevenson-Hinde & Simpson, 1982). These types of difficult behaviors (e.g., irritability, fussiness) are only one aspect of the regulatory disorder. We have found that other processes contribute to regulatory disorders. The underlying process deficits appear related to a dysfunction in the registration, processing, and organization of sensory-affective experience and the planning and sequencing of adaptive responses that may lead to a variety of behavioral, affective, and cognitive symptoms (Greenspan, 1992).

The symptoms of regulatory disorders have been described in a fragmented fashion without identifying the full range of symptoms or the underlying process deficits. However, descriptions of children with regulatory disorders highlight the range and importance of these symptoms. For example, the clinical significance of poor regulation of arousal and state is demonstrated by the high incidence of children with sleep disturbances who have behavioral disturbances, attention deficit disorder with hyperactivity, and depression (Mattison, Handford, & Vela-Bueno, 1986). Infants with problems associated with regulating sensorimotor systems (i.e., hypersensitivity to stimulation) tend to develop emotional difficulties in the school-aged years (Fish & Dixon, 1978; Walker & Emory, 1983). Similar consistencies have been reported between negative temperamental characteristics assessed during infancy (e.g., distractibility, difficult temperament) and poor behavioral control, dependency, and aggressive behaviors in the preschool years (Forsyth & Canny, 1991; Himmelfarb, Hock, & Wenar, 1985; Sroufe, Fox, & Pancake, 1983), reactive depression in late adolescence (Chess et al., 1983), and later learning disabilities and psychopathology (Rutter, 1977).

Impact of Regulatory Disorder in Infancy on Later Developmental Outcomes

We conducted a longitudinal study to investigate the behaviors of "fussy babies" diagnosed as regulatory disordered at 8 to 11 months of age. These infants exhibited sleep disturbances, hypersensitivities to sensory stimulation, irritability, poor self-calming, and mood and state deregulation (DeGangi, Porges, Sickel, & Greenspan, 1993). Examination of group differences revealed that children initially identified as regulatory disordered differed significantly from their normal peers in perceptual, language, and general cognitive skills at 4 years of age. Although the regulatory disordered sample did not differ from their normal counterparts in developmental parameters during infancy, at 4 years of age, five of the nine regulatory disordered infants displayed either motor or overall developmental delays. A high incidence of vestibular-based sensory integrative deficits (e.g., poor bilateral coordination and postural control), tactile defensiveness, motor planning problems, hyperactivity, and emotional-behavioral difficulties were present in the regulatory disordered population. The findings imply that regulatory disordered infants are at high risk for later perceptual, language, sensory-integrative, and behavioral difficulties in the preschool years. Further follow-up studies on 39 infants with mild to moderate regulatory disorders has shown that at age 3 they differ from their normal peers in sensory integration, mood regulation, attention, motor control, sleep, and behavioral control (DeGangi, Sickel, Wiener, & Kaplan, 1996).

Evolution of Symptoms of Regulatory Disorders Over Time

We conducted another study that examined the specific symptoms of regulatory disordered infants between 7 and 30 months of age and how they evolve over time (DeGangi & Breinbauer, 1997a). In the first year of life, symptoms included irritability, inconsolability, demandingness, poor self-calming, and sleep problems. The infants also showed sensory hypersensitivities to touch and light, a high need for movement, fear of novelty, problems giving clear gestural and vocal signals, and severe separation anxiety. These symptoms are related to the capacity to develop basic homeostasis (e.g., self-calming, regulation of arousal states, and physiological regulation) and early sensory processing. Many of these symptoms persisted in the second year of life; however, other symptoms emerged. Attentional problems were seen in some infants who were distractible and overstimulated by busy environments. Sensory problems were manifested by a dislike for restraint (e.g., car seats, being dressed), a dislike for new food textures, distress with loud sounds, and a fear of movement. In addition, interactive problems were demonstrated by difficulties with age-expected patterns of reciprocal interactions, difficulties with limit setting, need for total control of the environment, and problems in giving clear gestural signals. Persistent problems with basic homeostasis occurred in conjunction with difficulties with gestural communication (e.g., signal reading and signal giving), affective expression, attentional capacities, reciprocal play, and negotiating autonomy and control. It is possible that these symptoms are the early warning signs of later attentional, emotional, and behavioral problems.

In a longitudinal study of infants with regulatory disorders, we followed two age-matched regulatory disordered (RD) groups based on severity (N = 10 in mild RD group; N = 22 in moderate-severe RD group) and age-matched control groups (N = 38) that were initially tested between 7 and 30 months of age (DeGangi, Breinbauer, Roosevelt, Porges, & Greenspan, 2000). A fourth group with pervasive developmental disorders (PDD) (N = 18) also were tested. Problems with self-regulation, including sleep, feeding, state control, self-calming, sensory reactivity, mood regulation, and emotional and behavioral control, were documented during infancy. Children were retested at 36 months in their development, behavior, and play. Two child psychiatrists unfamiliar with the subjects' diagnostic classifications during infancy provided diagnoses at 36 months. At 36 months, 60% of children with mild regulatory disorders did not meet criteria for any disorders, whereas 95% of infants with moderate regulatory disorders had diagnoses that fell into two diagnostic clusters:

1. Delays in motor, language, and cognitive development
2. Parent-child relational problems

Most toddlers in the PDD group were diagnosed as having PDD or autism with mental retardation or borderline intelligence at 36 months. The early symptoms that related to later diagnostic outcomes for the clinical samples are discussed in the following sections.

Our findings support the notion that children with regulatory disorders have underlying deficits in self-regulation, attention and arousal, sensory processing, and emotional regulation However, different symptoms occur at different ages based upon the developmental level of the child. The symptoms of regulatory disordered infants evolve over time and eventually involve other process domains that build upon the basic capacities for regulation and sensory interest (including modulation) in the world.

Evaluation of regulatory symptoms and how they affect functional performance is important. Below is a description of the common symptoms seen in infants and children with regulatory disorders, how these symptoms are manifested, and their impact on developmental functioning.

Irritability

The most pervasive trait of infants with regulatory disorders is that of fussiness. Up to 54% of the infants with regulatory disorders are irritable (DeGangi et al., 1997a). They frequently escalate quickly from a pleasant mood to an intense cry, are inconsolable and demanding, and have difficulty self-calming. Once upset the fussy baby requires extreme efforts to calm down. The caregiver may spend from two to four hours a day attempting to calm his or her infant. With older infants, severe temper tantrums are often present. In many cases, the fussiness and irritability are very disruptive to the family and result in a high degree of family stress. Once the child reaches 2 years of age, these behaviors tend to diminish, but problems tolerating change emerge, yet the child remains extremely demanding. The task of learning how to resolve distress without help from others, to comply with requests, to delay gratification, and to anticipate social routines seems to eventually develop in the regulatory disordered child, but not until the child is almost 24 to 30 months of age. The development of internal control and related cognitive abilities may help the child with regulatory disorders to be better able to tolerate changes and modulate distress. These abilities have been described by Kopp (1989, 1987) as important to the development of emotion regulation. Difficulties with this most basic task seem to have a negative impact on the development of cognition, language, skilled movement, behavioral and emotional control, and sensorimotor modulation at 3 years (DeGangi, 2000).

Sleep

Sleep problems are fairly common among infants with regulatory disorders (up to 47% of children under 2 years). The child may typically wake frequently in the night and need extensive help to fall asleep at night (e.g., over an hour of preparatory activities). Our research also shows that many children with sleep problems have hypersensitivities to touch, a strong craving for movement, and high separation anxiety (DeGangi et al., 1997a). It seems that sleep problems are related to both biological and social regulation, and the ability to form a secure attachment to the caregiver (Anders, 1994).

Feeding

The feeding problems exhibited by infants with regulatory disorders usually include difficulty establishing a regular feeding schedule, distress around feeding with regurgitation, refusal to eat, and other feeding problems not related to specific allergies or food intolerance. Resistance to eating a variety of food textures often emerges after 9 months. Some infants spit out lumpy food textures or refuse to eat anything but a few preferred foods, usually consisting of firm, crunchy textures or pureed foods. This problem may relate to tactile hypersensitivities that cause the child to prefer certain food textures. Occasionally growth retardation or failure to thrive may be diagnosed secondary to the feeding disturbance. Craving certain foods is seen in 18 to 46% of 13- to 24-month-olds. In addition, reflux is a problem sometimes experienced by children with regulatory disorders. In our research, we found that early feeding problems led to social-emotional problems over time (DeGangi, 2000). In a preliminary follow-up study (DeGangi et al., 1996), we also found that mothers' feelings of depression and a lack of attachment toward their infants were related to feeding problems.

Sensory Processing

Many infants with regulatory problems respond by crying, withdrawal, or other negative behaviors when confronted with normal everyday sensory stimulation involving touch (i.e., being held by parent), movement (i.e., rough housing with parent), or sights and sounds (i.e., busy environment such as supermarket). The common sensorimotor challenges experienced by infants and toddlers with regulatory disorders include the following: overreactivity to loud noises, hypersensitivity to light and visual stimulation (e.g., busy environments such as shopping malls), fear of body movement in space, tactile defensiveness (e.g., dislike wearing clothing, resist cuddling, hate having their face washed, or dislike being stroked on the body), undersensitivity to touch (e.g., don't notice pain such as receiving a shot or when falling down), an undersensitivity to movement (e.g., craving vestibular stimulation), and motor planning problems (e.g., difficulty sequencing and organizing purposeful movement). Our data seem to suggest that underlying process deficits in any one or more senses (e.g., tactile, vestibular-proprioceptive) can have a profound effect on later developmental outcomes (DeGangi, 2000).

Attention

As the toddler with regulatory disorders develops, there appears to be a steady increase in attentional problems (up to 64%) (DeGangi et al., 1997a). These range from being overstimulated by busy environments and distractibility to sights and sounds to problems shifting attention or engaging. Parents often describe their toddler with regulatory problems as being intense, wide-eyed, or "hyper." Frequently the child will go from one toy to another, often not playing with any toy long enough to develop a toy preference. We found that children experiencing these symptoms early in life were more apt to develop cognitive problems and motor delays at 3 years (DeGangi, 2000).

Impact of Regulatory Problems on the Functional Emotional Developmental Capacities Observed in the Developmental Structuralist Model

Problems with social interactions that were reported in infants with regulatory problems included poor eye contact, somber affect, difficulties initiating and sustaining reciprocal interactions, difficulty reading the child's cues, aggressive behavior, difficulties responding to limits, severe separation anxiety, and a fearfulness of new people and situations (DeGangi et al., 1997a). A high need to control the environment was reported by caregivers stating that their children "ran the show" and did not respond to limits. Inflexibility in tolerating change and new situations as well as difficulties adapting to the demands of others seemed to underlie these problems.

Our study examining symptomatology showed developmental differences in the manifestations of these problems. Parents of 7- to 9-month-olds often reported that they had difficulty reading their child's cues. This seemed related to problems that some children have in organizing clear gestural signals. At 19 to 24 months, some of the children with regulatory disorders had difficulty organizing reciprocal interactions.

In a systematic study examining the play interactions of 94 children who were regulatory disordered and 154 controls ranging in age from 7 to 30 months, we found that infants with regulatory disorders showed more noncontingent responses, more aggression, less tactile exploration, and more flat affect when engaged in play with tactile materials (DeGangi et al., 1997b). However, no differences were found in the behaviors of infants with regulatory disorders and controls during symbolic and vestibular play. It is possible that children with regulatory disorders become distressed by sensory experiences involving touch, which affects their capacity to organize social interchanges. This is important since much of the early parent-child relationship involves touching. In comparison to the control group, the mothers of infants with poor self-regulation showed more anticontingent responses and less symbolic play despite the fact that their infants engaged in symbolic play. The mothers also engaged in more talking with their infant, less movement stimulation, and they showed a flat or depressed affect, particularly during rough-house play on movement equipment. The three play contexts examined in this study elicited different behaviors, thus validating the relevance of using different play conditions to observe mother-infant interactions.

Use of the FEAS in Evaluation of Infants and Children with Regulatory Disorders

The FEAS provides a systematic observational system that is useful in evaluating infants and children with disorders of self-regulation. Test items were developed to measure the domain of regulation and interest in the world. These items capture the child's capacity to modulate affect, mood, and activity level, to sustain attention with the caregiver and during play with objects, to motor plan organized actions while interacting with the caregiver, and to tolerate and take pleasure in sensorimotor exploration. Atypical behaviors shown in children with regulatory disorders are incorporated into the scoring of the FEAS. For example, sensory defensive responses may be observed through hypervigilance, avoidance of eye contact, a sluggish or withdrawn activity level, or an overly aroused activity level.

The FEAS provides a framework for observing the child's capacity to attach to his or her caregiver, an important aspect of assessment with children with regulatory disorders. Many of these children are disorganized or anxious in their attachment to their caregivers. They may have difficulty seeking affection, in being consoled, or in tolerating proximity due to sensory defensiveness. The child who is underreactive to touch and/or is fearful of movement may be overly clingy to the caregiver. The child with a regulatory disorder often has difficulty in approaching the caregiver in an organized way and will often trip, become disorganized motorically, or will become very upset by his or her inability to be consoled by a care-giver. Conversely, parents find it difficult to soothe their irritable child, feel demoralized and frustrated in their efforts to organize and calm their child, and often have difficulty reading their child's signals. The FEAS includes items that incorporate both typical and maladaptive child and care-giver behaviors related to attachment. Items measure different aspects of attachment, including pleasure that the child and parent display in being with one another, whether the dyad maintains a verbal or visual connec-tion with one another, the security and comfort that is offered to the child by the parent, affectionate responses with one another or signs of dis-comfort, and displeasure or sadness that may be expressed by the child if the caregiver should become unresponsive or disengaged.

As described previously, many children with regulatory disorders have difficulties with motor planning and intentional two-way communica-tion. The FEAS includes items that measure the child and parent's capac-ity to initiate and organize interactions through verbalizations, gestures, or actions, the capacity to respond contingently with one another, and the child's ability to motor plan, organize, and execute play interactions that are purposeful and intentional. Because our research has shown that mothers of regulatory disordered children often show a high percent of anticontingent and over-stimulating behaviors, it is useful to observe these behaviors using the FEAS parent scale.

Finally, because the FEAS is administered with three sets of play ob-servations including symbolic toys, tactile materials, and vestibular equip-ment, it is possible to observe variations in how the child with regulatory disorders interacts and organizes play when challenged by different play situations. Our research shows that these children do better during sym-bolic play, but become more disorganized during sensory play because of the sensory problems that often accompany the regulatory disorder.

Intervention Studies

In this last section, various intervention studies are described that provide further support for the developmental structuralist model and its related approaches to interactions (i.e., the Developmental, Individual-Difference, Relationship-based approach [ICDL, 2000]) that emphasize the importance of working through the parent-child relationship to address the child's functional emotional capacities and individual process-ing differences, as well as the caregiver's needs. There appears to be sub-stantial evidence that interventions need to address the caregiver-child re-lationship, in the context of the child's functional developmental emotional capacities, by including shared attention (Mundy & Crowson, 1997), affective reciprocity (Lewy et al., 1992; Tanguay, 1999), empathy and symbolic self-reflection (i.e., theory of mind) (Baron-Cohen, 1997), pragmatic language (Prizant et al., 1993), and symbolic play and abstract thinking (Minshew, 1997, 1999). In an analysis of early intervention stud-ies, Tsakaris (2000) described the outcomes of 27 studies on early inter-vention. Interventions focusing on content-based skills (e.g., explicit turn-taking) were less effective than interventions focusing on the context of relationships (e.g., dynamics between parent and child). All but two showed beneficial outcomes for short-term gains. Because of method-ological problems in measuring outcomes, only two studies demonstrated long-term gains over several years.

In a study by Provence and Naylor (1983), it was demonstrated that providing support to families with opportunities for socialization and self-reflection result in children who have better outcomes for school perfor-mance and fewer behavioral/emotional difficulties as they mature. Sally Provence recommended the use of broad measures of adaptation and so-cial competence for measuring program effectiveness rather than focusing exclusively on intelligence testing.

In a 4-year longitudinal study conducted by Greenspan and Wieder and their colleagues (Greenspan et al., 1987), intervention services were provided to multi-risk families with more than 200 children in the Clinical Infant Development Program (CIDP) at the National Institute of Mental Health (NIMH). Caregivers were worked with to facilitate their child's de-velopment with emphasis on developing an ongoing relationship between parent and child and fostering homeostasis, attachment, two-way com-munication, problem-solving interactions, and the emotional use of ideas. For example, infants who showed gaze aversion, lack of attachment, and irritability in the first few months of life were able to achieve improved regulatory and attachment patterns. Those infants in the intensive inter-vention group showed progress in being able to overcome early perinatal stress or developmental deviations in their emotional development.

There is a paucity of research investigating the outcome of therapy approaches for infants and toddlers with regulatory disorders. Because valid diagnostic criteria for young children are lacking, few systematic studies have been conducted. When infants are used as subjects, normal maturation often confounds the effects of therapy over time. In addition, outcome measures are often based on therapist ratings rather than objective and valid observations. These methodological problems have confounded or negatively affected the results of many studies (Weisz & Weiss, 1993).

There are, however, few studies examining the benefits of interventions suitable for infants and toddlers. Cramer and his colleagues (1990) contrasted the Fraiberg (1980) method of mother-infant psychotherapy and noninterpretive interactional guidance (MacDonough, 1989) with infants under 30 months of age showing behavioral disturbances. They found no differences in the two approaches; however, short-term gains were reported in symptom relief or removal and there were more harmonious mother-child interactions and better projective identification in as few as 10 treatment sessions provided once weekly.

Using a methodology that focused on the quality of attachment, Lieberman, Weston, and Pawl (1991) found that anxiously attached dyads receiving infant-parent psychotherapy improved in maternal empathy, the security of the infant's attachment, and the mother-child partnership. They found that the mother's emotional connection with the therapist significantly correlated with the mother's empathy toward her infant. Mothers who were more able to use the parent-infant psychotherapy to explore their own feelings toward themselves and their child were more empathic and more engaged with their toddlers at outcome than those who did not develop insights. In addition, their children showed more secure attachment, more reciprocity, and less anger and avoidance toward their mothers.

An infant-led psychotherapy program (e.g., Watch, Wait, and Wonder) and traditional psychotherapy were compared in a study with 67 clinically referred infants and their mothers (Cohen et al., 1999). Treatment was provided once weekly for five months. Dyads receiving the Watch, Wait, and Wonder approach showed more organized or secure attachment relationships and greater gains in cognitive development and emotion regulation than infants in the psychotherapy group. Mothers in the Watch, Wait, and Wonder group also reported greater parent satisfaction and competence and a decrease in depression compared to mothers in the psychotherapy group. Both methods of treatment helped in reducing the infant's presenting problems, decreasing parent stress and reducing maternal intrusiveness.

We conducted a study that examined the relative benefits of a child-centered infant psychotherapy approach vs. a structured developmental parent guidance approach in the treatment of irritability and inattention (DeGangi & Greenspan, 1997). The child-centered approach focused on the caregiver-child relationship and the child's spontaneous expression of developmental interests and capacities and individual differences (i.e., the developmental individual difference relationship-based approach). In contrast, the parent guidance approach was more structured and developmentally oriented. By contrasting these two interventions, we hoped to examine the contribution and role of parent and child in addressing the child's self-regulatory needs. In particular, we wished to examine how the child's locus of control (internally initiated vs. externally directed) would impact regulatory capacities and function. Subjects consisted of 24 infants between the ages of 14 and 30 months who had disorders of regulation including high irritability, sensory hypersensitivities, and a short attention span.

There were three groups of eight subjects, matched for age and symptoms. Twenty-four subjects had irritability and 21 had attentional problems. Subjects receiving treatment had a pretest, six weeks of either intervention A or B provided once weekly for an hour's session, followed by a retest four months after intervention. Subjects in the no-treatment group were retested between four and six months after initial testing. We used formalized assessment procedures of development, attention, and self-regulation to systemize the change that might occur over time.

Our results showed that child-centered therapy (CCA) was more effective than structured therapy (STR) and no treatment in treating inattention and irritability. Seventy-five percent of subjects resolved in their attentional problems after receiving CCA in contrast to 37.5% after STR and 0% after no treatment. For irritability, 57% of subjects resolved in their irritability after CCA, 28% after STR, and 0% after no treatment.

An important finding of this study was that children with regulatory problems can make progress in resolving problems related to inattention and irritability in six weeks of intervention using a relationship-based, child-centered therapy approach. Since these basic skills of self-regulation (e.g., organizing attention and regulating mood) were responsive to short-term intervention using CCA, it suggests that therapies focusing on the relationship between parent and child and the child's spontaneous expression of developmental interests are more useful than interventions that stress concrete developmental skills.

In a prospective study on 39 infants with regulatory disorders (e.g., high irritability and sensory processing problems during infancy) who were retested at 3 years of age, subjects who had received parent-child psychotherapy showed more motor and sensory integration problems than untreated subjects at 3 years of age (DeGangi et al., 1996). However, despite the fact that they had more constitutional problems, they did not show the emotional and behavioral problems that were found in the untreated group. In a study examining the effects of infant temperamental traits and early home-based intervention on psychiatric symptoms in adolescence, it was found that early intervention focusing on the parent-child relationship helped to protect subjects from developing psychiatric symptoms in adolescence (Teerikangas, Aronen, Martin, & Huttunen, 1998). These studies point to the importance of improving the parent-child relationship in preventing long-term emotional and behavioral problems in children at risk.

Summary

This chapter presents clinical research supporting the developmental structuralist model and theoretical model that is the basis for the FEAS. Empirical support for the developmental structuralist model and the FEAS assessment approach was provided for samples of infants with regulatory disorders and at-risk mother/infant dyads. In addition, research was presented that supports the different stages of the developmental structuralist model.

The intervention studies reported in this chapter demonstrate how treatment approaches directed toward improving the parent-child relationship and the functional emotional developmental capacities that are an outgrowth of this relationship tend to be associated with gains in the child's emotional, social, cognitive, and family functioning.

References

Adnopoz, J., Grigsby, K., & Nagler, S. (1991). Multiproblem families and high risk children and adolescents: Causes and management. In M.Lewis (Ed.), *Child and adolescent psychiatry: A comprehensive textbook* (pp. 1059–1066). Baltimore: Williams & Wilkens.

Anders, T. F. (1994). Infant sleep, nighttime relationships, and attachment. *Psychiatry, 57,* 11–21.

Baron-Cohen, S. (1997). *Mindblindness: An essay on autism and theories of mind.* Cambridge, MA: MIT Press.

Barron, A. P. & Earls, F. (1984). The relation of temperament and social factors to behavior problems in three-year-old children. *J Child Psychol Psychiatry, 25,* 23–33.

Bernstein, V., Jeremy, R., & Marcus, J. (1986). Mother-infant interaction in multiproblem families: Finding those at risk. In: Meeting of American Academy of Child Psychiatry. Toronto, Canada

Chess, S., Thomas, A., & Hassibi, M. (1983). Depression in childhood and adolescence. A prospective study of six cases. *J Nerv.Ment.Dis., 171,* 411–420.

Cohen, N. J., Muir, E., Lojkasek, M., Muir, R., Parker, C. J., Barwick, M., & Brown, M. (1999). Watch, wait, and wonder: Testing the effectiveness of a new approach to mother-infant psychotherapy. *Infant Mental Health Journal, 20,* 429–451.

Cohn, J. & Tronick, E. (1989). Specificity of infant responses to mother's affective behavior. *Journal of American Academy of Child and Adolescent Psychiatry, 28,* 242–248.

Cramer, B., Robert-Tissot, C., Stern, D. N., Serpa-Rusconi, S., DeMuralt, M., Besson, G., Palacio-Espasa, F., Bachmann, J., Knauer, D., Berney, C., & D'Arcis, U. (1990). Outcome evaluation in brief mother-infant psychotherapy: A preliminary report. *Infant Mental Health Journal, 11,* 278–300.

Dawson, G. & Galpert, I. (1990). Mother's use of imitative play for facilitating social responsiveness and toy play in young autistic children. *Development and Psychopathology, 2,* 151–162.

DeGangi, G. A. (1991). Regulatory disordered infants: Assessment of sensory, emotional, and attentional problems. *Infants and Young Children, 3,* 1–8.

DeGangi, G. A. (2000). *Pediatric disorders of regulation in affect and behavior: A therapist's guide to assessment and treatment.* New York: Academic Press.

DeGangi, G. A. & Breinbauer, C. (1997a). The symptomatology of infants and toddlers with regulatory disorders. *Journal of Developmental and Learning Disorders, 1,* 183–215.

DeGangi, G. A., Breinbauer, C., Roosevelt, J., Porges, S. W., & Greenspan, S. I. (2000). Prediction of childhood problems at three years in children experiencing disorders of regulation during infancy. *Infant Mental Health Journal, 21,* 156–175.

DeGangi, G. A., DiPietro, J. A., Greenspan, S. I., & Porges, S. W. (1991). Psychophysiological characteristics of the regulatory disordered infant. *Infant Behavior and Development, 14,* 37–50.

DeGangi, G. A. & Greenspan, S. I. (1988). The development of sensory functioning in infants. *Physical and Occupational Therapy in Pediatrics, 8,* 21–33.

DeGangi, G. A. & Greenspan, S. I. (1997). The effectiveness of short-term interventions in treatment of inattention and irritability in toddlers. *Journal of Developmental and Learning Disorders, 1,* 277–298.

DeGangi, G. A., Porges, S. W., Sickel, R. Z., & Greenspan, S. I. (1993). Four-year follow-up of a sample of regulatory disordered infants. *Infant Mental Health Journal, 14,* 330–343.

DeGangi, G. A., Sickel, R. Z., Kaplan, E. P., & Wiener, A. S. (1997b). Mother-infant interactions in infants with disorders of self-regulation. *Physical and Occupational Therapy in Pediatrics, 17,* 17–38.

DeGangi, G. A., Sickel, R. Z., Wiener, A. S., & Kaplan, E. P. (1996). Fussy babies: To treat or not to treat? *British Journal of Occupational Therapy, 59,* 457–464.

Diagnostic Classification Task Force. (1994). *Diagnostic classification of mental health and developmental disorders of infancy and early childhood.* Arlington, VA: ZERO TO THREE: National Center for Clinical Infant Programs.

Doherty, S. C. (1997). Identifying at-risk mother-infant behavior patterns: The Greenspan-Lieberman Observation Scale—Revised. *Journal of Developmental and Learning Disorders, 1,* 321–341.

Fish, B. & Dixon, W. J. (1978). Vestibular hyporeactivity in infants at risk for schizophrenia. Association with critical developmental disorders. *Arch.Gen.Psychiatry, 35,* 963–971.

Forsyth, B. W. & Canny, P. F. (1991). Perceptions of vulnerability 3½ years after problems of feeding and crying behavior in early infancy. *Pediatrics, 88,* 757–763.

Fraiberg, S. (1980). *Clinical studies in infant mental health: The first year of life.* New York: Basic Books.

Greenspan, S. I. (1979). Intelligence and adaptation: An integration of psychoanalytic and Piagetian developmental psychology. *Psychological Issues.* (Monograph 47/48). Madison, CT, International Universities Press.

Greenspan, S. I. (1981). Psychopathology and adaptation in infancy and early childhood: Principles of clinical diagnosis and preventive intervention. *Clinical Infant Reports, No. 1.* New York, International Universities Press.

Greenspan, S. I. (1989a). Conclusions: Theoretical perspectives on research regarding psychopathology and preventive intervention in infancy. In S. Greenspan, S. Wieder, A. Lieberman, R. Nover, & R. Lourie (Eds.), *Infants in multirisk families: Case studies in preventive intervention, Clinical Infant Reports No. 3* (pp. 499-536). Madison, CT: International Universities Press.

Greenspan, S. I. (1989b). *The development of the ego: Implications for personality theory, psychopathology, and the psychotherapeutic process.* Madison, CT: International Universities Press.

Greenspan, S. I. (1992). *Infancy and early childhood: The practice of clinical assessment and intervention with emotional and developmental challenges.* Madison, CT: Universities Press.

Greenspan, S. I. & Lieberman, A. F. (1980). Infants, mothers, and their interactions: A quantitative clinical approach to developmental assessment. In S.I. Greenspan & G. H. Pollock (Eds.), *The course of life: Psychoanalytic contributions toward understanding personality development* (pp. 271–312). Washington, DC: U.S. Government Printing Office.

Greenspan, S. I., Lieberman, A. F., Wieder, S. W., Nover, R. A., Lourie, R. S., & Robinson, M. E. (Eds). (1987a). *Infants in multirisk families: Case studies in preventive intervention, Clinical Infant Reports No. 3.* New York: International Universities Press.

Greenspan, S. I. & Lourie, R. S. (1981). Developmental structuralist approach to the classification of adaptive and pathologic personality organizations: Infancy and early childhood. *Am J Psychiatry, 138,* 725-735.

Greenspan, S. I., Nover, R. A., & Scheuer, A. Q. (1987b). A developmental diagnostic approach for infants, young children, and their families. In S.I. Greenspan, S. Wieder, R. A. Nover, A. F. Lieberman, R. S. Lourie, & M. E. Robinson (Eds.), *Infants in multirisk families: Case studies in preventive intervention, Clinical Infant Reports No. 3* (pp. 431–498). Madison, CT: International Universities Press.

Greenspan, S. I. & Porges, S. W. (1984). Psychopathology in infancy and early childhood: Clinical perspectives on the organization of sensory and affective-thematic experience. *Child Dev., 55,* 49–70.

Himmelfarb, S., Hock, E., & Wenar, C. (1985). Infant temperament and noncompliant behavior at four years: A longitudinal study. *Genetic, social and general psychology monographs.* 111, 7–21.

ICDL Clinical practice guidelines: Redefining the standards of care for infants, children, and families with special needs (2000). Bethesda, MD: Interdisciplinary Council on Developmental and Learning Disorders.

Kopp, C. B. (1987). The growth of self-regulation: Parents and children. In N. Eisenberg (Ed.), *Perspectives in developmental psychology* (pp. 34–55). New York: John Wiley & Sons.

Kopp, C. B. (1989). Regulation of distress and negative emotions: A developmental view. *Developmental Psychology, 25,* 343–354.

Lee, C. L. & Bates, J. E. (1985). Mother-child interaction at age two years and perceived difficult temperament. *Child Dev., 56,* 1314–1325.

Lewy, A. L. & Dawson, G. (1992). Social stimulation and joint attention in young autistic children. *J Abnorm.Child Psychol, 20,* 555–566.

Lieberman, A. F., Weston, D. R., & Pawl, J. H. (1991). Preventive intervention and outcome with anxiously attached dyads. *Child Dev., 62,* 199–209.

MacDonough, S. (1989). Interaction guidance: A technique for treating early relationships. Paper presented at the Fourth World Congress of Infant Psychiatry and Allied Disciplines. Lugano, Switzerland.

Mattison, R. E., Handford, H. A., & Vela-Bueno, A. (1986). Sleep disorders in children. *Psychiatr Med., 4,* 149–164.

McCollum, J. A. & Hemmeter, J. L. (1997). Parent-child interaction intervention when children have disabilities. In M. Guralnick (Ed.), *The effectiveness of early intervention* (pp. 549–579). Baltimore: Paul H. Brookes.

Minshew, N. J. (1997). Autism and the pervasive developmental disorders: The clinical syndrome. In B.K. Shapiro, P. J. Accardo, & A. J. Capute (Eds.), *Behavior belongs in the brain: Neurobehavioral syndromes* (pp. 49–68). Baltimore: York Press.

Minshew, N. J. (1999). Autism as a disorder of complex information processing and underdevelopment of neocortical systems. Paper presented at the Interdisciplinary Council on Developmental and Learning Disorder Third Annual International Conference. McLean, VA: Autism and Disorders of Relating and Communicating.

Mundy, P. & Crowson, M. (1997). Joint attention and early social communication: Implications for research on intervention with autism. *J.Autism Dev.Disord., 20,* 115–128.

Mundy, P., Sigman, M., & Kasari, C. (1990). A longitudinal study of joint attention and language development in autistic children. *J Autism Dev.Disord., 20,* 115–128.

Poisson, S., Hofheimer, S., Strauss, M., & Greenspan, S. (1983). Interobserver agreement and reliability assessment of the GLOS.

Prizant, B. M. & Wetherby, A. M. (1993). Communication assessment of young children. *Infants and Young Children, 5,* 20–34.

Provence, S. & Naylor, A. (1983). *Working with disadvantaged parents and their children: Scientific and practical issues.* New Haven: Yale University.

Rutter, M. (1977). Individual differences. In M. Rutter & L. Hersov (Eds.), *Child psychiatry: Modern approaches* (pp. 3–21). London: Blackwell Scientific Publications.

Sroufe, L. A., Fox, N. E., & Pancake, V. R. (1983). Attachment and dependency in developmental perspective. *Child Dev., 54,* 1615–1627.

Stevenson-Hinde, J. & Simpson, A. E. (1982). Temperament and relationships. In R. Porter & G. M. Collins (Eds.), *Temperamental differences in infants and young children* (pp. 51–65). Ciba Foundation Symposium. London: Pitman.

Tanguay, P. E. (1999). The diagnostic assessment of autism using social communication domains. Paper presented at the Interdisciplinary Council on Developmental and Learning Disorders' Third Annual International Conference. McLean, VA: Autism and Disorders of Relating and Communicating.

Teerikangas, O. M., Aronen, E. T., Martin, R. P., & Huttunen, M. O. (1998). Effects of infant temperament and early intervention on the psychiatric symptoms of adolescents. *J Am Acad.Child Adolesc.Psychiatry, 37,* 1070-1076.

Thelen, E. (1989). Self-organization in developmental processes: Can systems approaches work? In M. Gunnar (Ed.), *Systems in development: The Minnesota Symposium in Child Psychology* (pp. 77–117). Hillsdale, NJ: Erlbaum.

Tsakaris, E. (2000). A developmental analysis of intervention research. Paper presented at the Interdisciplinary Council on Developmental and Learning Disorder Fourth Annual International Conference. McLean, VA: Autism and Disorders of Relating and Communicating.

Wachs, T. D. & Gandour, M. J. (1983). Temperament, environment, and six-month cognitive-intellectual development: A test of the organismic specificity hypothesis. *International Journal of Behavioral Development, 6,* 135–152.

Walker, E. & Emory, E. (1983). Infants at risk for psychopathology: Offspring of schizophrenic parents. *Child Dev., 54,* 1269–1285.

Weisz, J. R. & Weiss, B. (1993). *Effects of psychotherapy with children and adolescents.* Newbury Park, CA: Sage.

Wieder, S., Jasnow, M., Greenspan, S., & Strauss, M. (1989). Antecedent psychosocial factors in mothers in multirisk families: Life histories of the 47 participants in the Clinical Infant Development Program. In S.I. Greenspan, S. W. Wieder, A. Lieberman, R. Nover, R. Lourie, & M. Robinson (Eds.), *Infants in multirisk families: Case studies in preventive intervention* (pp. 345–376). Madison, CT: International Universities Press.

IV

Evaluation and Diagnostic Classification

As the foregoing chapters have shown, both the clinical and research versions of the FEAS can assist the clinician in observing and profiling the infant or young child and his/her family's emotional functioning. The FEAS can, therefore, be an important contribution to understanding a child's overall development. In and of itself, however, it does not constitute a complete clinical evaluation. A comprehensive, developmentally based clinical evaluation and diagnostic formulation involves a number of elements and processes. These are described in the next two chapters.

8

Evaluation

Stanley I. Greenspan, M.D.
Serena Wieder, Ph.D.

The assessment of emotional functioning in infancy and early childhood is best done in the context of a full clinical evaluation. The full clinical evaluation of emotional and developmental disorders in infants and young children requires the clinician to take into account all facets of the child's experience. It is, therefore, necessary to have a model that looks at how constitutional-maturational (i.e., regulatory), family, and interactive factors work together as the child progresses through each developmental phase (Greenspan, 1992; Greenspan & Wieder, 1998).

It is also necessary to distinguish this developmentally based evaluation model from other approaches. As described in Chapter 1, the functional developmental model for evaluation is based on a theoretical framework of functional developmental capacities and individually different processing abilities that unfold as the infant grows and interacts with others. Using this model requires a clinician to assess each child's relative strengths as well as challenges as they simultaneously influence the child's functional capacities at each developmental level.

This type of assessment contrasts with that of the typical deficit model, where teams using standardized instruments, and often working in a single-session arena style, independently evaluate the developmental domains of fine motor, gross motor, language, cognitive, and social skills.

The deficit model typically presents assessment results in terms of deficits within each developmental domain, with general recommendations, and frequently omits critical areas of interactive relationships and emotional functioning.

The functional emotional developmental approach emphasizes multiple observations and in-depth interviews over time in both the natural environments and in child-centered settings. In addition, in the functional emotional developmental approach, the evaluations go beyond the assessment of skills and assess functioning within relationships. Standardized tools are also used, but are selected as needed for strategic purposes rather than as the core assessment. The evaluations always include multiple observations of the child and parent/caregiver in interactions and play, as well as in interaction with the evaluator. The relationship of the clinician with the family affects the evaluation, interpretation, and implementation of the intervention plan.

The Basic Model

The developmental model guiding the evaluation process, which was also described in earlier chapters, needs to be re-emphasized in the context of the evaluation process. This model can be visualized with the child's (or infant's) constitutional-maturational patterns on one side and the child's environment, including caregivers, family, community, and culture, on the other side. Both of these sets of factors operate through the child/parent (caregiver) relationship, which can be pictured in the middle. These factors and the child/parent relationship, in turn, contribute to the organization of experience at each of six different developmental levels, which may be pictured just beneath the child/parent relationship.

As we described in Chapters 1 and 2, each developmental level involves different tasks or goals. The relative effect of the constitutional-maturational, environmental, or interactive variables will, therefore, depend on and can only be understood in the context of the developmental level to which they relate. Thus, influencing variables are best understood as distinct and different influences on the six distinct developmental and experiential levels and not, in the traditional sense, as general influences on development or behavior. For example, as a child is beginning to engage in a relationship, the mother's tendency to be very intellectual and prefer talking over holding may make it relatively harder for the child to

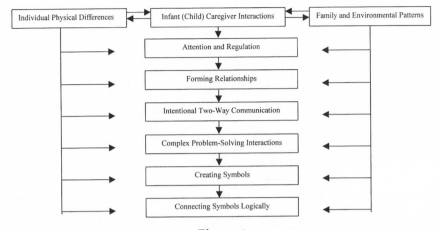

Figure 1

become deeply engaged in emotional terms. If, constitutionally, the child has slightly lower than average muscle tone and is hyposensitive with regard to touch and sound, her mother's intellectual and slightly aloof style may be doubly challenging, as neither the mother nor the child is able to take the initiative in engaging the other.

Functional Developmental Levels

As we discussed in some detail in Chapter 1, in this model, there are six functional developmental levels. To review briefly, they include the child's ability to accomplish the following:

1. *Self-Regulation and Interest in the World:* Attend to multisensory affective experience and, at the same time, organize a calm, regulated state and experience pleasure.
2. *Forming Relationships, Attachment, and Engagement:* Engage with and evidence affective preference and pleasure for a caregiver.
3. *Two-Way, Purposeful Communication:* Initiate and respond to two-way pre-symbolic gestural communication.
4. *Behavioral Organization, Problem-Solving, and Internalization (A Complex Sense of Self):* Organize chains of two-way communication (opening and closing many circles of communication in a row), maintain communication across space, integrate affective polarities, and

synthesize an emerging pre-representational organization of self and other.

5. *Representational Capacity*: Represent (symbolize) affective experience (e.g., pretend play or functional use of language), which calls for higher-level auditory and verbal sequencing ability.

6. *Representational Differentiation (Building Logical Bridges Between Ideas and Emotional Thinking)*: Create representational (symbolic) categories and gradually build conceptual bridges between these categories. This ability creates the foundation for such basic personality functions as reality testing, impulse control, self-other representational differentiation, affect labeling and discrimination, stable mood, and a sense of time and space that enables logical planning. This ability rests not only on complex auditory and verbal processing abilities, but on visual-spatial abstracting capacities as well.

To make a developmental assessment of the functional level, the clinician should evaluate each of the six developmental levels in terms of whether or not the child has successfully negotiated the level, and whether there is a deficit at any level that the child has not successfully negotiated. A deficit occurs when the level has not been mastered at all. Sometimes a child may have successfully negotiated a level, but not for the full range of emotional themes. For example, a toddler may use two-way gestural communication to negotiate assertiveness and exploration by pointing at a certain toy and vocalizing for a parent to play with him. The same child may either withdraw or cry in a disorganized way when he wishes for increased closeness and dependency instead of, for example, reaching out to be picked up or coming over and initiating a cuddle. This behavior would indicate that a child has a constriction at that level. Sometimes a child is able to negotiate a level with one parent and not the other, with one sibling and not another, or with one substitute caregiver but not another. If it should reasonably be expected that a particular relationship is secure and stable enough to support a certain developmental level, but that level is not evident in that relationship, then the child has a constriction at that level as well.

If the child has reached a developmental level, but the slightest stress, such as being tired, having a mild illness (e.g., a cold), or playing with a new peer leads to a loss of that level, then the child has an *instability* at that level.

A child may have a defect, constriction, or instability at more than one level. Also, a child may have a defect at one level and a constriction or instability at another. Therefore, the clinician should make a judgment based on how fully each child has negotiated each developmental level. It is also useful for the clinician to indicate which areas or relationships are not incorporated into each developmental level. Consider the following areas of expected emotional range: dependency (closeness, pleasure, assertiveness [exploration], curiosity, anger, empathy [for children over 3½ years]); stable forms of love; self-limit-setting (for children over 18 months); interest and collaboration with peers (for children over 2 years); participation in a peer group (for children over 2½ years); and the ability to deal with competition and rivalry (for children over 3½ years).

Constitutional-Maturational Patterns

A child's constitutional-maturational characteristics are the result of genetic, prenatal, perinatal, and maturational variations and/or deficits. These characteristics can be observed as part of the following patterns:

- Sensory reactivity, including hypo- and hyperreactivity in each sensory modality (tactile, auditory, visual, vestibular, and olfactory). Sensory processing in each sensory modality (e.g., the capacity to decode sequences, configurations, or abstract patterns).
- Sensory-affective reactivity and processing in each modality (e.g., the ability to process and react to degrees of affective intensity in a stable manner).
- Motor tone
- Motor planning and sequencing.

An instrument to clinically assess aspects of sensory functions in a reliable manner has been developed and is available (DeGangi & Greenspan, 1988, 1989a, 1989b).

Sensory reactivity (hypo- or hyper-) and sensory processing can be observed clinically. Is the child hyper- or hyposensitive to touch or sound? How does the child react in terms of vision and movement in space? In each sensory modality, does the 4-month-old "process" a complicated pattern of information input or only a simple one? Does the 4 ½-year-old have a receptive language problem and is, therefore, unable to sequence words he or she hears together or follow complex directions? Is the 3-year-old an early comprehender and talker, but slower in visual-spatial processing?

If spatial patterns are poorly comprehended, a child may be facile with words and sensitive to every emotional nuance, but have no context. Such children never see the "forest" and get lost in the "trees." In the clinician's office, this child may forget where the door is or have a hard time picturing that mother is only a few feet away in the waiting room. In addition to lacking straightforward "pictures" of spatial relationship (i.e., how to get to the playground), such a child may also have difficulty with seeing the emotional big picture. If the mother is angry, the child may think the earth is opening up and he is falling in because he cannot comprehend that his mother was nice before and she will probably be nice again.

A child with a lag in the visual-spatial area may become overwhelmed by the affect of the moment. This reaction is often intensified when the child also has precocious auditory-verbal skills. The child, in a sense, overloads and does not have the ability to see how it all fits together. Thus, at a minimum, it is necessary for the clinician to have a sense of how the child reacts in each sensory modality, how the child processes information in each modality, and, particularly, as the child gets older, a sense of the child's auditory-verbal processing skills in comparison to visual-spatial processing skills.

It is also necessary for the clinician to look at the motor system, including motor tone, motor planning (fine and gross), and postural control. Observing how a child sits, crawls, or runs; maintains posture; holds a crayon; hops, scribbles, or draws; and makes rapid alternating movements will provide a picture of the child's motor system. A child's security in regulating and controlling his or her body plays an important role in how that child uses gestures to communicate the ability to regulate dependency (being close or far away); his or her confidence in regulating aggression ("Can I control my hand that wants to hit?"); and an overall physical sense of self.

Other constitutional and maturational variables have to do with movement in space, attention, and dealing with transitions.

Parent and Family Contributions

In addition to constitutional and maturational factors, it is important to describe the family contribution with regard to each developmental level. If a family system is aloof, it may not negotiate engagement well; if a family system is intrusive, it may overwhelm or overstimulate a baby. Obviously, if a baby is already overly sensitive to touch or sound, the caregiver's intrusiveness will be all the more difficult for the child to handle. We see, therefore, the interaction between the maturational pattern and the family pattern.

A family system may throw so many meanings at a child that he or she is unable to organize a sense of reality. Categories of me/not-me may become confused, because one day a feeling is yours, the next day it is the mother's, next day it is the father's, the day after it is little brother's; anger may turn into dependency, and vice versa. If meanings shift too quickly, a child may be unable to reach the fourth level–emotional thinking. A child with difficulties in auditory-verbal sequencing will have an especially difficult time.

The couple is a unit in itself. How do husband and wife operate, not only with each other, but how do they negotiate on behalf of the children, in terms of the developmental processes? A couple with marital problems could still successfully negotiate shared attention, engagement, two-way communication, shared meanings, and emotional thinking with their children. But the marital difficulties could disrupt any one or a number of these developmental processes.

Each parent is also an individual. How does each personality operate vis-à-vis these processes? Although it may be desirable to have a general mental health diagnosis for each caregiver, one also needs to functionally observe which of these levels each caregiver can naturally and easily support. Is the parent engaged, warm, and interactive (a good reader of cues)? Is he or she oriented toward symbolic meanings (verbalizing meanings) and engaging in pretend play, and can the caregiver organize feelings and thoughts, or does one or the other get lost between reality and fantasy? Are there limitations, in terms of these levels, and if so, what are they?

Each parent also has specific fantasies that may be projected onto the children and interfere with any of the levels. Does a mother see her motorically active, distractible, labile baby as a menace and therefore overcontrol, overintrude, or withdraw? Her fantasy may govern her behavior. Does a father whose son has low motor tone see his boy as passive and inept, and therefore pull away from him or impatiently "rev" him up?

In working only with the parent-child interaction, and not the parent's fantasy, one may be dealing with only the tip of the iceberg. The father may be worried that he has an overly passive son, or the mother may be worried that she has a monster for a daughter (who reminds her of her retarded sister). All these feelings may be "cooking," and they can drive the parent-child interactions.

The Process of Clinical Assessment

Each clinician has a personal way of conducting an evaluation. However, any assessment should (1) encompass certain baseline data, (2) organize data by indicating how each factor contributes to the child's ability to develop, and (3) suggest methods of treatment. A comprehensive assessment usually involves the following elements: presenting challenges and "complaints," a review of current functioning, developmental history, family patterns, child and parent (caregiver) sessions (i.e., observing interactions), additional consultations, and formulation. A brief outline of a formal assessment with a discussion of selected elements follows.

Formal Assessment

1. *Review of current challenges and functioning*, including
   - Each functional developmental capacity (e.g., from attention and engagement to thinking);
   - Each processing capacity (e.g., auditory, motor planning and sequencing, visual-spatial, and sensory modulation);
   - In relevant contexts (e.g., at home with caregivers and siblings, with peers, in educational settings).
2. *History, including history of the preceding review items, beginning with prenatal development.*
3. *Two or more observational sessions of child-caregiver interactions with coaching and/or interactions with clinician (each sessions should be 45 minutes or more).* These observational sessions should provide the basis for forming a hypothesis about the child's functional emotional developmental capacities, individual processing and motor planning differences, and interactive and family patterns.
4. *Exploration of caregiver(s) personalities, marital and family patterns, and siblings.* This exploration should focus on the caregiver/family/sibling patterns in their own right and in relationship to their role in enabling the child to negotiate the functional developmental milestones (minimum of one 45-minute session).
5. *Biomedical evaluations* (e.g., extended sleep EEG, metabolic work-up, genetic studies, and nutrition)
6. *Speech and language evaluation.*

7. *Evaluation of motor and sensory processing,* including
   - Motor planning
   - Sensory modulation
   - Perceptual motor capacities
   - Visual-spatial capacities.
8. *Evaluation of cognitive functions, including neuro-psychological and educational assessments.*
9. *Mental health evaluations of family members, family patterns, and family needs.*

   NOTE: The evaluations listed in number 5 — 9 should only be carried out to answer specific questions that arise from the history, review of challenges, and current functioning and observations of the child-caregiver interactions patterns and family functioning.

Presenting Challenges and "Complaints" (Overall Picture)

Therapists frequently spend an entire session on the presenting "complaints" or overall picture, which includes the development of the "problems," the child (or infant) and his/her family's current functioning, and preliminary observation of the child both with the caregiver(s), and, in the case of a child over 3 years old, without them as well.

We (the authors and colleagues) will usually suggest that the parents bring the child with them to the first session. Even though we spend most of the time talking to the parents, we have our eyes on the child and we watch spontaneous interactions between them. If an older child (3 or 4 years of age) is involved, we will have the parents leave the child at home the first time, if possible, so the parents can talk more freely.

We begin by asking the parents, "How can I help?" We encourage the parents to elaborate about the child's problem, whether it has to do with sleeping, eating, or being too aggressive or too withdrawn. If we ask a question, it is usually to clarify something they have said, such as, "Can you give me some examples of that?" "How is this different now from what it was six months ago, and when wasn't it a problem?" We try to find out when the problem started, how it evolved, and its nature and scope. For example, if a 2½-year-old is aggressive with peers, we want to know whether it is with all peers or only certain children. We are interested in what precipitated the problem and what may be contributing to it. Was there a change within the family, such as the father getting a new job? Was there marital tension? Were new developmental abilities emerging that paradoxically were stressful to the child?

When the parents say, "Well, I think we have told you everything about the problem," then we will ask, "Is there more to tell about Johnny or Susie that would help fill out the picture?" We find it much more helpful to ask open-ended questions than to ask specific questions about cognitive, language, or motor development at this point. We can gather together more relevant information when the parents elaborate spontaneously. Parents also reveal their own feelings and private family matters if the therapist is empathetic in helping them describe their child. Therefore, we as clinicians strive to be unstructured; ask facilitating, elaborative questions rather than yes-or-no or defining questions, and never be in a hurry to fill out a checklist.

We use the initial session to establish rapport with the family and child to begin a collaborative process. Our experience is that the developmental process discussed earlier in relation to the child—mutual attention, engagement, gestural communication, shared meanings, and the categorizing and connecting of meanings—may occur between an empathetic clinician and the parents. How the clinician relates to the parents reflects how they will be encouraged to relate to their baby. If the therapist asks hurried questions, with yes-or-no answers, he or she sets up an untherapeutic model. It usually takes parents a long time to decide to come for help; they should be able to tell their story without being hurried or criticized.

As part of this presenting picture, we find it important to learn about all the areas of the child's current functioning. If the primary focus is initially on aggression and distractibility, we want to know the child's other age-expected capacities. We consider if the child is at the age-appropriate developmental level and, if so, the full range of emotional inclinations. Is the 8-month-old capable of reciprocal cause-and-effect interchanges? Is a 4-month-old wooing and engaging? Is a 2½-year-old exhibiting symbolic or representational capacities? Does the child do pretend play? Does she use language functionally? How does the child negotiate needs? At each of these levels, how is the child dealing with dependency, pleasure, assertiveness, anger, and so forth?

Toward the end of the first session, we may fill in more gaps by asking questions about sensory, language, cognitive, and fine and gross motor functioning. Usually, we have a sense of these capacities and patterns from anecdotes and more general descriptions of behavior. We listen for indications of the child's ability to retain information, how the child does or does not follow commands, word retrieval skills, word association skills, and fine and gross motor and motor planning skills.

Some clinicians write down what parents say right after the session; others write during the session. Taking notes need not be an interference if the clinician stops throughout to make good contact. We take detailed notes during the first 15 or 20 minutes because we want as much information as we can get in the parents' words.

By the end of the first session, we have a sense of where the child is developmentally. We also have a sense of the range of emotional themes the child can deal with at his developmental level, as well as an awareness of the support, or lack of support, the child gets from his fine and gross motor, speech and language, and cognitive abilities. We also form an impression of the support the child gets from the parents. We observe how the parents communicate and organize their thinking, the quality of their engagement, their emotional availability, and their interest in the child. We have a good sense of their relative comfort or discomfort with each emotional theme. In general, we use the initial meeting to observe how the parents attend, engage, intentionally communicate, construct and organize ideas, and are able or not able to incorporate a range of emotional themes into their ideas as they relate to their child and to us as the therapists.

Developmental History

In the second session, we construct a developmental history for the child. (However, sometimes martial or other family problems burst out during the first session. The parents may be at each other's throats; the mother and/or the father may be extremely depressed. In such cases, the focus of the second session is on the individual parent problems, as well as family functioning.)

We will usually start the session in an unstructured manner, allowing parents to describe how their child's development unfolded and what they think is important. We encourage them to alternate between what the baby or child was like at different stages and what they felt was going on as a family and as individuals in each of those stages. We try to start with how (or if) the couple planned for the child and progress through the pregnancy and delivery. Next, we cover the six developmental stages previously described to organize a developmental history.

Family Patterns

The next session focuses in greater depth on the functioning of the caregiver and family at each developmental phase. For example, the mother may say that she was a little depressed or angry, or that there were marital problems at different stages in the child's development.

Sometimes clinicians who are only beginning to work with infants and families feel reluctant to talk to the parents about any difficulties in the marriage. However, we use an open and supportive approach to elicit relevant information. We might ask, "What can you tell me about yourselves as people, as a married couple, as a family?" We are also interested in concrete details of a history of mental illness, learning disabilities, or special developmental patterns in either of the parents' families.

Some families will not hesitate to discuss marital difficulties or other problems. Sometimes there will be discussion of how the "problem child" relates to the father and mother in terms of "power struggles." If they describe a pattern, for example, between mother and child or father and child, we are likely to ask, "Does that same pattern operate in other family relationships–between mother and father, for example?" Is the pattern a carryover from a parent's own family? By following the couple's lead, we try to develop a picture of the marriage, careers of one or both parents, relationship with other children and between all the children, the parents' relationship with their own families of origin, as well as friendships and community ties.

Sometimes the family as a whole functions in a very fragmented, presymbolic way. They gesture, "behave at" each other, overwhelm each other, or withdraw from one another, but they don't share any meanings with one another. Nothing is negotiated at a symbolic level. Even though each individual may be capable of functioning on a symbolic level, something about the family dynamics cancels out that ability. In this context, we want to know how the family handles dependency, excitement, and sexuality, as well as anger, assertiveness, empathy, and love.

For each unit of the family–the parents, each parent-child relationship, as well as the family as a whole–we want to find out how the different emotional themes were dealt with at different developmental levels.

Child (or Infant) and Parent Sessions

We focus the next two sessions on the child. We conduct the session differently with an older child (a 3- or 4-year-old, for example) than with an infant. With an infant, we may ask the parent to play with the baby to "show me how you like to be with or play with your baby or child." The parents may ask, "What do you want me to do?" "Anything you like," is our response. We offer the use of the toys in the office or tell them they may bring a special toy from home.

We watch as each parent plays with the child in an unstructured way for about 15 or 20 minutes. We are looking for the developmental level, the range of emotional themes at each level, and the use of and support that the child is able to derive from motor, language, sensory, and cognitive skills. We are also watching for the parents' ability to support or undermine the developmental level, the range in that level, and the use of sensory, language, and motor systems. After we watch the mother and father separately, we watch the three of them together to see how they interact as a group because sometimes the group situation is more challenging. Later, we will join them to do some coaching and/or start to play with the child (briefly in the first session and for a longer period in the second session).

During this time, we want to see the child interacting at his or her highest developmental level, as well as how the child relates to a new person whom he or she knows only slightly. In addition, we want to determine how to bring out the highest developmental level at which the child can function. For example, if a child is withdrawn or self-absorbed and repetitively moving a truck, we will suggest joining the play, trying to move the truck together, put up a fence (one's hands) or take another car and, with great joy and enthusiasm, announce "Here I come!" to entice the child into interaction. Sometimes marching or jumping with an aimless child or lying next to a passive, withdrawn child and offering a back rub or tickle will draw the child in. If a child shows signs of symbolic functioning and the parents do not support symbolic functioning (i.e., in their 3-year-old), we will try, through coaching or directing, to initiate pretend play. If an 8-month-old is being overstimulated, we will try to introduce cause-and-effect interactions. If a 4-month-old looks withdrawn, we'll try to flirt to pull him in. We will try to calm down a fussy 5-month-old by using visual or vocal support, gentle tactile pressure, and a change of positions. We will work hands-on with an infant to explore tactile sensitivity, motor tone, motor planning, and preference for patterns of movement in space.

We learn a great deal through observation. By way of example, we might offer a doll to a child moving a train to see if he gives it a ride (suggesting symbolic capacities) or playfully obstruct the path of a child aimlessly wandering around the room to see if he ducks under our arms or smiles or simply turns and wanders away. We also might say to a child who is moving a train, "Oh boy, I can see that you know how to make this train go!" The child may put a doll on the train, make the doll a conductor, and add a passenger. The passenger may have a baby while the train is going through a tunnel, while, at the same time, a doctor makes sure the baby is all right. A 3-year-old who generates such a "drama" is sophisticated cognitively and evidences a rich fantasy life.

With children who can connect ideas together (e.g., hold a back-and-forth conversation), and depending on the child's comfort in being separated from his caregiver, we may reverse the sequence. We may have the first session with the child alone to explore how he or she engages, attends, initiates intentional two-way communication, problem solves, and shares and categorizes meanings.

During this time alone, a 3½-year-old may stand in the middle of the room and look us over while we look at him. If we don't try to control the situation too quickly and can tolerate 10 or 15 seconds of ambiguity, the child may start to play, ask us a question about the toys, or talk about his family. What the child has to say, without us saying, "Tell me what your mother told you about why you are here" or "Do you want to play with the toys?" can be very valuable. A child may look around and say, "I heard there were toys here. Where are they?" Such a statement indicates an organized, intentional child who has figured out why he is there and acts on his understanding. Another child may look puzzled and, after a silence, ask in a formal manner, "Can I sit down?"

Some 4-year-olds will talk to us throughout the session. We can have an almost adult-to-adult kind of dialogue about school or home, nightmares or worries, or just a chat about anything, as one might have with a neighbor. Other children will behave aggressively and want to jump on us or wrestle. They become too familiar too quickly.

We observe the way the child relates to us, that is, the quality of engagement—overly familiar, overly cautious, or warm. We look for how intentional the child is in the use of gestures and how well he or she sizes up the situation and us (without words). We try to determine the emotional range and the child's way of dealing with anxiety (e.g., does the child become aggressive or withdrawn?). We also note, during interaction with a child, the child's physical status, speech, receptive language, visual-spatial problem-solving skills (e.g., searching for a toy), gross and fine motor skills, and general state of health and mood. In general, we want to systematically describe the child's ability to attend, engage, initiate and be purposeful with affects and motor gestures, open and close many communication circles to problem solve, create ideas (pretend play), and converse and think logically.

The next step is to learn what is on the child's mind. If the child is symbolic, we look at the content of the play and dialogue, as well as the sequence of themes that emerge. Often, observing how a child shifts from one activity or theme to another (e.g., aggression to protectiveness or exploration to repetition) will provide some initial hypotheses. Our role as therapist is to be reasonably warm, supportive, and skillful in engaging the child and helping him or her evidence and elaborate upon his or her capacities.

Formulation

After learning about the child's current functioning and history and observing the child and family first hand, we should have a convergence of impressions. If a picture is not emerging, we may need to spend another session or two developing the history or observing further.

We ask ourselves a number of questions related to the child's assessment. How high up in the developmental progression has the child gone in terms of:

- Self-regulation and interest in the world,
- Forming relationships, attachment, and engagement,
- Two-way, purposeful communication,
- Behavioral organization, problem-solving, and internalization (a complex sense of self),
- Representational capacity,
- Representational differentiation (building logical bridges between ideas and emotional thinking), and
- Moving into the advanced stages of logical and abstract thinking (e.g., triangular thinking, relativistic thinking, reflective thinking with a stable internal standard).

We evaluate how well a child has mastered the earlier phases and, if the child has not fully mastered a level, what are the unresolved issues? For example, does a child still have challenges in terms of attentional capacities, the quality of engagement, and/or intentional abilities?

Determining the developmental level tells us how the child organizes experience. To use a metaphor, it provides a picture of the "stage" upon which a child plays out the "drama." The presenting symptoms–nightmares, waking up at night, refusal to eat, as well as other concerns and inclinations–make up the drama. The stage may be age-appropriate. For example, a 4-year-old who can categorize representational experience has a drama of being aggressive to other children, but this drama is being played out on a stage that is age-appropriate. This child has the capacity to comprehend the nature of aggression and use "ideas" to figure out his or her behavior.

On the other hand, there may be major deficits in the stage (i.e., attending, being intentional, representing experience, or differentiating experience). If there are flaws in the stage, we want to pinpoint the nature of those flaws. For example, if a child is not engaged with other people, that child may be perseverative and self-stimulatory because she can't interact or she may be aggressive because she basically has no sense of other people's feelings. She may not even see people as human. Alternatively, another child may be aggressive because she cannot represent feelings and, therefore, acts them out. Still another child may represent and differentiate his feelings, but have conflicts about her dependency needs.

We also look at the range of experience organized at a particular developmental level. If a child is at an age-appropriate developmental level, does he/she accommodate such things as dependency, assertiveness, curiosity, sexuality, and aggression at that level? On the other hand, even if a child is at the right developmental level, the stage may be narrow. In other words, he might be only at that developmental stage when it applies to assertiveness, but not when it applies to dependency. When it comes to excitement, he may function at a much lower level. In other words, if he dances the wrong step, he could fall off the stage. We also look at the stability of the developmental organization: does even a little stress lead to a loss of function or are the functions stable?

To continue our metaphor, if the stage has cracks or holes in it because the child has major problems stemming from earlier developmental issues, we will say there are defects in the stage. If the stage is solid (no defects), it is either very flexible and wide or very narrow and constricted (e.g., it will tolerate a drama of assertiveness but it will not tolerate a drama of intimacy or excitement). In addition, a stage is stable or unstable.

Next, we want to know about the contributing factors. One set of factors relates to observations about family functioning; the other set of factors relates to the assessment of the child's individual differences. The parent-child interactions are the mediating factors. The developmental formulation or profile describes: (1) the child's functional developmental level; (2) the contributing processing profile (e.g., overreactive to sound, auditory and visuospatial and motor planning difficulties); and (3) the contributing family patterns (e.g., high energy, overloading, and confusing family pattern), as well as the observed interaction patterns of each of the significant caregivers and the types of interactions that would be hypothesized to enable the child to move up the developmental ladder and decrease his/her processing difficulties.

Summary

In this chapter we have outlined the practical clinical steps involved in conducting a comprehensive developmentally based evaluation. This discussion will hopefully complement the material presented in the earlier chapters.

References

DeGangi, G. A. & Greenspan, S. I. (1988). The development of sensory functioning in infants. *Physical and Occupational Therapy in Pediatrics, 8(3)*, 21–33.

DeGangi, G. A. & Greenspan, S. I. (1989a). *Test of sensory functions in infants.* Los Angeles: Western Psychological Services.

DeGangi, G. A. & Greenspan, S. I. (1989b). The assessment of sensory functioning in infants. *Physical and Occupational Therapy in Pediatrics, 9,* 21–33.

Greenspan, S. I. (1992). *Infancy and early childhood: The practice of clinical assessment and intervention with emotional and developmental challenges.* Madison, CT: International Universities Press.

Greenspan, S. I. & Wieder, S. (1998). *The child with special needs: Intellectual and emotional growth.* Reading, MA: Addison Wesley.

9

Developmentally Based Diagnostic Classification of Emotional Disorders in Infancy and Early Childhood

Stanley I. Greenspan, M.D.
Serena Wieder, Ph.D.

The Diagnostic and Statistical Manual of Mental Disorders of the American Psychiatric Association (DSM-IV; American Psychiatric Association, 1995) tends to focus on the phenomenology of mental disorders; that is, on clusters of symptoms or patterns of behavior.

Mental health professionals are familiar with the traditional diagnostic categories, such as affective disorders and schizophrenia. Childhood categories include attention deficit disorder, anxiety disorder, conduct disorder, pervasive developmental disorder, and others.

However, there is general agreement that in the current diagnostic framework there are very few categories that apply to the first 3 to 4 years of life. Attachment Disorder of Infancy focuses on reactive attachment disorder, such as the baby's reaction to being deprived of a human relationship. Other categories, such as Specific Developmental Disorder, which can relate to a motor or language delay, can also be appropriate for infancy. But there are woefully few symptom-oriented disorders that are geared specifically to infants. Some mental health professionals apply symptom complexes constructed for problems with older children downward toward infancy. For example, anxiety disorders can describe symptoms of excessive fear and anxiety exhibited by infants and young children, as well as by older children. Similarly, mood disorders may also apply to younger children (when they manifest characteristics often seen in depression with older children). Symptoms of distractibility associated with attention deficit disorder are seen in preschoolers and even toddlers. Conduct disorders describe children who have difficulty with social behavior and controlling their impulses. Pervasive developmental disorder and autism are applied to a broad age range and encompass children with severe impairments in social relationships, language, and overall communication.

However, the diagnostic categories applied to older children are inadequate to characterize the difficulties of infants and young children. Furthermore, in addition to symptom-oriented descriptions, therapists require an appropriate developmental approach to diagnosis. It is important to capture the developmental process, including strengths and problems, such as failure to attain a specific developmental level, evidenced by the ability to regulate aggression or behavior, to relate to others, or to have self-esteem. In addition, because all learning takes place as part of a relationship, diagnoses must also capture the importance of the parent/caregiver-child relationship (as the process that helps the child develop adaptive capacities).

In order to characterize adequately an infant or young child's diagnostic patterns, one must look at them from many sides. One needs to discuss the infant's presenting symptoms and behavior (phenomenology), as well as the developmental level or process, and, as indicated, the parent/caregiver/child interactions, family patterns, and other aspects of development. For example, is the symptom just a sign of momentary stress, a sign of adaptation, or a signal that some underlying developmental process, such as relationships, is not being properly negotiated?

Therefore, a multiaxial approach is recommended: (1) a symptom-oriented or phenomenologically oriented diagnosis; (2) a developmentally based diagnosis; (3) a relationship and/or family-based diagnosis; and (4) an "other" category to cover developmental or physical problems (e.g., a motor or language delay or a chronic physical illness). Although these multiple diagnoses will not necessarily in themselves always capture the interactive pattern, it would be captured in an accompanying description. Additionally, the interactive pattern would be hinted at in both the family and the infant's pattern. For example, a problem with regulation and shared attention would obviously be a statement not just about the infant's inattentiveness or the parents' inability to engage the infant, but about the way this process is being mediated.

In this approach, the clinician looks at each developmental level; the child's constitutional and maturational contributions, and the interactive and family contributions, to see how these influence the infant's or child's ability to negotiate each particular developmental level. The symptoms or behaviors that result from this negotiation comprise the symptom-oriented diagnosis. The developmental level and pattern lead to the developmental diagnosis. The family and interactive patterns contribute to the relationship, interactional, or family diagnosis. The "others" category captures other lines of development, such as sensory reactivity and processing and language, motor, physical health, and related systems. One may describe these dimensions formally or in a narrative paragraph.

Developmental Diagnoses

The framework for developmental evaluation and diagnoses was discussed in the prior chapter. The goal is to profile each child as a unique individual in terms of his/her developmental level, interactional patterns, and constitutional-maturational contributions, as well as family-environmental contributions. The clinician may wish to follow the following format.

The clinician should make a determination regarding each of the six developmental levels in terms of whether it has been successfully negotiated or not, and whether there is a deficit at any level that has not been successfully negotiated. Sometimes these levels have been successfully negotiated, but are not applied to the full range of emotional themes and there is a constriction or an instability at that level.

Symptom-Oriented and Phenomenologically Based Diagnoses

In addition to the developmental profile, it is also useful to have a developmental approach to symptom-oriented diagnoses. Based on the considerations discussed above, we initiated an effort to create a more developmentally based diagnostic system. The first version of that classification system was presented in *Infancy and Early Childhood: The Practice of Clinical Assessment and Intervention with Emotional and Developmental Challenges* (Greenspan, 1992). In addition, as Chair and Co-Chair of the Diagnostic Classification Committee of ZERO TO THREE: The National Center for Infants, Toddlers, and Families, the authors of this chapter worked together with a number of colleagues to create the DC: 0–3 Diagnostic Classification System (Diagnostic Classification Task Force, 1994). This classification system presents a developmentally based approach to symptoms and phenomenology-oriented diagnoses in infancy and early childhood.

In the pages that follow, we will present an overview of the developmental approach to classification that also includes more recent advances. As part of a developmental approach, three broad categories are suggested, under which most symptoms and patterns can be listed. While for each symptom-oriented diagnosis one must understand the developmental processes that are involved and the contribution of the constitutional-maturational and interactive and family dynamics, the descriptive diagnoses are helpful for administrative and some clinical purposes.

Descriptive symptom-oriented diagnoses may be divided into three general categories, each of which has its specific developmental roots and preventively oriented psychotherapeutic approaches. These three categories are interactive disorders, regulatory disorders, and multi-symptom disorders.

Interactive Disorders

Interactive disorders are characterized by a particular caregiver-child interaction or by the way the child perceives and experiences his emotional world. These disorders lack a significant constitutional or maturational component. Symptoms in this category include anxiety, fears, behavioral control problems, and sleeping and eating difficulties. This category, because it involves symptoms stemming from interactive patterns, would also include situational reactions of a transient nature, such as a mother returning to work or certain responses to trauma where the response does not involve multiple aspects of development.

Regulatory Disorders

Regulatory disorders have a significant and clearly demonstrable maturational or constitutional component (Greenspan, 1989). They also have an
interactive component. These disorders involve attentional and behavioral problems, such as irritability, aggression, distractibility, poor frustration tolerance, tantrums, and sleeping and eating difficulties.

Disorders of Relating and Communicating, Including Multisystem Developmental Disorders and Autistic Spectrum Disorders

A third category of disorders involves multiple aspects of development, including social relationships and language, cognitive, motor, and sensory
functioning. Related to this category is autism and pervasive developmental disorders, which involve multiple deficits, including significant
disruption in the ability to form, sustain, and interact in relationships.
Another type of disorder that involves multiple aspects of development is
where an environmental stress leads to a global disruption in multiple areas of functioning. For example, when an infant evidences a failure-to-
thrive syndrome, motor, cognitive, language, affective, and physical
growth may slow down or cease altogether. Types of neglect or abuse may
produce a similar global disruption in functioning. Recently we have
added a new classification system for disorders of relating and communicating that focuses on neurodevelopmental patterns. It will be described
later in this chapter.

Within these groups, one can classify most of the DSM-IV infant and
early childhood mental health disorders and their classification. The following sections will consider each of the three types of broad disorders in
terms of general features and treatment implications.

These three broad categories have implications for therapy and pre-
vention. In the first category, difficulties that are a part of the infant-caregiver interaction pattern, there are only minimal contributions, if any,
from constitutional-maturational differences and there are no significant
irregularities, delays, or dysfunctions in core areas of functioning, such as
motor, sensory, language, and cognition. In other words, in this category,
the primary difficulty is in the interactions between the child and the care-

giver. The caregiver's own personality, fantasies, and intentions, the child's own emerging organization of experience, and the way these come together through the interactions, will be the primary focus for understanding the nature of the difficulty and for intervention.

The second category of regulatory disorders focuses on a group of infants and young children in which there are significant constitutional and maturational factors. Here sensory over- or underreactivity, sensory processing, or motor tone and motor planning difficulties, along with the child-caregiver interaction, the caregiver's personality and fantasies, and the family dynamics, are part of the problem.

One may argue that all infants and children have unique constitutional and maturational variations, including the first group in which the focus is the caregiver-infant interaction. To be sure, this statement in a relative sense is true. The distinction is that, for the regulatory disorders, the constitutional and maturational factors are not just present as individual differences, but are a significant part of the child's problem. Therefore, in the second group, one wants not just to understand individual differences as part of the nature of the caregiver-infant interaction patterns, one wants to make the constitutional and maturational factors a major focus in their own right (alongside the interaction patterns and the family dynamics). Here, where possible, one will utilize intervention strategies that help the infant strengthen or organize in a more adaptive way constitutional and maturational variations. One will also seek to understand how the infant's constitutional and maturational variations are a stimulus for the parents' particular fantasies and how the infant's constitutional and maturational variations bring out certain maladaptive personality dynamics in the caregivers, parents, or family as a unit.

The third group, the multisystem, pervasive developmental problems, includes those groups of infants and young children that in addition to variations in constitutional and maturational patterns, have significant delays or dysfunctions in multiple core areas of functioning, such as language, motor, sensory, and cognition. Here difficulties exist at a number of levels. The child evidences problems in infant-caregiver interaction patterns, parents' perceptions, and family dynamics. There are also regulatory difficulties in terms of significant contributions from constitutional and maturational variations. Furthermore, either these regulatory patterns are so extreme that they are consistent with significant delays in sensory, motor, cognitive, or language patterns, or they are associated with significant dysfunctions and delays in these core areas of functioning. In this third category, therefore, there are three broad areas of concern and focus for intervention-interactive, including family and caregiver variables; the regulatory factors; and the delays and dysfunctions in core areas of functioning.

One may question in this group whether the main difficulty isn't only delays and dysfunctions in multiple core areas of functioning in the child. We suggest that there are almost always difficulties in the interactive patterns and caregiver and family dynamics. It is rare, even with the most flexible and adaptive parents, that the infant and young child's developmental challenges, which combine regulatory problems and significant delays and dysfunctions, do not result in difficulties in the caregiver-infant interaction or in the family dynamics. The nature of the challenge the infant or young child presents and the lack of expectable feedback, due to language and visual-spatial-motor processing difficulties, almost always creates a significant stress on the interaction patterns and the family dynamics. Most families and most caregivers seem prepared for certain types of communication patterns with infants and young children. When these biologically expectable interaction patterns are not forthcoming, special approaches are often needed. The degree of the family contribution will vary considerably depending on the infant or child or the family and caregiver's preexisting patterns. With this last group, therefore, interventions must focus simultaneously on the family dynamics, the infant-caregiver interaction patterns, the regulatory patterns, and the developmental delays and dysfunctions in core areas, such as motor, language, cognition, and sensory functions. We will now discuss each broad category. For further discussion of evaluation challenges and related intervention strategies, see *DC 0–3* (Diagnostic Classification Task Force, 1994), *Infancy and Early Childhood* (Greenspan, 1992), *The Child With Special Needs* (Greenspan & Wieder, 1998), *The Challenging Child* (Greenspan & Salmon, 1995).

Interactive Disorders

Interactive disorders occur when anxiety, fear, labile mood, conduct problems, or some other aspect of feeling, thought, or behavior is part of the child's interaction with his caregiver(s) or family, and/or feelings, wishes, and conflicts within the child, or both. Consider the following examples.

An 8-month-old may be so fearful that he does not crawl, interact, or explore; he may cry every time the mother moves a few steps away. He wants to be picked up all the time, and is afraid. A 19-month-old toddler may pinch, poke, or bite other children. He hits his mother when she tries to discipline him. A 4-year-old avoids his peers and stands off in a corner of the room. If another child behaves assertively, he becomes frightened and freezes. He is fearful of even looking at animals in the zoo. Another 4½-year-old is aggressive with peers. A 3-year-old has nightmares and won't go to her preschool program. See the following cases referenced in *Infancy and Early Childhood* (Greenspan, 1992): 1 (p. 31), 3 (p. 56), 4 (p. 60), 6 (p. 101), 12 (p. 157), 13 (p. 167), 14 (p. 175), and 18 (p. 238), which illustrate interactive difficulties.

In order to understand the interactive patterns associated with these types of symptoms, the first step is to determine which interactive patterns, in terms of the characteristic interactions of each developmental level, have been negotiated successfully and which have not.

By way of an example, consider a withdrawn 4-year-old who never engaged or formed relationships well. As a baby, he tended to disengage, particularly when confronted with anger or other intense feelings; the parents never knew quite how to woo him back. Under the pressure of peer competition, he feels angry and withdraws.

On the other hand, another 4-year-old child who engaged well, learned the gestural system of communication, learned to represent or symbolize his emotions, tends not to be able to distinguish clearly aggression from warm and loving feelings. This child becomes frightened whenever he feels aggressive; he anticipates rejection, and he rejects first, often becoming aloof and withdrawn. Although the behavior of the two children may look the same, very different sets of reasons and underlying interactive dynamics are involved. When the second child comes into the playroom, he is warm and engaged, he uses interactive gestures, and he plays out themes such as aggression and love, which demonstrates that he can represent experiences. However, in the play, one begins to see that he confuses aggressive and loving themes; as these themes become merged and chaotic, he may withdraw from the play when it reaches a critical point.

The first child, who withdraws because he never engaged, will come into the playroom with a somewhat aloof and cautious manner; he may not warm up at all, or only very slowly; anytime there is some suggestion of emotion or the situation does not feel quite "right," he will withdraw.

One senses that the major issue between the adult and the first child is the quality of intimacy and engagement, whereas with the second child, one can feel secure about his engagement and communication and go on to focus on his ability to represent feelings and resolve conflict. A child's behavior in the playroom provides clues to the types of interventions that were difficult to negotiate and the types of interventions that should be a part of the psychotherapeutic process.

The first child had difficulty negotiating the most basic patterns of interaction and relatedness, especially in the context of strong emotion. Both he and his caregivers were unsure of themselves and were unable to woo one another. The therapist will try not to repeat this pattern by waiting for the child to begin talking about his feelings, because the child will experience this as a replay of the interactive pattern he never learned to negotiate. Instead, the therapist will try to empathize with the child's uncertainty about how to be close and explore associated fears.

The second child had difficulty negotiating complex symbolized feelings in the context of an ongoing relationship. The therapist will need to discover what about the child's relationships made it difficult for him to learn that aggressive and loving feelings can be part of the same relationship pattern.

Interactive disorders can be evidenced from early infancy up through childhood (and into adulthood as well). The characteristics of these disorders, at each age and developmental phase, will be based on the developmental challenges of the particular phase the infant or child and his caregiver are negotiating. One particular type of interactive pattern that has been the subject of a great deal of research relates to attachment patterns (Aber & Baker, 1990; Ainsworth, Bell, & Stayton, 1974; Arend, Gove, & Sroufe, 1979; Bowlby, 1969; Cassidy, 1990; Cassidy & Marvin, 1988; Easterbrooks & Goldberg, 1990; Egeland & Farber, 1984; Goldberg & Easterbrooks, 1984; Main, M, Kaplan, N., and Cassidy, J., 1985; Marvin & Stewart, 1991; Maslin-Cole & Spieker, 1990; Matas, Arend, & Sroufe, 1978; Pastor, 1981; Sroufe, 1983; Sroufe, Fox, & Pancake, 1983; Waters, Wippman, & Sroufe, 1979). Clinicians should incorporate this and related research into their clinical thinking, but be cautious about generalizations that take attention away from the unique characteristics of each infant, caregiver, and family. For example, a study by Marion Yarrow (personal communication, 1990) suggests that "securely attached infants of depressed mothers had more difficulty as older children than less securely attached counterparts."

Regulatory Disorders

Regulatory disorders, a relatively new diagnostic construct (Greenspan, 1992)[1], involve some of the same behaviors as interactive disorders, including nightmares, withdrawal, aggressiveness, fearfulness, attentional difficulties, and difficulty with groups. But these disorders involve symptoms that are a part of both interactive patterns and *clearly demonstrable constitutional and maturational patterns.* See cases 1 (p. 311), 2 (p. 421), 4 (p.. 60), 5 (p. 82), 7 (p. 109), 8 (p. 122), 9 (p. 131), 11 (p. 147), 15 (p. 186), 16 (p. 203), 18 (p. 238), 22 (p. 289) from *Infancy and Early Childhood* (Greenspan, 1992) and *DC: 0–3* (Diagnostic Classification Task Force, 1994) for illustrations of regulatory difficulties.

Regulatory disorders are first evident in infancy and early childhood. They are characterized by difficulties the infant has in regulating physiological, sensory, attentional, and motor or affective processes, and organizing a calm, alert, or affectively positive state. The causes of these disorders are unclear. One may observe regulatory difficulties in infants whose prenatal, perinatal, and early developmental functioning (i.e., motor, cognitive, and language) has appeared unremarkable. At the same time clinically, one may see a large number of infants with regulatory difficulties where there has been maternal substance abuse (Greenspan, 1990; Porges & Greenspan, 1990) and the infant is small for gestational age or of low birth weight. There are suggestions that these infants have difficulties organizing adaptive functions involving feelings, behaviors, and learning. Difficulties can range from mild to severe and may affect one or more areas of development.

For example, poorly organized or modulated responses may show themselves in the following ways:

- The physiological or state repertoire (e.g., irregular breathing, startles, hiccups, gagging);
- Gross motor activity (e.g., poor tonus, jerky movements);
- Fine motor activity (e.g., poorly differentiated or sparse, jerky, or limp movements);
- Attentional organization (e.g., driven or unable to settle down vs. perseverating in a small detail);

---

[1]Serena Wieder, Ph.D., collaborated in the original clinical definition and description of regulatory disorders.

- Affective organization: this would include both the predominant affective tone as well as the range of affect and degree of modulation expressed (e.g., infant can vary from being completely flat to screaming frantically, but be predominantly sober, depressed, or unhappy);
- Sleep, eating, or elimination patterns (e.g., difficulty with failing or staying asleep or returning to sleep).

Infants and children may clinically present with sleep or feeding difficulties, deficits in their speech and language development, as well as their ability to play alone or with others. Parents may also complain that their children easily lose their temper (e.g., get angry or jealous) and do not adapt well to changes in state or other required transitions. Because sensory, motor, and affective experiences impact upon the infant and young child continuously through routine handling, if such handling is not sensitive to individual differences, irregular conditions in the environment, and/or changes in routine, these infants and children and their caregivers can be strongly affected.

There is a long-standing assumption and growing evidence, including documentation of differences in sensory reactivity and physiologic regulation, that fussy or difficult infants have symptoms that are part of a pattern of constitutional and early maturational variation (DeGangi, DiPietro, Greenspan, & Porges, 1991; Greenspan, 1990; Porges et al., 1990). However, it is also recognized that early caregiving patterns can be influenced by and exert considerable influence on how these constitutional and maturational patterns develop and become part of the child's evolving personality (Portales, Porges, & Greenspan, 1990). With regard to the presumed "constitutional" or "biological" base for sensory, motor, and integrative patterns, there has been a tendency toward using general terms such as overly sensitive or reactive without delineating as specifically as possible the sensory pathway or motor functions involved. As interest in these children increases, it is important to systematize descriptions of the sensory, motor, and integrative patterns that we presume are involved.

Criteria

A classification of regulatory disorders is outlined below. These disorders are operationally defined as having a distinct behavioral pattern coupled with difficulty in sensory, sensorimotor, or organizational processing that affects daily adaptation and interactions/relationships. When behavioral and constitutional-maturational elements are not present, other diagnoses may be more appropriate. For example, an infant who is irritable and withdrawn after being abandoned may be evidencing an expectable type of relationship or attachment difficulty. An infant who is irritable and overly reactive to routine interpersonal experiences, in the absence of a clearly identified sensory, sensorimotor, or processing difficulty, may be evidencing an anxiety or mood disorder.

In addition to the behavioral symptoms, therefore, at least one category of sensory, sensorimotor, or processing difficulty must be present to make this diagnosis. These are listed below together with different behavioral categories in the following sections.

- The child is over- or underreactive to loud or high- or low-pitched noises.
- The child is over- or underreactive to bright lights or new and striking visual images (e.g., colors, shapes, complex fields).
- Tactile defensiveness is apparent (e.g., overreactivity to changing clothes, bathing, stroking of arms, legs, or trunk; avoids touching "messy" textures, etc.) and/or underreactive to touch or pain.
- The child is under- or overreactive to movement in space (e.g., brisk horizontal or vertical movements such as in tossing a child in the air, playing merry-go-round, jumping, etc.).
- The child is under- or overreactive to odors.
- The child is under- or overreactive to temperature.
- Poor motor tone is apparent (gravitational or postural insecurity, oral-motor difficulties—avoids certain textures).
- The child has less than age-appropriate motor planning skills (e.g., complex motor patterns such as alternating hand banging).
- The child has less than age-appropriate fine motor skills.
- The child has less than age-appropriate auditory-verbal discrimination or integration capacity (e.g., an 8-month-old should be able to imitate distinct sounds, a 2½-year-old follow or repeat requests, or a 3-year-old put together words and actions).
- Less than age-appropriate visual-spatial discrimination or integration capacity is apparent (e.g., a 2½-year-old should know where to turn to get to a friend's house, an 8-month-old should recognize different facial configurations, a 3-year-old should be able to put together certain spaces, such as a room, with activities).

Regulatory Disorders: Four Types

Type I: Hypersensitive Type

1. The child is often overly reactive to routine sensory experiences such as light touch, loud noises, or bright lights.
2. The child tends to have at least one of the following:
   a. Tends to be easily upset (e.g., irritable, often crying or unhappy), cannot soothe self, finds it difficult to return to sleep and/or recover from frustration or disappointment.
   b. The child may also be negative and controlling ("the fearful little dictator").
   c. The child can be fearful, cautious, and clinging (e.g., at 4 months, even when sitting in mother's lap, may take more than 15 minutes to "flirt" with a new person, looking serious and worried; or at 8 months, may cry, pull away, and squirm intensely when a new person tries to pick her up even after 15 minutes of gentle wooing).
   d. The child dislikes changes in routine or new experiences, including visiting other people's homes, school, and so on. When frightened of new experiences, he or she clings to mother or father (e.g., wants to be picked up and held). The child will not explore new surroundings even for a few minutes.
   e. The child tends to shy away from new peers even after 18 months of age.
   f. Night wakings tend to be associated with a strong desire to be held by mother until asleep again or for entire night.
   g. In school settings, the child tends to be overwhelmed by a large group (circle times tend to be difficult) and seeks a one-on-one relationship with the teacher.

Type II: Underreactive Type

1. The child is often underreactive to and has difficulty processing auditory-verbal experiences. In addition, he or she may be either over- or underreactive to tactile and visual-spatial experiences, as well as having muscle tone and motor planning difficulties.
2. At least one of the following also applies:
   a. The child tends to be unfocused or inattentive, "tuned out."
   b. The child tends to be withdrawn, but responds, to some degree, to wooing.

c. The child will intermittently stare off into space or at distant objects.

d. The child is preoccupied with his own inner sensations or, at later ages, with his own thoughts or feelings (or private pretend play) and/or is withdrawn. For example, at 4 months of age the infant tends to scan his environment but not focus in on mother's or father's face and/or voice with intentional affect (e.g., focused smiling); at 8 months of age the infant may play with a block or seem to focus on an object for an inordinate amount of time, excluding his parents' inviting overtures; at 2 years of age, the child may wander about aimlessly; at 3½ years of age, he or she may play with building blocks or a special doll house, lost in private "thoughts" or fantasy games. Note that none of these characteristics is so pervasive as to constitute an autistic pattern.

Type III: Active-Aggressive Type

1. The infant often has a mixed pattern of sensory over- or underreactivity, motor planning difficulties, as well as at times fine motor lags. Also, this child tends toward poor motor modulation and motor discharge patterns, particularly when frustrated, angry, or vulnerable (e.g., crawling or running into things or people, making loud noises or sounds, unable to attend in an age-expected manner). He or she seems to be looking at or listening fleetingly to each sound or sight so that attention and study of any one thing is lacking; is unable to attend in age-expected manner. For example, by 4 months, an infant should be able to attend for 5 or more seconds; by 8 months, for 20 or more seconds; and by 18 months, for a few minutes at a time. By 9 to 12 months, the infant seems to be looking at or listening fleetingly to each sound or sight so that attention and study of any one thing is lacking.

2. The child also has at least one of the following characteristics:

   a. He tends to be overly active.

   b. He tends to be destructive and/or aggressive. For example, by 9 to 12 months, the child may already be pulling other children's hair deliberately; by 18 months, he may be hurting others with biting and kicking; may break toys and hurt animals.

   c. He tends to find it difficult to inhibit excitement (gets carried away) or shift "states" (e.g., go to sleep).

Type IV: Mixed Type

1. The child tends to have mixed features of mild to moderate severity of types I through III, with no one set of characteristics dominating. For example, he or she may be fearful but also aggressive.
2. The child tends to have some mixed features of types I through III, though one or another may predominate, with at least one significant sensory processing difficulty, auditory-verbal, visual-spatial, and/or perceptual-motor, contributing to the behavioral difficulties. When social withdrawal or aimless or idiosyncratic behavior is a significant symptom, it is not so severe as to constitute an autistic disorder because there is either intermittent or ongoing reciprocal social relating or the ability to be socially engaged by a skilled therapist sensitive to both the underlying processing difficulties and their associated emotional patterns.

Clinical Illustrations and Discussion

There are many ways in which regulatory processes influence development. For example, consider a 15-month-old who experiments with being independent—walking or crawling away from his mother—as well as maintaining a sense of security. The child begins to abstract, in a preverbal way, a sense of who he is as a person, who the mother is, and who the father is. But, if a child is unable to process sounds across the room, and his mother says, "Hey, that's terrific! You're building a great tower," he looks at her face and is confused. He does not get any reassurance, because he cannot decode the rhythm of her voice. He has to come over and cling to her. Meanwhile, she gets upset with his clinging and, without realizing that he can't decode her sound, she ushers him away. The child who can decode the mother's sounds, plays with his tower, looks over, hears his mother's reassuring sounds, and thinks, "Oh, that's great. You like it. I'll do some more." The child who decodes the rhythm feels as if he's in his mother's lap, because he receives her warmth across space. When one talks to a loved one who is far away, one feels warm on the telephone, because one decodes the affect in the voice. The child who cannot decode sound will therefore have greater difficulty in developing independence.

The child with visual-spatial processing difficulty may have a difficult time maintaining his internal mental representation, especially under the pressure of intense affects. The visual-spatial vulnerability makes it hard to maintain the internal mental image. If for example the representation of a significant caregiver is lost, a child may expectedly experience a sense of loss and even depression or anxiety and fear. An interesting hypothesis regarding depression in children and adults relates to this phenomenon. Perhaps the biologic vulnerability for depression is mediated through a visual-spatial vulnerability that in turn creates a vulnerability in the stability of mental representations. The loss of the representation leads to dysphoric affects. The dysphoric affects, in this model, are secondary.

If motor planning is impaired and the child cannot control his body, his difficulty will affect his confidence in dealing with aggression. He tries in play to touch his father's nose, but instead he hits his father in the eye and makes him mad. The child didn't intend to hit his father; his arm didn't work the way he wanted. Thus the child's confidence in his body and his ability to modulate aggression is not going to be optimally established.

For the child who is tactilely hyperreactive, his protection from the outside world is overly fragile. How is that going to affect the way he perceives other people's aggression? How is he going to react when another 2-year-old hits him in the back? When mother tries to hold a 4-month-old who is sensitive to light touch, if she rubs his skin lightly, he may squirm away, and she may misperceive that he is rejecting her.

In a study of 8-month-olds (DeGangi & Greenspan, 1988; Doussard-Roosevelt, Walker, Portales, Greenspan, & Porges, 1990; Portales et al., 1990) we were able to further observe how critical these types of constitutional and maturationally based regulatory difficulties are to the child's developmental patterns. In infants with a variety of symptoms, such as eating or sleeping problems and temper tantrums, we were able to demonstrate that a very high percentage had constitutional and maturational differences that were part of the difficulty. The babies were either hypo- or hyperreactive in one or another sensory modality or had sensory processing or motor tone or motor planning difficulties. These differences in turn seemed to contribute to a skewing of the parent-infant interaction pattern, which in turn was affecting personality development. These children were also found to have differences in physiological regulation (DeGangi et al., 1991). These differences persisted and were evident at 18 months. There were also signs of family distress at 18 months (Portales et al., 1990). It appeared that the maturational differences were affecting not only the child's personality, but also derailing the family to some extent. A small group of these infants that were followed to age 4 evidence a greater number of behavioral and learning problems than a comparison group (DeGangi,

Porges, Sickel, & Greenspan, 1993). Therefore, children who have constitutional and maturational unevenness tend to be especially challenging. They have a harder time in their interactions with their caregivers. Family functioning tends to be stressed. Eventually there may be more behavioral and learning difficulties.

Disorders Of Relating And Communicating (including Multisystem Developmental Disorders)

The third category of disorders involves problems in multiple aspects of a child's development including social relationships and language and cognitive, motor, and sensory functioning. This category includes multisystem developmental disorders (MSDD) and the DSM-IV category of pervasive developmental disorders (PDD) (i.e., autistic spectrum disorders). The main distinction between MSDD and PDD is that children with MSDD reveal capacities or potential for engagement and closeness in relating but may show difficulties in relating and communicating *secondary* to sensory processing, regulatory, and motor planning difficulties. These children are quite responsive to comprehensive intervention and become relatively quickly engaged and interactive.

Before describing this third group of disorders it is important to note that another type of disorder that involves multiple aspects of development can occur when an environmental stress or trauma leads to a global disruption in multiple areas of functioning. For example, when an infant evidences a failure-to-thrive syndrome, the infant's motor, cognitive, language, affective, and physical growth may slow down or cease altogether. Persistent types of neglect or abuse may produce a similar global disruption in functioning, including reactive attachment.

In addition, it is important to distinguish how regulatory disorders differ from MSDD or PDD. Regulatory disorders involve processing capacities but do not derail overall relating and communicating, whereas MSDD or PDD do. Developmental disorders also involve regulatory difficulties in terms of significant constitutional and maturational variations. In several disorders of relating and communicating, difficulties in the interactive patterns and caregiver and family dynamics almost always occur. It is rare, even with the most flexible and adaptive parents, that the infant and young child's developmental challenges, which combine regulatory problems and significant delays and dysfunctions, do not create difficulties in the caregiver-infant interaction or in the family dynamics. The nature of the challenge the child presents, and the lack of expectable feedback due to language and visual-spatial-motor processing difficulties, almost always places a significant stress on the interaction patterns and the family dynamics. Most families and most caregivers seem prepared for certain types of communication patterns with infants and young children. When these biologically expectable interaction patterns are not forthcoming, special approaches are often needed. The degree of the family contribution will vary considerably depending on the infant or child or the family's and caregiver's preexisting patterns. Interventions must, therefore, focus simultaneously on the family dynamics, the infant-caregiver interaction patterns, the regulatory patterns, and the child's developmental delays and dysfunctions in core areas, such as motor, language, cognition, and sensory functions.

A New Classification for Disorders of Relating and Communicating: Non-Progressive Neurodevelopmental Disorders of Relating and Communicating

This section proposes an expanded conceptualization of problems in relating and communicating, including MSDD and PDD. In the five years since the publication of *Diagnostic Classification 0–3* (Diagnostic Classification Task Force, 1994), and the 7 years since Greenspan (1992) proposed multi-system developmental disorders in *Infancy and Early Childhood*, clinicians have collected additional diagnostic, treatment, and outcome data on several hundred more children with severe disorders of relating, communicating, and thinking. This extensive clinical information enables us to divide non-progressive developmental disorders of relating and communicating into several broad groups that can capture a child's developmental capacities, such as the degree to which a child can communicate, as well as the child's underlying processing differences (e.g., the child's relative strengths in visual-spatial or auditory processing). Existing classification (e.g., autism and PDD, as well as MSDD) do not sufficiently capture the individual profiles that describe and help plan for an intervention for a given child and family. As we have discussed elsewhere, each child with an autistic spectrum disorder will differ in his or her sensory reactivity, processing, and functional developmental profiles. Therefore, a reconceptualization of the existing classification system (including MSDD and PDD), which can incorporate relevant develop-mental dimensions, may prove helpful. The dimensions that need to be considered include:

- *The child's ability to connect affect (intent) with sequences of behavior and/or symbols.* The affect serves as a signaling system telling the motor system what to do and allows the child to initiate, be spontaneous, and engage in meaningful gestures and symbolic acts;
- *The child's functional developmental level of presymbolic and early symbolic capacities.* The child's ability to engage in complex problem solving through gestures and early expression of ideas;
- *The child's engagement with others,* as evidenced by mutual or shared attention and mutual pleasure;
- *Motor planning.* The child's ability to initiate action, both imitate or have an idea, plan how to execute it, and then sequence the steps necessary to do or express what he or she wants or is thinking;
- *Auditory-verbal processing.* Memory and comprehension, including receptive understanding (e.g., semantics, reasoning, and logic) and expression (e.g., retrieval and pragmatics);
- *Visual-spatial processing.* Memory and comprehension, including part-whole discrimination, organization, tracking, directional stability, time sense, and visual-motor (e.g., construction and sequencing);
- *Sensory reactivity and regulation.* Sensory registration, orientation, interpretation, and responding or reacting (under and overreactive or well-modulated) in different sensory modalities;
- *Symbolic thinking and rate of progress.* The rate the child climbs the symbolic ladder to becoming an imaginative, representational, and abstract thinker, the better the rate of progress.

The following section offers a classification of neurodevelopmental disorders of relating, communicating, and thinking, based on a child's presenting profile and the child's potential for early response to a comprehensive, developmentally based intervention program. This proposed classification is based on constructing developmental profiles implementing a comprehensive intervention program and following a large number of children and families (Greenspan, 1992; Greenspan & Wieder, 1997; Greenspan et al., 1998). It is an initial clinical descriptive effort that will hopefully create a framework for further research. It identifies four broad groups, some of which divide into smaller subtypes. Children within each group and subtype are described with respect to the preceding developmental dimensions. This section includes some case studies to help illustrate the characteristics and responses typical of children within each group.

Group I

Children whose presenting profile places them within this group tend to make very rapid progress, often moving within 2 to 3 years from patterns of perseveration, self-stimulation, and self-absorption to warm, emotionally pleasurable engagement, spontaneous use of language, and abstract levels of symbolic play, with healthy peer relationships and solid academic skills. The overall group evidences the following identifying criteria, with four subtypes defined by unique patterns of processing differences.

Identifying Criteria

Children within Group I:

- Evidence difficulty connecting affect (or intent) to motor planning and sequencing as well as to symbol formation; therefore, behavior tends to be repetitive, self-stimulatory, fragmented, or lacks clear meaning or purpose;
- Either partially have, or within the first few months of intervention acquire, the ability to engage in preverbal, gestural problem-solving interactions with caregivers (e.g., taking a caregiver by the hand, leading her to the toy room, and showing her the desired toy);
- Either partially have, or within the first few months of intervention acquire, the capacity for warm engagement with positive affect, as evidenced by affectionate behavior with smiles and looks of delight at primary caregivers;
- Possess relatively strong motor planning (e.g., child can sequence three or more motor actions, including sounds or words, though not at an age-appropriate level, such as taking a car in and out of the garage, making car noises, and moving the car around the house);

- Either have, or within the first few months of intervention acquire, solid imitative skills for motor actions and/or sounds and/or words (e.g., can imitate actions, such as "touch your nose" or "touch your head," as well as simple sounds and words, such as "up" or "go"). The children use this skill to progress, over time, toward early stages of imaginative play.

Additional Characteristics

Children within Group I also display:

- Hypersensitivity to sensation, such as touch and sound. Although the children are often underreactive to movement and, occasionally, to pain, the overall tendency of the children is to be overreactive;
- Relatively strong or weak visual-spatial processing;
- Relatively mild to moderate auditory processing impairment with good progress once intervention begins;
- All the children in this group progress into imaginative play quickly, climbing the symbolic ladder from pretending real-life experiences to representational play, and are able to build logical bridges between ideas and become abstract thinkers.

Sequence of Progress

Children within Group I often show rapid improvement in engagement, purposeful gesturing, range of affect expressed, and shared attention with caregivers and, over time, with peers. They also rapidly improve in imitative skills because of their better motor planning abilities, leading to language and imaginative play sequences. During the first year or two of intervention, many of the children become excited about their emerging language skills and enter a stage of hyper-ideation in which they talk about everything, but in a very fragmented (free-associative) manner. Over time, they learn to be more logical as the environment challenges them to build bridges between their ideas. During the early stage of becoming more logical, they tend to continue some preoccupations and perseverative tendencies with special interests, topics of conversation, or playthings (e.g., roads, cars, certain types of visual displays). During this early stage, some children have profile descriptions similar to that of Asperger's syndrome.

However, when interventions emphasize creative interactions and dialogues (e.g., using their interests as a take-off for creative interactions), these children gradually become more spontaneous, flexible, creative, and empathetic. Over time, they progress to higher and higher levels of abstract reasoning and social skills.

Subgroups Patterns Within Group I

There are four different patterns within Group I. Children within these subgroups meet all the basic identifying criteria for the basic group, but display different, unique patterns of processing capacities.

Group I-A: Relatively strong auditory, visual-spatial, and motor-planning capacities, and a tendency toward overreactivity to sensation.
Children within Group I-A make the most rapid progress. Over time, and possibly by the time they enter school, these children may even evidence precocious academic skills (e.g., abstract thinking, reading, or arithmetic). This subgroup has:

- A tendency toward relatively strong short-term auditory memory and expressive abilities (e.g., may recite the alphabet and numbers, fill in the blanks to songs and stories, and when older, memorize scripts from TV shows or books);
- Relatively strong visual-spatial memory skills (e.g., knows where things are, good sense of direction, good at puzzles, recognizes letters and shapes);
- A tendency to be more reactive to sensation and emotional states, showing more intense joy as well as frustration. These children develop better modulation over time.

Group I-B: Relatively strong auditory processing but weaker visual-spatial and motor-planning capacities, with a tendency to be underreactive.
While also making rapid progress, children in this group evidence:

- A tendency to remain more fragmented in their thinking and may have a harder time learning math (especially word problems), interpreting the meaning of what they read, and "seeing the forest for the trees" intellectually and socially;
- Relatively strong short-term auditory memory;

- Relatively weaker visual-spatial memory and processing capacities than children in Group I-A;
- Relatively weaker motor planning abilities than children in Group I-A;
- A tendency to be more underreactive with some sensory hypersensitivity. They have a longer fuse, but also tend to process information more slowly.

Group I-C: Relatively stronger visual-spatial and motor-planning capacities but weaker auditory processing, and a tendency toward sensory underreactivity.

Children within Group I-C make solid, consistent progress, but not quite as rapidly as those in Groups I-A and I-B above. They evidence:

- A tendency to take a longer time to progress, especially in learning to use words, but they can use symbolic toys as a language to express many ideas. Group I-C children do not tend to evidence a dramatic hyper-ideation learning phase since language develops more slowly, but they are able to elaborate and sequence ideas through the use of toys and gestures, aided by their better motor-planning abilities;
- Relatively stronger visual-spatial memory and processing;
- Relatively weaker auditory processing and memory/retrieval;
- A tendency toward sensory underreactivity, but may get more emotional, especially when their weaker auditory processing and poor verbal communication leave them frustrated or frightened.

Group I-D: Relatively strong auditory, verbal ,and visual-spatial memory but relatively weaker verbal and visual-spatial comprehension and motor planning, and a tendency to be overreactive and become overloaded.

Children in Group I-D tend to make consistent progress with good rote verbal skills, but have a narrower range of ideas. These children do not usually go through the hyperideation phase and have a weaker ability for higher-level processing of auditory and visual information. These children have:

- A narrower range of acceptable emotions. Unless the environment can be more soothing and interactive, they tend to be more rigid and anxious;

- Become more easily overloaded without the resources to comprehend and integrate. Consequently, these children resort to constrictions and rigidity and are more anxious and fearful because of their oversensitivity, with more challenges with reality testing. This subtype has many similarities to what others have described as Asperger's syndrome;
- Both auditory and visual-spatial memory as relative strengths;
- Relatively weaker auditory and visual-spatial comprehension;
- Relatively weaker motor planning;
- A tendency to be more overreactive, especially to unexpected sensation or events, but also to be underreactive in some modalities. They may have reduced muscle tone.

Group I Case Illustration

Two-and-a-half-year-old David presented with self-absorption, perseveration, and self-stimulation, no peer play, and lack of eye contact and pleasure in relating to his parents. During his evaluation, David spent most of his time reciting numbers in a rote sequence, spinning and jumping around aimlessly and randomly, and lining up toys and cars, while making self-stimulatory sounds. David, however, showed strengths in his ability to indicate what he wanted when extremely motivated; occasional displays of affection; the capacity to imitate actions, sounds, and words; and the ability to recognize pictures and shapes. With a comprehensive program, David quickly became more engaged and began imitating some pretend-oriented sequences. He gradually began using his language purposefully and creatively. He then went through the sequence of progress described previously and, at present, is in a regular school, where he excels in reading and English as well as in math. He has a number of close friends, a sense of humor, and insights into other people's feelings. His remaining challenges are with fine-motor sequencing (penmanship) and his tendency to become somewhat anxious and argumentative when in a competitive situation.

Group II

Children in Group II have greater challenges than those in Group I. They make slower, but consistent, progress with each hurdle requiring a great deal of time-consuming work. Typically, these children can initially engage a little bit, be partially purposeful, and intermittently do some problem solving. However, they take much longer to become consistent, preverbal problem-solvers and to learn to use imitation as a basis for language and imaginative play. When they achieve these milestones, they do not generally go through a stage of hyper-ideation and rapid learning, but rather move through each new capacity very gradually. Although many children in this group still make progress, most are not able to participate in all the activities of a regular classroom with a large class size, as are the children in Group I. They can benefit, however, from appropriately staffed inclusion or integrated programs, or from special needs language-based classrooms in which the other children are interactive and verbal.

Identifying Criteria

Children within Group II:

- Evidence difficulty connecting affect (or intent) to motor planning and sequencing as well as to symbol formation; therefore, their behavior tends to be repetitive, self-stimulatory, fragmented, or lack clear meaning or purpose;
- Can be partially purposeful, often oriented to basic needs, but do not have solid mastery of preverbal, gestural problem-solving capacities (i.e., cannot do 20+ circles of problem-solving interaction and communication in a row);
- Possess an intermittent, but not full, capacity to engage with caregivers. These children initially rely more on sensorimotor stimulation and, when self-absorbed or avoidant, need to be wooed and pursued;
- Have motor-planning skills that tend to be limited to two or fewer sequential actions (e.g., putting the car in the garage and taking it out, rolling the car toward a single destination);
- Do not yet evidence spontaneous imitative skills, other than perhaps some occasional ability to copy a familiar motor pattern, such as building with blocks, or setting up or drawing a scene that they memorized;
- Possess relatively limited auditory processing capacities, through which they can verbally express what they want better than they can

understand what others say. They have a greater reliance on the use of scripts.

Group II children also tend to be characterized by the following, which are not, necessarily, early identifying criteria:

- Mixed reactivity to sensation with a tendency toward being under-reactive and self-absorbed and/or underreactive and craving (as well as mixtures of the two), with some children tending to be more reactive;
- Relative degrees of compromise in visual-spatial processing but may have good visual memory and, sooner or later, may learn to read but with weak comprehension skills.

Sequence of Progress

Children within Group II have the capacity to become joyfully engaged, but may require wooing and persistent pursuit. They also have the capacity to move from simple, purposeful gestures to complex problem-solving, preverbal interactions and, eventually, use of imitation as the basis for learning words and becoming involved in pretend play. They learn primarily through what they see and may get very immersed in videos and books (before being encouraged to do more interactive work). They also may borrow scripts and scenes to begin to embark on symbolic play as well. However, mastery of each of these steps, from engagement to using simple and then complex gestures and on to using words and ideas, tends to be very gradual. Children in this group may evidence a wide range of patterns of progress in the transition from preverbal gesturing to use of ideas. Some children in this group take a long time to progress beyond intermittent, need-based, short verbal phrases. Some of the children who are not able to develop imitative skills readily benefit from more semi-structured challenges to imitate actions, sounds, and words. This work, however, must be part of a comprehensive program. As the children in this group develop language, their mastery of each step from creative elaboration to logical discussion is a gradual and time-consuming process. The children in this group can easily become mired in the use of more fragmented, concrete, and early types of logic and have great difficulty—in comparison to the children in Group I—in progressing to more abstract and creative thinking. Some children learn to read before they are fluent and conversant. Peer relationships are both possible and desired, but Group II children develop relationships very gradually in conjunction with advances in their functional thinking capacities. These children benefit from semi-structured, sensorimotor games before they move on to symbolic levels in play. Their capacities for experiencing warmth and pleasure with other children often precede their ability to interact and communicate creatively. Nonetheless, with continued work, these children will continue to progress.

Subgroup Patterns Within Group II

Group II divides into two different patterns, both of which meet all the general criteria for the group.

Group II-A: Relatively strong visual-spatial memory and relatively weak visual processing, auditory processing, and motor-planning capacities, with a tendency toward overreactivity.
Children within Group II-A are more easily engaged and spontaneous. They tend to have:

- Moderate compromises in auditory processing (very difficult to respond to the words of others) but develop language, retrieve often-used phrases, and borrow fragments of scripts from books and videos, which they use for symbolic play. Although their language develops slowly and tends to be descriptive of what is seen or associative, these children slowly become more logical and able to reason. The children within this subtype also speak more spontaneously, which is related to their more reactive and often demanding nature;
- Moderate compromises in visual-spatial processing (easily lost, poor sense of direction, can't find things), but possess visual memory as a relative strength;
- Moderate compromises in auditory processing;
- Moderate compromises in motor planning;
- More reactivity and to be intermittently sensation seeking.

Group II-B: Relatively strong visual-spatial memory, while other visual-spatial processing is moderately impaired. Moderate to severe auditory processing and motor-planning problems. Group II-B differs from Group

II-A in that Group II-B children are underreactive with overreactivity to certain sounds.

Children within Group II-B tend to be more self-absorbed and avoidant, requiring more encouragement to speak. They tend to have:

- Moderate compromises in auditory processing, but they do learn to speak, with greater difficulty in understanding the unpredictable speech of others. They have retrieval difficulties and rely on often-repeated phrases and scripts. The early conversations of these children tend to be short and repetitive;
- More underreactivity. They also tend to be more self-absorbed than children in Group II-A and have to be wooed to respond. They benefit from visual communication strategies, and often learn to read sooner than to speak fluently or spontaneously;
- Moderate compromises in visual-spatial processing (easily lost, poor sense of direction, can't find things) but their visual memory is a relative strength;
- Moderate to severe compromises in auditory processing;
- Moderate to severe difficulties with motor planning and low muscle tone;
- Hypersensitivity and overreactivity to sensation, with some sensation-seeking behavior.

Group II Case Illustration

Three-year-old Joey presented with a great deal of avoidant behavior, always moving away from his caregivers and having only fleeting eye contact. He frequently engaged in very simple perseverative and self-stimulatory behavior, such as rapidly turning the pages of his books or pushing his Thomas® train round and round the track. Joey could purposefully reach for his juice or take a block from his parents, but he was not able to negotiate complex preverbal interactions or, for that matter, imitate sounds or words. Four years after his program began, Joey (6½) now shows abilities to relate with real pleasure and joy, use complex gestures to lead his parents places, and describe what he wants in sentences, such as "Give me juice now!" Joey can respond to simple questions ("What do you want to do?" "Play with my trains!"), and have short sequences of back-and-forth communication with four or five exchanges of short phrases. He is also able to engage in early imaginative play, having his action figures fly around the room with great joy and delight. He is not yet able to consistently answer "why" questions. He also is able to play with peers only with some adult involvement and when there is action or a structured game. However, he continues to make progress at a consistent but slow pace. Interestingly, Joey only occasionally displays perseverative, self-stimulatory patterns.

Group III

Children in this group have moderate to severe auditory and visual-spatial processing, with more severe motor planning that impedes purposeful communication and problem solving. They are capable of intermittent problem solving interactions, but cannot sustain their interactions. They are intermittently engaged in purposeful activities, with much self-absorption and/or aimless behavior. It is this "in-and-out" quality, with presymbolic "islands" of problem solving, that characterizes this group. Their islands may involve the use of words, pictures, signs, and other two- to three-step gestures or actions to communicate their basic needs. Some children will use toys as if they were real as long as they are the actors (e.g., they will eat pretend foods or feed a life-size baby doll) but they do not usually represent themselves or others through figures. Some children with severe oral-motor dyspraxia will not speak more than a few ritualized words, if at all, but they may evidence pre-verbal communication through a few signs, or picture communication, or through the use of a favorite toy. Some children learn to recognize logos and may read words.

Identifying Criteria

Children within Group III evidence:

- Very intermittent purposefulness at the presymbolic level, which is seen in islands of problem solving. Group III children cannot sustain interactions; that is, they cannot complete more than four or five circles of problem-solving interactions;
- Very intermittent capacity to engage with caregivers, and usually engage as a result of sensorimotor stimulation. These children tend to break off into aimless, self-absorbed, or avoidant behavior;

- Relatively strong auditory processing, which enables them to say a few words or phrases when in need or desiring something. Their receptive language is relatively stronger when it consists of often-used phrases in routines and/or accompanied by visual support and context. Their more severe motor planning, oral-motor, and/or visual-spatial challenges make it difficult for them to convey just what they understand receptively;
- Very limited motor planning, with most actions limited to two or three sequential actions that are often repeated again and again. Group III children often seek hand-over-hand assistance for actions;
- Very weak imitation skills. Group III children do not imitate spontaneously and learn only through tremendous repetition;
- Relatively weak visual-spatial processing (e.g., disorganized, poor discrimination, poor searching, easily lost);
- Relatively strong visual memory. Mixed reactivity to sensation, with a tendency toward being underreactive and self-absorbed and/or underreactive and craving (as well as mixtures of the two), with some children tending to be more passive and with low muscle tone.

Sequence of Progress

Group III children tend to progress slowly, given the severity of their processing difficulties and their intermittent engagement and problem solving. The key to intervention is to "bring them in" to more sustained pleasurable interactions through persistent pursuit and by playing simple games, such as peek-a-boo, hide and seek, chase, tickling, horsy rides, and other sensorimotor fun activities. More consistent engagement will create more motivation and lead to more interactive problem solving. The heightened affect inherent in having a "problem," such as getting a parent to do more roughhousing, finding a treasured Thomas® toy train, or getting more cookies, will motivate the child to process more information or input, be it visual or auditory. For example, the child will learn the sequence needed to get shoes, coat, key, and mom's purse in order to go outside. Once engaged, the caregiver's affect cueing will help the child expand his or her perceptions as well as sustain the child's attention to the input. The child's desire or objections will then motivate her to go beyond her motor planning constraints and respond in some form. With more sustained engagement and interactions, children in this group also can become more responsive to complex imitation, visual communication strategies, and practiced learning. They can go on to early levels of symbolic play.

Group III Case Illustration

Sarah ran in looking for her Winnie-the-Pooh and climbed up on the stool in front of the shelves, but she could not move the little figures in the basket around to search for her beloved character. The next moment, she pulled the basket off the shelf and all the figures fell out. She then looked in the next basket without bothering to look at the fallen figures on the floor. Her mom intervened before Sarah could drop the second basket and offered to help. Sarah echoed, "Help!" and grabbed her mother's hands and put them in the basket. Her mother had to point to Winnie before Sarah actually saw the figure. Sarah grabbed it and ran off to lie on the couch. Mom then brought Tigger over to say hello. Sarah grabbed Tigger and ran to the other side of the room. She held her figures tightly and turned away when mom came over again. Mom then took Eeyore and started to sing, "Ring around the rosie . . ." moving her figure up and down. This time, Sarah looked and filled in "down" to "all fall down," but she then moved rapidly away and went over to the mirror. Sarah's pattern of flight and avoidance after getting what she wanted, followed by not knowing what to do next, was quite typical. Sarah's intervention program began when she was 3 years old. She slowly learned the labels for things she wanted and to protest. She recognized and could express familiar phrases like "come and eat," "go out," and "bath time." She became quite engaged with sensorimotor play and loved to be swung and tickled. She even began to play imaginatively with toys, first dipping her toes into the water of the play pool and then letting Winnie "jump" in. She began to imitate more words and actions. She also tried to solve problems to get her figures, but only when she was very motivated or very angry, and usually only after energetic sensorimotor play pulled her in. Her expressive language expanded to include more and more phrases indicating what she wanted, but her weak receptive processing made it difficult for her to answer any questions. She relied on visual and affect cues to understand what was said to her. This transferred to puppet play and even simple role-play as a cook or doctor. Sarah's problem solving also progressed very slowly because of her very poor motor planning, but she became more easily engaged and more responsive to semi-structured and structured approaches to learning. Between ages 4 and 5, she learned to count and identify colors, and loved to paint and cut with scissors. By age 6½, Sarah demonstrated some pre-academic abilities, and was able to read some sight words. She now enjoys being with other children and joins the crowd running around, hiding, and chasing, but she does not yet play interactively, although she has learned the various social rituals, such as greeting, sharing, and protesting. Sarah can also spontaneously communicate "feel happy" with a big smile, and "feel mad" with a frown.

Group IV

Children in this group are characterized by significant challenges in being purposeful, which are related to their very severe motor-planning problems, as well as by significant auditory and visual-spatial processing difficulties. Children in Group IV fall into two subgroups. Both subgroups differ from Group III in that children have more severe challenges in all processing areas, especially motor planning (including oral-motor dyspraxia). As a consequence, children within the Group IV subgroups progress very unevenly, and slowly, having the most difficulty in developing intentional problem-solving patterns, expressive language, and motor planning. Over time, with continuing therapeutic work, they become engaged and partially interactive through gestures and action games.

Group IV-A Identifying Criteria

Children within Group IV-A evidence:

- An intermittent capacity to engage with caregivers. Initially, they tend to be very avoidant, with great difficulty in understanding what others want of them and being purposeful. They wander around aimlessly or lie down passively, with intermittent bursts of sensory-seeking behavior;
- Severe motor planning, which impedes sequences of more than one or two steps. Group IV-A children usually initiate actions to have their basic needs met. They are very dependent on adult actions to obtain what they want, although they are very persistent in communicating their desires through simple and, eventually, more complex gestures;

- Limited imitation abilities, usually restricted to single-step actions, such as pushing, pulling, or throwing an object;
- Relatively strong visual-spatial processing with moderate compromises; stronger visual memory, but weaker organization and visual-motor abilities (easily lost, poor sense of direction, can't find things, poor discrimination);
- Severe auditory processing difficulties. These children may learn some need-based words but rely on visual cues to understand what others say. Some children with more severe oral-motor dyspraxia do not speak but do have a narrow range of meaningful visual symbolic schemas (such as cars or trains) that they may enjoy and use repeatedly. Some children do eventually learn to say or sign some words through much practice and repetition.

Children within Group IV-A also:

- Show a wide range of reactivity. They tend to be primarily over or underreactive to sensation, with a greater tendency to be avoidant rather than self-absorbed. Participate in presymbolic play when toys relating to real life experiences (e.g., baby doll, slide, pool, school bus) are readily in sight and modeled, but do not usually find or organize the toys themselves. (Structure and visual communication strategies are very helpful in learning pre-academic and adaptive skills.) They may learn to enjoy simple puzzles and cause-and-effect toys;
- Evidence symbolic understanding, as shown by their attachments to video and TV figures and their desires for specific books and videos. However, their very poor motor planning impedes purposeful play.

Group IV-A Sequence of Progress

With persistent pursuit, these children can become more engaged, enjoy being around their families, and become better problem solvers to get what they want. Because of severe motor planning difficulties, they do not often initiate purposeful steps, but can readily undo what they do not want and then have difficulty knowing what to do next. They often resort to the repetition of ideas (e.g., simple sequences with favorite toys, such as pushing a toy train on tracks through the tunnel). They may learn words (usually through ritualized phrases), songs, and filling-in-the-blank. Eventually, they retrieve the words for highly desired objects or objections while in high-affect states. Some children show visual-spatial learning on semi-structured tasks, such as matching, pointing to pictures, and assembling easy puzzles, but they cannot sequence actions to express ideas independently. They function at a presymbolic level. Other children are unable to retain even repetitive learning, but do best when work focuses on their natural interests (e.g., to go outside, get food, play horsy). Some children with a relatively strong visual-spatial capacity read logos or words, but their receptive understanding remains highly dependent on visual cues and context. With work on experiencing pleasure and consistent engagement, these children can diminish frustration, self-destruction, and aggression and can increase their adaptation to surroundings and their expectations. Over time, some children evidence unexpected strengths, moving on to presymbolic problem solving and increased rate of learning.

Group IV-A Case Illustration

Harold was able to progress only very slowly to imitating sounds and words, even with an intensive program organized to facilitate imitation. He could say one or two words spontaneously when angry or insistent on getting something, but otherwise he had to be prompted and pushed to speak. Every utterance was extremely difficult for him, and he would sometimes stare at a caregiver's mouth to try and form the same movements. His severe dyspraxia also interfered with his evidencing pretend play, although from the different facial expressions and the gleam in his eye when he engaged in playful interactions with his parents, it appeared he was playing little "tricks." He sometimes held onto toy objects, such as a Nerf ® sword or magic wand, and used them in ritualized ways, but he could not use toys to sequence new ideas. He could engage and even initiate sensorimotor interactions during which he expressed pleasure and affection. Although games with his brother had to be orchestrated, he did enjoy running around the schoolyard and the pool with other children. In the second year of intervention, Harold was able to interact and communicate with three or four back-and-forth exchanges about what he wanted, such as pulling his dad over to the refrigerator and finding the hotdogs. He could even retrieve a few words at such moments (e.g., "Hotdog" "What else?" "French fries"). Harold became more consistently engaged over time, with islands of presymbolic ability, and he became more aware of what was going on around him. He no longer wandered aimlessly and would pick up trucks to push or select other cause-and-effect toys and simple puzzles. He let others join him but invariably turned the interaction into sensorimotor play, which brought him great pleasure. His pre-academic progress was also very slow, even with lots of structure, repetition, and practice, but he did make progress in learning to complete "work" and self-care.

Group IV-B Identifying Criteria

Children in Group IV-B tend to evidence patterns of regression and/or more overt neurological involvement (e.g., persistent seizures). Children within this subgroup usually begin with enormous challenges and make very limited progress, no progress at all, or vacillate between a little progress and regression. Group IV-B children display:

- Fleeting to intermittent engagement. They tend to have severe processing challenges in all areas and yet, at the same time, can become more engaged and happier and, in learning this, to become partially purposeful in solving problems when they want something;
- Fleeting to intermittent purposeful behavior related to very strong needs. It is hard for this group to progress consistently into complex preverbal problem-solving strategies or into the use of ideas, words, or complex spatial problem solving. During times of progress, their developmental abilities may improve to the level of children in Group IV-A or Group III;
- Severe motor planning difficulties. These children may intermittently use cause-and-effect toys brought to them (e.g., a simple popup toy) but they often only engage in repetitive touching, banging, or self-stimulation. They frequently have severe oral-motor dyspraxia and have little or no imitative ability;
- Extremely limited auditory processing capacity;
- Extremely limited visual-spatial processing;
- A tendency to be underreactive to sensation. These children often evidence low muscle tone and passivity. They may also evidence more overt neurological symptoms.

Group IV-B Sequence of Progress

With a comprehensive program, these children can become more engaged and happier. Over time, they can learn to be intermittently purposeful, engaged, and involved in preverbal, gestural problem solving, but are unable to develop symbolic capacities. With structure, visual communication strategies, repetition and practice, they can develop basic adaptive skills for home and school. They will often find it difficult to move into complex, preverbal problem solving.

Group IV-B Case Illustration

Margaret had severe perinatal complications and evidenced low muscle tone from shortly after birth. She achieved her motor milestones very slowly, sitting up at 9 months, crawling at 12 months, and walking, with some asymmetry noted, at 17 months. Other than showing some pleasure in cuddling during the first year and some purposeful mouthing toward the end of the first year, she did not progress into consistent, purposeful interaction or complex, preverbal problem solving. At the time of the first visit, she tended to perseverate by rubbing a favorite spot on the carpet and by staring toward the light, but could smile and show some fleeting pleasure with sensory-based play. With a comprehensive program, Margaret has progressed slightly. She has become more robustly engaged, with deeper smiles and pleasure, and more purposeful reaching. She engages in some exchange of facial expressions, which she sometimes uses to indicate preferences. At present, however, she has not progressed into complex, behavioral problem-solving interactions. Margaret has recently begun evidencing a seizure disorder, for which she has been placed on medications.

The classification of neurodevelopmental disorders of relating, communicating, and thinking described above provides a way of grouping developmental challenges according to their unique developmental profile. In so doing, they provide assistance in individualized intervention planning and in the search for neurobiological correlates and mechanisms.

Conclusion

In this chapter we have discussed a developmental approach to the classification of disorders in infancy and early childhood. We discussed three broad categories (interactive disorder, regulatory disorder, and disorders of relating, communicating) and presented new directions in developmentally based classification.

References

Aber, J. & Baker, A. J. (1990). Security of attachment in toddlerhood: Modifying assessment procedures for joint clinical and research purposes. In M. T. Greenberg, D. Cicchetti, & E. M. Cummings (Eds.), *Attachment in the Preschool Years* (pp. 427–463). Chicago: University of Chicago Press.

Ainsworth, M., Bell, S. M., & Stayton, D. (1974). Infant-mother attachment and social development: Socialization as a product of reciprocal responsiveness to signals. In M. Richards (Ed.), *The Integration of the Child into a Social World* (pp. 99–135). Cambridge, England: Cambridge University Press.

American Psychiatric Association (1995). *Diagnostic and statistical manual of mental disorders.* (4th ed.) Washington, DC.

Arend, R., Gove, F. L., & Sroufe, L. A. (1979). Continuity of individual adaptation from infancy to kindergarten: A predictive study of ego-resiliency and curiosity in preschoolers. *Child Dev., 50,* 950–959.

Bowlby, J. (1969). *Attachment and loss.* (Vols. Vol. 1) London: Hogarth Press.

Cassidy, J. (1990). Theoretical and methodological considerations in the study of attachment and self in young children. In M. T. Greenberg & D. Cicchetti (Eds.), *Attachment in the Preschool Years* (pp. 87–120). Chicago: Chicago University Press.

Cassidy, J. & Marvin, R., with the Attachment Working Group of the John D. and Catherine T. MacArthur Network on the Transition from Infancy to Early Childhood. (1988). *A system for coding the organization of attachment behavior in 3 or 4 year old children.* Washington, DC.

DeGangi, G. A., DiPietro, J. A., Greenspan, S. I., & Porges, S. W. (1991). Psychophysiological characteristics of the regulatory disordered infant. *Infant Behav. & Develop., 14,* 37–50.

DeGangi, G. A. & Greenspan, S. I. (1988). The development of sensory functioning in infants. *Physical and Occupational Therapy in Pediatrics, 8*(3), 21–33.

DeGangi, G. A., Porges, S. W., Sickel, R. Z., & Greenspan, S. I. (1993). Four-Year Follow-Up of A Sample of Regulatory Disordered Infants. *Infant Mental Health Journal, 14,* 330–343.

Diagnostic Classification Task Force (1994). *Diagnostic classification: 0–3: Diagnostic classification of mental health and developmental disorders of infancy and early childhood.* Arlington, VA: ZERO TO THREE: National Center for Clinical Infant Programs.

Doussard-Roosevelt, J. A., Walker, P. S., Portales, A., Greenspan, S. I., & Porges, S. W. (1990). Vagal tone and the fussy infant: Atypical vagal reactivity in the difficult infant. *Infant Behav. & Develop. 13,* 352 (abstract).

Easterbrooks, M. A. & Goldberg, W. A. (1990). Security of toddler-parent attachment: Relation to children's sociopersonality functioning during kindergarten. In M. T. Greenberg, D. Cicchetti, & E. M. Cummings (Eds.), *Attachment in the Preschool Years* (pp. 221–245). Chicago: University of Chicago Press.

Egeland, B. & Farber, E. A. (1984). Infant-mother attachment: Factors related to its development and changes over time. *Child Dev., 55,* 753–771.

Goldberg, W. A. & Easterbrooks, M. A. (1984). Toddler development in the family. Impact of the father involvement and parenting characteristics. *Developmental Psychology, 55,* 740–752.

Greenspan, S. I. (1989). *The development of the ego: Implications for personality theory, psychopathology, and the psychotherapeutic process.* New York: International Universities Press.

Greenspan, S. I. (1990). Regulatory disorders: Clinical perspectives. Presented at the National Institute on Drug Abuse RAUS Review Meeting on Methodological Issues in Controlled Studies on Effects of Prenatal Exposure to Drugs of Abuse, June 8–9. Richmond, VA.

Greenspan, S. I. (1992). *Infancy and early childhood: The practice of clinical assessment and intervention with emotional and developmental challenges.* Madison, CT: International Universities Press.

Greenspan, S. I. & Salmon, J. (1995). *The challenging child: Understanding, raising, and enjoying the five "difficult" types of children.* Reading, MA: Addison Wesley.

Greenspan, S. I. & Wieder, S. (1997). Developmental patterns and outcomes in infants and children with disorders in relating and communicating: A chart review of 200 cases of children with autistic spectrum diagnoses. *Journal of Developmental and Learning Disorders, 1,* 87–141.

Greenspan, S. I. & Wieder, S. (1998). *The child with special needs: Intellectual and emotional growth.* Reading, MA: Addison Wesley.

Main, M, Kaplan, N., & Cassidy, J. (1985). Security in infancy, childhood and adulthood: A move to the level of representation. *Monographs of the Society for Research in Child Development, 50*

Marvin, R. & Stewart, R. B. (1991). A family systems framework for the study of attachment. In M. T. Greenberg, D. Cicchetti, & E. M. Cummings (Eds.), *Attachment in the Preschool Years* (pp. 51–87). Chicago: University of Chicago Press.

Maslin-Cole, C. & Spieker, S. J. (1990). Attachment as a basis of independent motivation: A view from risk and nonrisk samples. In M. T. Greenberg, D. Cicchetti, & E. M. Cummings (Eds.), *Attachment in the Preschool Years* (pp. 245–272). Chicago: University of Chicago Press.

Matas, L., Arend, R., & Sroufe, L. (1978). Continuity of adaptation in the second year: The relationship between quality of attachment and later competence. *Child Development, 49,* 547–556.

Pastor, D. (1981). The quality of mother-infant attachment and its relationship to toddlers' initial sociability with peers. *Developmental Psychology, 23,* 326–335.

Porges, S. W. & Greenspan, S. I. (1990). Regulatory disordered infants: A common theme. Presented at the National Institute on Drug Abuse RAUS Review Meeting on Methodological Issues in Controlled Studies on Effects of Prenatal Exposure to Drugs of Abuse, June 8–9. Richmond, VA.

Portales, A. W., Porges, S. W., & Greenspan, S. I. (1990). Parenthood and the difficult child. *Infant Behav. & Development, 13,* 573 (abstract).

Sroufe, L. A. (1983). Infant-caregiver attachment and patterns of adaptation in preschool: The roots of maladaptation and competence. (pp. 41–83). Hillsdale, NJ: Erlbaum.

Sroufe, L. A., Fox, N. A., & Pancake, V. (1983). Attachment and dependency in developmental perspective. *Child Development, 54,* 1615–1627.

Waters, E., Wippman, J., & Sroufe, L. A. (1979). Attachment, positive affect, and competence in the peer group: Two studies in construct validation. *Child Dev., 50,* 821–829.

Appendices

Appendix A

Means, Discrimination Indices, and T-Value Tables for Caregiver and Child Behaviors

Table A-1.
Means, Discrimination Indices, and T-Values: 7- to 9-Month-Old
Data (Caregiver Behaviors)

CAREGIVER BEHAVIORS

Developmental Level	Mean		RD DIS	MP DIS	t-value (df = 53)
	Normal	RD			
Self-Regulation and Interest in the World:					
1. Interest in toys	1.97	1.79	.18		
2. Interest in child	1.97	1.68	.29a		2.78**
3. Pleasant affect	1.89	1.42	.47b	.78c	3.19**
4. Provides touch	.81	.89	.37a	.64c	
5. Provides movement	.89	.32	.57b	.22a	2.18*
Self-Regulation Subscale	*7.53*	*6.10*		*MP 5.83*	
Forming Relationships, Attachment, and engagement:					
6. Relaxed with child	1.92	1.58	.34a	.42b	2.83**
7. Looks with affection	1.97	1.68	.29a	.64c	2.78**
8. Enjoys being with child	1.83	1.68	.15		
Forming Relationships Subscale	*5.67*	*4.95*		*MP 4.42*	
Two-Way, Purposeful Communication:					
9. Opens circles	1.86	1.68	.18		
10. Responds to child contingently	1.58	1.37	.21a	.25a	
11. Parallel play	1.61	1.47	.14	.61c	
12. Plays at appropriate level	1.81	1.47	.34a	.64c	
13. Waits for child to respond	1.56	1.58	0	.23a	2.11*
Two-Way Communication Subscale	*8.16*	*7.52*		*MP 6.67*	
TOTAL CAREGIVER SCORE	**21.42**	**18.58**		**MP 18.67**	

Key: RD, regulatory disordered; MP, multi-problem family; DIS, discrimination index; df, degrees of freedom
a = small DIS (.20–.39); b = medium DIS (.40–.59); c = large DIS (.60+)
* = p<.05; ** = p<.01

Note: MP = Discrimination index between normals and multi-problem/high-risk babies reported and mean values for subtests and total tests. Means are not reported for multi-problem group except for subscale and total test scores because N was only 6 for this age group; t scores reflect statistical differences between means for normal and RD groups.

Table A-1.
Means, Discrimination Indices, and T-Values: 7- to 9-Month-Old Data (Child Behaviors)

CHILD BEHAVIORS

Developmental Level	Mean		RD DIS	MP DIS	t-value (df = 53)
	Normal	RD			
Self-Regulation and Interest in the World:					
1. Interested in toys	1.97	1.84	.13	.30a	
2. Explores objects freely	1.97	1.68	.29a	.47b	2.45*
3. Remains calm	1.97	1.89	.08	.47b	
4. Comfortable with touch	1.67	1.47	.20a	1.34c	
5. Enjoys movement	1.44	.63	.81c	1.11c	3.51***
6. Overly visual	1.78	1.58	.20a	.78c	
7. Happy, content affect	1.86	1.11	.75c	1.03c	4.84***
8. Underreactivity	1.64	1.47	.17	1.14c	
9. Overreactivity	1.36	1.00	.36a	.69c	
Self-Regulation Subscale	*13.89*	*11.11*		MP 7.33	
Forming Relationships, Attachment, and Engagement					
10. Interest in caregiver	1.94	1.26	.68c	1.11c	4.75***
11. Curiosity in caregiver games	1.89	1.11	.78c	.49b	5.14***
12. Closeness to caregiver	1.86	1.16	.70c	1.19c	3.78***
13. Gaze aversion	1.83	1.47	.36a	.83c	2.19*
14. Social references	1.75	1.00	.75c	1.25c	4.23***
Forming Relationships Subscale	*9.50*	*6.1*		MP 5.67	
TOTAL CHILD SCORE	**23.38**	**17.21**		**MP 13.00**	
TOTAL SCALE	**44.80**	**35.78**		**MP 31.67**	

Key: RD, regulatory disordered; MP, multi-problem family; DIS, discrimination index; df, degrees of freedom
a = small DIS (.20–.39); b = medium DIS (.40–.59); c = large DIS (.60+)
* = p<.05; ** = p<.01; *** = p<.001

Note: MP = Discrimination index between normals and multi-problem/high-risk babies reported and mean values for subtests and total tests. Means are not reported for multi-problem group except for subscale and total test scores because N was only 6 for this age group; t scores reflect statistical differences between means for normal and RD groups.

Table A-2.
Means, Discrimination Indices, and T-Values: 10- to 12-Month-Old Data (Caregiver Behaviors)

CAREGIVER BEHAVIORS

Developmental Level	Mean Normal	Mean RD	RD DIS	MP DIS	t-value (df = 47)
Self-Regulation and Interest in the World:					
1. Interest in toys	2.00	1.81	.19		
2. Interest in child	1.93	1.90	.03 .93c		
3. Pleasant affect	1.89	1.67	.22a.89c		
4. Provides touch	1.43	1.52	0	1.43c	
5. Provides movement	1.36	.86	.50b	1.36c	
Self-Regulation Subscale	*8.60*	*7.76*		*MP 4.0*	
Forming Relationships, Attachment, and engagement:					
6. Relaxed with child	1.96	1.71	.25a	.46b	
7. Looks with affection	2.00	1.86	.14	1.00c	
8. Enjoys being with child	2.00	1.86	.14	.50b	
9. Overly anxious	1.86	1.61	.25a		
Forming Relationships Subscale	*7.82*	*7.04*		*MP 5.50*	
Two-Way, Purposeful Communication:					
10. Allows child to explore	1.82	1.71	.11		
11. Responds to child contingently	1.68	1.71	0		
12. Parallel play	1.86	1.95	0	.86c	
13. Plays at appropriate level	1.89	1.67	.22a		
14. Waits for child to respond	1.71	1.67	.04	.71c	
Two-Way Communication Subscale	*8.96*	*8.71*		*MP 8.50*	
Behavioral Organization and Elaboration (Complex Sense of Self)					
15. Initiates reciprocal interactions	1.32	1.14	.18	.32a	
16. Uses gestures in circles of communication	1.75	1.67	.08	.25a	

(Continued)

Table A-2.
(Continued)

CAREGIVER BEHAVIORS

Developmental Level	Mean		RD DIS	MP DIS	t-value (df = 47)
	Normal	RD			
17. Uses touch in circles of communication	1.39	1.05	.34a	1.39c	
Behavioral Organization Subscale	*4.46*	*3.85*		*MP 2.50*	
TOTAL CAREGIVER SCORE	**29.86**	**27.38**		**MP 20.50**	

Key: RD, regulatory disordered; MP, multi-problem family; DIS, discrimination index; df, degrees of freedom
a = small DIS (.20–.39); b = medium DIS (.40–.59); c = large DIS (.60+)

Note: MP = Discrimination index between normals and multi-problem/high-risk babies reported and mean values for subtests and total tests. Means are not reported for multi-problem group except for subscale and total test scores because N was only 6 for this age group; t scores reflect statistical differences between means for normal and RD groups.

Table A-2.
Means, Discrimination Indices, and T-Values: 10- to 12-Month-Old Data (Child Behaviors)

CHILD BEHAVIORS

Developmental Level	Mean		RD DIS	MP DIS	t-value (df = 47)
	Normal	RD			
Self-Regulation and Interest in the World:					
1. Interested in toys	1.89	1.90	0		
2. Explores objects freely	1.82	1.90	0	.32a	
3. Remains calm	1.96	2.00	0		
4. Comfortable with touch	1.89	1.90	0	1.89c	
5. Enjoys movement	1.25	.67	.58b	1.25c	2.25*
6. Overly visual	1.71	1.76	0	.21a	
7. Happy, content affect	1.82	1.52	.40b	1.32c	2.10*
8. Underreactivity	1.68	.95	.73c	.68c	3.20**
9. Overreactivity	1.21	.90	.31a	1.21c	
Self-Regulation Subscale	*15.25*	*13.52*		*MP 8.50*	
Forming Relationships, Attachment, and engagement:					
10. Interest in caregiver	1.96	1.81	.15	1.46c	
11. Curiosity in caregiver games	1.71	1.71	0	1.71c	
12. Closeness to caregiver	1.86	1.38	.48b	1.36c	2.39*
13. Gaze aversion	1.96	1.67	.29a	.46b	2.56*
14. Social references	1.79	1.62	.17	1.49c	
Forming Relationships Subscale	*9.29*	*8.19*		*MP 3.00*	
Two-Way, Purposeful Communication:					
15. Opens circles of communication	1.50	1.43	.07	1.00c	
16. Closes circles	1.75	1.48	.27a	.75c	
17. Shows anger or aggression	1.93	1.71	.22a	.93c	

(Continued)

Table A-2.
(Continued)

CHILD BEHAVIORS

Developmental Level	Mean		RD DIS	MP DIS	t-value (df = 47)
	Normal	RD			
18. Uses language	1.57	1.24	.23a	1.57c	
Two-Way Communication Subscale	6.75	5.86		MP 2.50	
TOTAL CHILD SCORE	**32.19**	**27.57**		**MP 14.00**	
TOTAL SCALE	**61.14**	**54.95**		**MP 34.50**	

Key: RD, regulatory disordered; MP, multi-problem family; DIS, discrimination index; df, degrees of freedom
a = small DIS (.20–.39); b = medium DIS (.40–.59); c = large DIS (.60+)
* = p<.05; ** = p<.01

Note: MP = Discrimination index between normals and multi-problem/high-risk babies reported and mean values for subtests and total tests. Means are not reported for multi-problem group except for subscale and total test scores because N was only 6 for this age group; t scores reflect statistical differences between means for normal and RD groups.

Table A-3.
Means, Discrimination Indices, and T-Values: 13- to 18-Month-Old Data (Caregiver Behaviors)

CAREGIVER BEHAVIORS

Developmental Level	Mean		RD DIS	MP DIS	t-value (df = 69)
	Normal	RD			
Self-Regulation and Interest in the World:					
1. Interest in child	2.00	1.91	.09		
2. Pleasant affect	1.92	1.77	.15	.48b	
3. Provides touch	1.61	1.54	.07	1.5c	
4. Provides movement	1.50	.94	.56b	1.5c	2.54*
Self-Regulation Subscale	7.03	6.17		MP 3.44	
Forming Relationships, Attachment, and Engagement:					
5. Relaxed with child	1.97	1.63	.34a		3.09**
6. Looks with affection	1.86	1.80	.06	.30a	
7. Enjoys being with child	1.97	1.77	.20a	.53b	
8. Overly anxious	1.94	1.69	.25a		2.47*
Forming Relationships Subscale	7.75	6.88		MP 7.0	
Two-Way, Purposeful Communication:					
9. Allows child to explore	1.97	1.66	.31a	.41b	2.69**
10. Responds to child contingently	1.81	1.66	.15	.81c	
11. Parallel play	1.89	1.91	0	.22a	
12. Plays at appropriate level	1.92	1.71	.21a	.25a	
13. Waits for child to respond	1.92	1.66	.26a		2.23*
Two-Way Communication Subscale	9.5	8.60		MP 7.66	
Behavioral Organization and Elaboration (Complex Sense of Self)					
14. Initiates reciprocal interactions	1.81	1.37	.44b	.25a	3.11**
15. Uses gestures in circles of communication	1.78	1.29	.49b	.67c	2.74**
16. Uses touch in circles of communication	1.58	.94	.64b	1.25c	3.09**
17. Shows pleasure with child	1.03	1.00	0	.25a	

(Continued)

Table A-3.
(Continued)

CAREGIVER BEHAVIORS

Developmental Level	Mean		RD DIS	MP DIS	t-value (df = 69)
	Normal	RD			
18. Appropriate limits	1.67	1.63	.04		
Behavioral Organization Subscale	7.86	6.22		MP 5.33	
TOTAL CAREGIVER SCORE	32.14	27.89		MP23.44	

Key: RD, regulatory disordered; MP, multi-problem family; DIS, discrimination index; df, degrees of freedom
a = small DIS (.20–.39); b = medium DIS (.40–.59); c = large DIS (.60+)
* = p<.05; ** = p<.01

Note: MP = Discrimination index between normals and multi-problem/high-risk babies reported and mean values for subtests and total tests. Means are not reported for multi-problem group except for subscale and total test scores because N was only 6 for this age group; t scores reflect statistical differences between means for normal and RD groups.

Table A-3.
Means, Discrimination Indices, and T-Values: 13- to 18-Month-Old Data (Child Behaviors)

CHILD BEHAVIORS

Developmental Level	Mean		RD DIS	MP DIS	t-value (df = 69)
	Normal	RD			
Self-Regulation and Interest in the World:					
1. Interested in toys	1.94	1.83	.11		
2. Explores objects freely	1.97	1.80	.17		
3. Remains calm	1.97	1.80	.17		
4. Comfortable with touch	1.83	1.46	.37a	1.83c	2.27*
5. Enjoys movement	1.17	.97	.20a	1.17c	
6. Happy, content affect	1.75	1.46	.29a	.42b	2.03*
7. Underreactivity	1.56	.63	.93c	.89c	4.83***
8. Overreactivity	1.47	.77	.70c	.47b	3.50***
Self-Regulation Subscale	*13.67*	*10.71*		*MP 8.89*	
Forming Relationships, Attachment, and Engagement:					
9. Interest in caregiver	1.86	1.60	.26a	.75c	
10. Sense of security	1.94	1.77	.17		
11. Curiosity in caregiver games	1.81	1.57	.24a		
12. Gaze aversion	1.72	1.54	.18	.98c	
13. Social references	1.75	1.54	.21a	.53b	
Forming Relationships Subscale	*9.08*	*8.03*		*MP 6.89*	
Two-Way, Purposeful Communication:					
14. Opens circles of communication	1.78	1.60	.18		
15. Responds contingently	1.83	1.49	.34a		2.50*
16. Shows anger or aggression	1.81	1.80	.01	.70c	
17. Uses language	1.72	1.06	.66c	.72c	3.72***

(Continued)

Table A-3.
(Continued)

CHILD BEHAVIORS

Developmental Level	Mean		RD DIS	MP DIS	t-value (df = 69)
	Normal	RD			
Two-Way Communication Subscale	7.14	5.94		MP 5.89	
TOTAL CHILD SCORE	30.22	24.97		MP 23.11	
TOTAL SCALE	62.36	52.86		MP 46.56	

Key: RD, regulatory disordered; MP, multi-problem family; DIS, discrimination index; df, degrees of freedom
a = small DIS (.20–.39); b = medium DIS (.40–.59); c = large DIS (.60+)
* = p<.05; ** = p<.01; *** = p<.001

Note: MP = Discrimination index between normals and multi-problem/high-risk babies reported and mean values for subtests and total tests. Means are not reported for multi-problem group except for subscale and total test scores because N was only 6 for this age group; t scores reflect statistical differences between means for normal and RD groups.

Table A-4.
Means, Discrimination Indices, and T-Values: 19- to 24-Month-Old Data (Caregiver Behaviors)

CAREGIVER BEHAVIORS

Developmental Level	Mean		RD DIS	t-value (df = 83)
	Normal	RD		
Self-Regulation and Interest in the World:				
1. Pleasant affect	1.93	1.76	.17	2.10*
2. Provides touch	1.50	1.15	.35a	
3. Provides movement	.50	.90	0	
Self-Regulation Subscale	*3.93*	*3.80*		
Forming Relationships, Attachment, and Engagement:				
4. Relaxed with child	1.89	1.85	.04	
5. Looks with affection	1.95	1.88	.07	
6. Enjoys being with child	1.98	1.88	.10	
Forming Relationships Subscale	*5.82*	*5.60*		
Two-Way, Purposeful Communication:				
7. Allows child to explore	1.82	1.73	.09	
8. Responds to child contingently	1.77	1.76	.01	
9. Parallel play	1.73	1.78	0	
10. Plays at appropriate level	1.93	1.88	.05	
11. Waits for child to respond	1.77	1.73	.04	
Two-Way Communication Subscale	*9.02*	*8.87*		
Behavioral Organization and Elaboration (Complex Sense of Self)				
12. Initiates reciprocal interactions	1.82	1.73	.09	
13. Uses gestures in circles of communication	1.50	1.61	0	
14. Uses touch in circles of communication	.82	1.02	0	
15. Elaborates on child's play	1.50	1.32	.18	
16. Allows child to assert self	1.93	1.56	.37a	3.00**
17. Shows pleasure with child	1.80	1.46	.34a	2.49*

(Continued)

Table A-4.
(Continued)

CAREGIVER BEHAVIORS

Developmental Level	Mean		RD DIS	t-value (df = 83)
	Normal	RD		
18. Appropriate limits	1.89	1.83	.05	
Behavioral Organization Subscale	*11.25*	*10.54*		
TOTAL CAREGIVER SCORE	**30.02**	**28.83**		

Key: RD, regulatory disordered; DIS, discrimination index; df, degrees of freedom
a = small DIS (.20–.39); b = medium DIS (.40–.59); c = large DIS (.60+)
* = p<.05; ** = p<.01

Note: t scores reflect statistical differences between means for normal and RD groups.

Table A-4.
Means, Discrimination Indices, and T-Values: 19- to 24-Month-Old Data (Child Behaviors)

CHILD BEHAVIORS

Developmental Level	Mean		RD DIS	t-value (df = 83)
	Normal	RD		
Self-Regulation and Interest in the World:				
1. Interested in toys	1.98	1.73	.25a	3.10**
2. Explores objects freely	1.98	1.80	.18	2.36*
3. Remains calm	1.95	1.88	.07	
4. Comfortable with touch	1.86	1.56	.30a	2.14*
5. Enjoys movement	.57	1.15	0	
6. Happy, content affect	1.75	1.66	.09	
7. Focused on objects	1.86	1.63	.23a	2.02*
8. Underreactivity	.68	.90	0	
9. Overreactivity	1.55	1.07	.48b	2.66**
Self-Regulation Subscale	*14.18*	*13.39*		
Forming Relationships, Attachment, and Engagement:				
10. Interest in caregiver	1.95	1.83	.12	
11. Sense of security	1.98	1.90	.08	
12. Curiosity in caregiver games	1.84	1.68	.16	
13. Closeness to caregiver	1.95	1.66	.29a	2.84**
14. Gaze aversion	1.59	1.59	0	
15. Social references	1.93	1.76	.17	2.29*
16. Communicates across space	1.61	1.27	.34a	
Forming Relationships Subscale	*12.86*	*11.68*		
Two-Way, Purposeful Communication:				
17. Opens circles of communication	1.89	1.76	.13	
18. Initiates purposeful actions	1.95	1.76	.19	2.12*
19. Responds contingently	1.93	1.80	.13	
20. Shows anger or aggression	1.73	1.66	.07	
21. Uses language	1.86	1.56	.30a	2.35*

(Continued)

Table A-4.
(Continued)

CHILD BEHAVIORS

Developmental Level	Mean Normal	RD	RD DIS	t-value (df = 83)
Two-Way Communication Subscale	9.36	8.54		
Behavioral Organization and Elaboration (Complex Sense of Self)				
22. Organizes several circles of communication	1.68	1.34	.34a	2.29*
23. Imitates caregiver ideas	1.34	1.02	.32a	
Behavioral Organization Subscore	3.02	2.37		
TOTAL CHILD SCORE	39.43	35.98		
TOTAL SCALE	69.45	64.80		

Key: RD, regulatory disordered; DIS, discrimination index; df, degrees of freedom
a = small DIS (.20–.39); b = medium DIS (.40–.59); c = large DIS (.60+)
* = p<.05; ** = p<.01
Note: t scores reflect statistical differences between means for normal and RD groups.

Table A-5.
Means, Discrimination Indices, and T-Values: 25- to 35-Month-Old Data (Caregiver Behaviors)

CAREGIVER BEHAVIORS

Developmental Level	Mean Normal	RD	DIS	t-value (df = 33)	PDD	DIS	t-value (df = 37)
Self-Regulation and Interest in the World:							
1. Interacts calmly	1.95	1.88	.07		1.65	.30a	2.41*
2. Pleasant affect	1.89	1.75	.14		1.65	.24a	
3. Provides touch	1.58	1.38	.20a		1.05	.53b	
4. Provides movement	.47	1.13	0		.65	0	
Self-Regulation Subscale	*5.89*	*6.12*			*5.0*		
Forming Relationships, Attachment, and Engagement:							
5. Relaxed with child	1.95	1.69	.26a	2.10*	1.40	.55b	3.03**
6. Looks with affection	2.00	1.94	.06		1.70	.30a	
7. Enjoys being with child	1.89	1.87	.02		1.55	.34a	
8. Overly anxious	1.89	1.75	.12		1.60	.29a	
Forming Relationships Subscale	*7.73*	*7.25*			*6.25*		
Two-Way, Purposeful Communication:							
9. Allows child to explore	1.95	1.75	.20a		1.45	.50b	2.74**
10. Responds to child contingently	2.00	1.87	.13		1.45	.55b	
11. Parallel play	2.00	1.75	.25a		1.80	.20a	
12. Plays at appropriate level	1.89	1.69	.20a		1.45	.44b	2.06*
13. Waits for child to respond	1.95	1.62	.33a	2.11*	1.40	.55b	2.62*
Two-Way Communication Subscale	*9.78*	*8.68*			*2.92*		
Behavioral Organization and Elaboration (Complex Sense of Self)							
14. Initiates reciprocal interactions	1.95	1.50	.45b	2.29*	.80	1.15c	5.79**
15. Uses gestures in circles of communication	1.42	1.00	.42b		1.50	0	
16. Uses language in communication	2.00	1.69	.31a		1.80	.20a	

(Continued)

Table A-5.
(Continued)

CAREGIVER BEHAVIORS

Developmental Level	Mean Normal	RD	DIS	t-value (df = 33)	PDD	DIS	t-value (df = 37)
17. Elaborates on child's play	1.58	1.44	.14		.95	.63c	
18. Allows child to assert self	1.95	1.87	.12		1.50	.45b	
19. Shows pleasure with child	1.63	1.31	.32a		.70	.93c	4.10***
20. Appropriate limits	1.79	1.38	.31a		1.55	.24a	
Behavioral Organization Subscale	*12.31*	*10.18*			*4.58*		
Representational Capacity							
21. Encourages symbolic play	1.79	1.62	.17		.95	.84c	
22. Elaborates on pretend play idea	1.21	1.31	0		.10	1.11c	4.61**
23. Allows child to express closeness	1.26	1.31	0		.05	1.21c	5.34**
24. Asks questions during play	.79	.88	0		.10	.69c	2.86**
25. Allows child to express assertiveness	.89	1.00	0		.10	.79c	3.41**
Representational Capacity Subscore	*6.05*	*6.62*			*2.42*		
TOTAL CAREGIVER SCORE	**41.79**	**38.88**			**29.00**		

Key: RD, regulatory disordered; DIS, discrimination index; PDD, pervasive developmental disorder; df, degrees of freedom
a = small DIS (.20–.39); b = medium DIS (.40–.59); c = large DIS (.60+) ; * = p<.05; ** = p<.01; *** = p<.001

Note: t scores reflect statistical differences between means for normal and RD groups.

Table A-5.
Means, Discrimination Indices, and T-Values: 25- to 35-Month-Old Data (Child Behaviors)

CHILD BEHAVIORS

Developmental Level	Mean Normal	RD	DIS	t-value (df = 33)	PDD	DIS	t-value (df = 37)
Self-Regulation and Interest in the World:							
1. Interested in toys	2.00	1.87	.15		1.55	.45b	
2. Explores objects freely	2.00	1.94	.06		1.30	.70c	
3. Remains calm	2.00	1.87	.13		1.45	.55b	
4. Comfortable with touch	1.95	1.50	.45b	2.53*	1.10	.85c	4.51**
5. Enjoys movement	.63	1.31	0		.85	0	
6. Overly visual	1.47	1.81	0		1.35	.12	
7. Happy, content affect	1.84	1.50	.34a		1.15	.69c	3.63***
8. Focused on objects	1.95	1.87	.08		1.00	.95c	4.13***
9. Underreactivity	.89	.94	0		.30	.59b	2.13*
10. Overreactivity	1.42	1.19	.23a		.70	.72c	3.00**
Self-Regulation Subscale	*16.16*	*15.81*			*10.75*		
Forming Relationships, Attachment, and Engagement:							
11. Interest in caregiver	1.84	1.81	.03		1.20	.64c	2.90**
12. Sense of security	2.00	1.87	.13		1.40	.60c	
13. Curiosity in caregiver games	1.74	1.62	.12		.85	.89c	3.74**
14. Displeasure if caregiver unresponsive	1.47	1.25	.22a		1.15	.32a	
15. Recovers from distress	1.58	1.62	0		1.25	.33a	
16. Closeness to caregiver	1.74	1.75	0		.85	.89c	3.94**
17. Gaze aversion	1.26	1.69	0		.65	.61c	2.27*
18. Social references	2.00	1.81	.19		.95	1.05c	
19. Communicates across space	1.47	1.44	.03		.40	1.07c	4.20**
Forming Relationships Subscale	*15.11*	*14.88*			*8.7*		
Two-Way, Purposeful Communication:							
20. Opens circles of communication	1.95	1.69	.25a		.95	1.0c	4.25**

(Continued)

Table A-5.
(Continued)

CHILD BEHAVIORS

Developmental Level	Mean Normal	RD	DIS	t-value (df = 33)	PDD	DIS	t-value (df = 37)
21. Initiates purposeful actions	1.95	1.81	.14		.80	1.15c	7.63**
22. Responds contingently	1.84	1.75	.09		1.10	.74c	3.13**
23. Shows anger or aggression	1.47	1.75	0		1.30	.17	
24. Uses language	1.89	1.81	.09		.85	1.04c	4.63**
Two-Way Communication Subscale		9.11	8.81		5.00		
Behavioral Organization and Elaboration (Complex Sense of Self)							
25. Organizes several circles of communication	1.53	1.44	.09		.35	1.18c	6.65**
26. Imitates caregiver idea	1.11	1.38	0		.30	.81c	3.42**
Behavioral Organization Subscale	2.63	2.81			.65		
Representational Capacity							
27. Engages symbolic play	1.53	1.62	0		.10	1.43c	7.1***
28. Pretend play of one idea	1.16	.81	.35a		0	1.16c	
29. Uses language to communicate wishes	.95	1.06	0		.15	.80c	3.12**
30. Uses pretend play to express closeness	.79	1.00	0		.05	.74c	3.3**
Representational Capacity Subscore	3.37	3.94			.30		
TOTAL CHILD SCORE	46.37	46.25			25.40		
TOTAL FOR SCALE	88.16	85.12			54.40		

Key: RD, regulatory disordered; DIS, discrimination index; PDD, pervasive developmental disorder; df, degrees of freedom
a = small DIS (.20–.39); b = medium DIS (.40–.59); c = large DIS (.60+) ; * = p<.05; ** = p<.01; *** = p<.001

Note: t scores reflect statistical differences between means for normal and RD groups.

Table A-6.
Means, Discrimination Indices, and T-Values: 3- to 4-Year-Old Data
(Caregiver Behaviors)

CAREGIVER BEHAVIORS

Developmental Level	Mean Normal	RD	DIS	PDD	DIS	MP	DIS
Self-Regulation and Interest in the World:							
1. Interacts calmly	1.88	1.74	.14	1.84	.04	1.94	0
2. Pleasant affect	1.88	1.43**	.41b	1.42**	.46b	1.38	.50b
3. Provides touch	.76	.86	0	.89	0	.19	.57b
Self-Regulation Subscale	*4.73*	*4.55*		*4.47*		*3.62*	
Forming Relationships, Attachment, and Engagement:							
4. Relaxed with child	1.91	1.72	.19	1.68	.23a	1.69	.22a
5. Looks with affection	1.91	1.57*	.34a	1.58*	.33a	1.5	.41b
6. Enjoys being with child	1.85	1.53	.32a	1.63	.22a	1.56	.29a
7. Maintains connection across space	1.94	1.81	.13	1.68	.26a	1.81	.13
Forming Relationships Subscale	*7.61*	*6.63*		*6.57*		*6.56*	
Two-Way, Purposeful Communication:							
8. Allows child to explore	1.88	1.71	.17	1.47*	.41b	1.69	.19
9. Responds to child contingently	1.94	1.74	.20a	1.42*	.52b	1.63	.31a
10. Parallel play	1.71	1.64	.07	1.79	0	1.50	.21a
11. Plays at appropriate level	1.94	1.57**	.37a	1.37**	.57b	1.50	.44b
12. Waits for child to respond	1.88	1.72	.16	1.42**	.42b	1.56	.32a
Two-Way Communication Subscale	*9.35*	*8.37*		*7.47*		*7.87*	
Behavioral Organization and Elaboration (Complex Sense of Self)							
13. Initiates reciprocal interactions	1.91	1.67	.24a	1.00**	.91c	1.87	.04
14. Uses gestures in circles of communication	1.44	1.00*	.44b	1.16	.28a	1.31	.07
15. Uses language in communication	1.94	1.79*	.15	1.63**	.31a	1.87	.07
16. Elaborates on child's play	1.82	1.50*	.32a	.74**	1.08c	1.69	.13
17. Allows child to assert self	1.91	1.79	.12	1.37**	.54b	1.75	.16

(Continued)

Table A-6.
(Continued)

CAREGIVER BEHAVIORS

Developmental Level	Mean						
	Normal	RD	DIS	PDD	DIS	MP	DIS
18. Shows pleasure with child	1.71	1.22**	.49b	.63**	1.07c	1.44	.27a
19. Appropriate limits	1.88	1.38**	.50b	1.42*	.46b	1.31	.57b
Behavioral Organization Subscale	*12.61*	*10.36*		*4.23*		*11.25*	
Representational Capacity	/////	/////	/////	/////	/////	/////	/////
20. Encourages symbolic play	1.71	1.55	.16	1.21*	.50b	1.50	.21a
21. Elaborates on pretend play idea	1.62	1.29	.33a	.37**	1.25c	1.25	.37a
22. Allows child to express closeness	1.62	1.19*	.43b	.26**	1.36c	1.25	.37a
23. Asks questions during play	1.35	1.03	.32a	.37**	.98c	.81	.54b
24. Allows child to express assertiveness	.71	.95	0	.11*	.50c	.94	0
Representational Capacity Subscore	*7.05*	*6.29*		*2.31*		*5.87*	
Representational Differentiation	/////	/////	/////	/////	/////	/////	/////
25. Elaborates on child's pretend play	1.15 .67	.48b	.37**	.78c	.75	.40b	
26. Connects three or more ideas into sequence	.56	.50	.06	.11**	.45b	.69	0
27. Helps child to elaborate on emotional themes	1.09	.48	.61c	.11**	.98c	.94	.15
Representational Differentiation Subscore	*2.79*	*1.65*		*.58*		*2.37*	
TOTAL CAREGIVER SCORE	**44.18**	**37.88**		**29.37**		**37.56**	

Key: RD, regulatory disordered; DIS, discrimination index; PDD, pervasive developmental disorder; MP, multi-problem family

a = small DIS (.20–.39); b = medium DIS (.40–.59); c = large DIS (.60+) ; * = p<.05; ** = p<.01

Note: t scores reflect statistical differences between means for normal and RD groups.

Table A-6.
Means, Discrimination Indices, and T-Values: 3- to 4-Year-Old Data (Child Behaviors)

CHILD BEHAVIORS

Developmental Level	Mean						
	Normal	RD	DIS	PDD	DIS	MP	DIS
Self-Regulation and Interest in the World:							
1. Interested in toys	2.00	1.93	.07	1.47	.53b	2.00	0
2. Explores objects freely	2.00	1.95	.05	1.47	.53b	1.94	.06
3. Remains calm	2.00	1.93	.07	1.63	.37a	2.00	0
4. Comfortable with touch	1.53	1.33	.20a	1.58	0	.13	1.4c
5. Happy, content affect	1.82	1.47**	.35a	1.16**	.66c	1.38	.44b
6. Focused on objects	2.00	1.78	.22a	1.53	.47b	2.00	0
7. Underreactivity	1.09	.98	.11	.53*	.56b	.44	.65c
8. Overreactivity	1.09	.90	.19	.79	.30a	1.50	0
Self-Regulation Subscale	*13.65*	*12.62*		*10.69*		*11.5*	
Forming Relationships, Attachment, and Engagement:							
9. Interest in caregiver	1.97	1.71	.26a	1.00**	.97c	1.75	.22a
10. Sense of security	2.00	1.83	.13	1.42	.58b	1.94	.06
11. Curiosity in caregiver games	1.85	1.31**	.54b	1.32**	.53b	1.69	.16
12. Displeasure if caregiver unresponsive	1.82	1.59	.23a	1.32*	.60c	1.56	.26a
13. Closeness to caregiver	2.00	1.57	.43b	.79	1.21c	1.63	.37a
14. Gaze aversion	1.35	1.47	0	.79*	.54b	1.38	0
15. Social references	1.94	1.57**	.37a	1.42**	.52b	1.87	.07
16. Communicates across space	1.76	1.43**	.33a	.11	1.65c	1.50	.26a
Forming Relationships Subscale	*14.71*	*12.47*		*7.00*		*13.31*	
Two-Way, Purposeful Communication:							
17. Opens circles of communication	2.00	1.88	.12	1.00	1.00c	1.75	.25a
18. Initiates purposeful actions	1.97	1.74*	.23a	1.26**	.61c	2.00	0
19. Responds contingently	1.88	1.78	.10	1.26**	.62c	1.87	.01
20. Uses language	2.00	1.76	.34a	.79	1.31c	1.81	.19

(Continued)

Table A-6.
(Continued)

CHILD BEHAVIORS

Developmental Level	Mean Normal	RD	DIS	PDD	DIS	MP	DIS
Two-Way Communication Subscale	7.86	7.15		4.31		7.44	
Behavioral Organization and Elaboration (Complex Sense of Self)							
21. Organizes several circles of communication	1.97	1.62**	.35a	.32**	1.65c	1.75	.22a
22. Imitates caregiver idea	1.06	.83	.23a	.21**	.85c	1.50	0
Behavioral Organization Subscale	3.03	2.45		.53		3.25	
Representational Capacity							
23. Engages symbolic play	1.82	1.62	.20a	.58**	1.24c	1.38	.44b
24. Pretend play with caregiver	1.38	1.29	.09	.32**	1.06c		
25. Uses language to communicate wishes	1.88	1.52*	.36a	.21**	1.67c	1.00	.88c
26. Uses pretend play to express closeness	1.56	1.22	.34a	.11**	1.45c	1.00	.46b
27. Expresses themes of pleasure	.85	.52*	.33a	0	.85c	.50	.35a
28. Expresses themes of assertiveness	1.00	.55*	.45b	.11**	.89c	.88	.12
29. Creates pretend drama of two or more ideas	1.71	1.17	.54b	.21**	1.5c	1.00	.71c
Representational Capacity Subscore	8.82	6.60		1.21		5.75	
Representational Differentiation							
30. Pretend play of two ideas logically connected	1.47	1.05*	.42b	.11**	1.36c	.88	.59b
31. Elaborates on play sequence; responds to questions	.56	.41	.15	.11**	.45b	.38	.18
32. Communicates themes of two or more ideas about closeness	1.32	.71**	.41b	.11**	1.21c	.75	.57b
33. Communicates themes about pleasure	.38	.40	0	0	.38b	.50	0
34. Communicates themes about assertiveness	.62	.36	.26a	.11*	.51b	.63	0

(Continued)

Table A-6.
(Continued)

CHILD BEHAVIORS

Developmental Level	Mean		DIS	PDD	DIS	MP	DIS
	Normal	RD					
Representational Differentiation Subscore	*4.35*	*2.93*		*.42*		*3.13*	
TOTAL CHILD SCORE	**52.42**	**44.58**		**24.16**		**44.38**	
TOTAL FOR SCALE	**96.59**	**82.46**		**53.53**		**81.94**	

Key: RD, regulatory disordered; DIS, discrimination index; PDD, pervasive developmental disorder; MP, multi-problem family

a = small DIS (.20–.39); b = medium DIS (.40–.59); c = large DIS (.60+) ; * = p<.05; ** = p<.01

Note: t scores reflect statistical differences between means for normal and RD groups.

Table B-1.
Means and F Values for Subtest and Total Test Scores: 7- to 9-Month-Olds

Subtest	Mean for Groups			F df = 2,60	p value
	Normal	RD	MP		
Caregiver					
Self-regulation and interest in the world	7.53	6.10	5.83	4.279	<.05
Forming relationships, attachment, and engagement	5.67	4.95	4.42	4.603	<.05
Two-way, purposeful communication	8.16	7.52	6.67	1.429	N.S.
Total Caregiver Score	*21.42*	*18.57*	*16.86*	*3.33*	*<.01*
Child					
Self-regulation and interest in the world	13.89	11.11	7.33	14.301	<.001
Forming relationships, attachment, and engagement	9.50	6.1	5.67	14.150	<.001
Total Child Score	*23.38*	*17.21*	*13.00*	*5.64*	*<.001*
TOTAL FOR SCALE	**44.80**	**35.78**	**31.67**	**17.98**	**<.001**

Key: RD, regulatory disordered; MP, multi-problem family; df, degrees of freedom

Table B-2.
Means and F Values for Subtest and Total Test Scores: 10- to 12-Month-Olds

Subtest	Mean for Groups			F df = 2.50	p value
	Normal	RD	MP		
Caregiver	/////////	/////////	/////////	/////////	/////////
Self-regulation and interest in the world	8.60	7.76	4.0	5.874	<.01
Forming relationships, attachment, and engagement	7.82	7.04	5.50	4.353	<.05
Two-way, purposeful communication	8.96	8.71	8.50	.173	N.S.
Behavioral organization, problem-solving, and internalization	4.46	3.85	2.5	1.714	N.S.
Total Caregiver Score	*29.86*	*27.38*	*20.50*	*4.29*	*<.05*
Child	/////////	/////////	/////////	/////////	/////////
Self-regulation and interest in the world	15.25	13.52	3.50	6.112	<.01
Forming relationships, attachment, and engagement	9.29	8.19	3.00	9.775	<.001
Two-way, purposeful communication	6.75	5.86	2.50	4.683	<.05
Total Child Score	*32.19*	*27.57*	*14.00*	*10.63*	*<.001*
TOTAL FOR SCALE	**61.14**	**54.95**	**34.50**	**8.431**	**<.001**

Key: RD, regulatory disordered; MP, multi-problem family; df, degrees of freedom

Table B-3.
Means and F Values for Subtest and Total Test Scores: 13- to 18-Month-Olds

Subtest	Mean for Groups			F df = 2.79	p value
	Normal	RD	MP		
Caregiver					
Self-regulation and interest in the world	7.03	6.17	3.44	16.088	<.001
Forming relationships, attachment, and engagement	7.75	6.88	7.00	4.23	<.05
Two-way, purposeful communication	9.5	8.6	7.66	5.479	<.01
Behavioral organization, problem-solving, and internalization	7.86	6.22	5.33	5.963	<.01
Total Caregiver Score	*32.14*	*27.89*	*23.44*	*10.249*	*<.001*
Child					
Self-regulation and interest in the world	13.67	10.71	8.89	18.55	<.001
Forming relationships, attachment, and engagement	9.08	8.03	6.78	4.24	<.05
Two-way, purposeful communication	7.14	5.94	5.89	4.131	<.05
Total Child Score	*30.22*	*24.97*	*23.11*	*8.987*	*<.001*
TOTAL FOR SCALE	**62.36**	**52.86**	**46.56**	**11.956**	**<.001**

Key: RD, regulatory disordered; MP, multi-problem family; df, degrees of freedom

Table B-4.
Means and F Values for Subtest and Total Test Scores: 19- to 24-Month-Olds

Subtest	Mean for Groups		F df = 1.85	p value
	Normal	RD		
Caregiver	/////	/////	/////	/////
Self-regulation and interest in the world	3.93	3.80	2.02	<.05
Forming relationships, attachment, and engagement	5.82	5.60	2.39	<.01
Two-way, purposeful communication	9.02	8.87	1.30	N.S.
Behavioral organization, problem-solving, and internalization	11.25	10.54	1.39	N.S.
Total Caregiver Score	*30.02*	*28.83*	*1.45*	*N.S.*
Child	/////	/////	/////	/////
Self-regulation and interest in the world	14.18	13.39	5.71	<.001
Forming relationships, attachment, and engagement	12.86	11.68	2.78	<.001
Two-way, purposeful communication	9.36	8.54	2.55	<.01
Behavioral organization, problem-solving, and internalization	3.02	2.37	1.52	N.S.
Total Child Score	*39.43*	*35.98*	*4.40*	*<.001*
TOTAL FOR SCALE	**69.45**	**64.80**	**2.62**	**<.01**

Key: RD, regulatory disordered; df, degrees of freedom

Table B-5.
Means and F Values for Subtest and Total Test Scores: 25- to 35-Month-Olds

Subtest	Mean for Groups			F df = 3.57	p value
	Normal	RD	PDD		
Caregiver					
Self-regulation and interest in the world	5.89	6.12	5.00	1.318	N.S.
Forming relationships, attachment, and engagement	7.73	7.25	6.25	4.461	<.01
Two-way, purposeful communication	9.78	8.68	2.92	3.734	<.05
Behavioral organization, problem-solving, and internalization	12.31	10.18	4.58	3.375	<.05
Representational capacity	6.05	6.62	1.40	9.355	<.001
Total Caregiver Score	*41.79*	*38.88*	*29.00*	*7.803*	*<.001*
Child					
Self-regulation and interest in the world	16.16	15.81	10.75	11.869	<.001
Forming relationships, attachment, and engagement	15.11	14.88	8.70	11.844	<.001
Two-way, purposeful communication	9.11	8.81	5.00	12.621	<.001
Behavioral organization, problem-solving, and internalization	2.63	2.81	.65	12.509	<.001
Representational capacity	3.37	3.94	.30	10.807	<.001
Total Child Score	*46.37*	*46.25*	*25.40*	*21.019*	*<.001*
TOTAL FOR SCALE	**88.16**	**85.12**	**54.40**	**16.921**	**<.001**

Key: RD, regulatory disordered; PDD, pervasive developmental disorder; df, degrees of freedom

Table B-6.
Means and F Values for Subtest and Total Test Scores: 3- to 4-Year-Olds

Subtest	Mean for Groups				F df = 3.126	p value
	Normal	RD	PDD	MP		
Caregiver						
Self-regulation and interest in the world	4.73	4.55	4.47	3.62	1.296	N.S.
Forming relationships, attachment, and engagement	7.61	6.63	6.57	6.56	2.12	N.S.
Two-way, purposeful communication	9.35	8.37	7.47	7.87	2.68	<.05
Behavioral organization, problem-solving, and internalization	12.61	10.36	4.23	11.25	6.988	<.001
Representational capacity	7.05	6.29	2.31	5.87	8.474	<.001
Representational differentiation	2.79	1.65	.58	2.37	5.09	<.01
Total Caregiver Score	*44.18*	*37.88*	*29.37*	*37.56*	*5.799*	*<.001*
Child						
Self-regulation and interest in the world	13.65	12.62	10.69	11.5	5.307	<.01
Forming relationships, attachment, and engagement	14.71	12.47	7.0	13.31	21.287	<.001
Two-way, purposeful communication	7.86	7.15	4.31	7.44	14.482	<.001
Behavioral organization, problem-solving, and internalization	3.03	2.45	.53	3.25	21.027	<.001
Representational capacity	8.82	6.60	1.21	5.75	20.172	<.001
Representational differentiation	4.35	2.93	.42	3.13	6.178	<.001
Total Child Score	*52.42*	*44.58*	*24.16*	*44.38*	*25.484*	*<.001*
TOTAL FOR SCALE	**96.59**	**82.46**	**53.53**	**81.94**	**15.66**	**<.001**

Key: RD, regulatory disordered; PDD, pervasive developmental disorder; MP, multi-problem family;
df, degrees of freedom

Appendix B

Research Version of the Functional Emotional Assessment Scale

Functional Emotional Assessment Scale

Administration
and
Scoring Form

Stanley I. Greenspan, M.D.
and
Georgia A DeGangi, Ph.D., OTR

Interdisciplinary Council on
Developmental and Learning Disorders
Bethesda, MD

Protocol Booklet - Research Version

Caregiver Behaviors

Name of Child: _____   Date of Testing: _____

Age of Child: _____

Person Playing
With Child: Mother: ___   Father: ___
              Caregiver: ___   Examiner: ___

General Scoring

Scoring is on a two-point scale for most items, except where indicated, and is:
  0 = not at all or very brief
  1 = present some of time, observed several times
  2 = consistently present, observed many times
  Indicate N/O for behaviors that are not observed.

Where indicated to convert a score, transform the scoring as follows:
  0 becomes a 2
  1 = 1
  2 becomes a 0

Scores for symbolic play should be entered in the SYM column and scores for sensory play entered in the SENS column. When the examiner facilitates play with the child, enter scores in the EXAM column. The last column may be used for entering scores for additional caregivers (e.g., mother, father, foster parent, babysitter) observed playing with the child.

Scores are interpreted for the primary caregiver playing with the child for the symbolic and sensory play situations. If scores do not differ for symbolic and sensory play, then only one score is interpreted. However, if behaviors differ for the different play situations, then two scores are calculated, one for symbolic play, one for sensory play. These are interpreted using the cutoff scores presented in the profile form.

	SYM	SENS	EXAM
SELF-REGULATION AND INTEREST IN THE WORLD			
1. Shows interest in toys through facial or verbal expressions of interest or by handling and touching toys, but not so absorbed by toys that the caregiver plays with toys alone, ignoring the child.			
2. Shows sustained interest in child, focuses on child's signals (gestures, vocalizations), keeping child involved in play.			
3. Interacts calmly with child, able to wait for child's responses.			
4. Shows pleasant or animated, happy affect throughout play. *Scoring:* 0 = flat, somber, or depressed affect. 1 = content, but neutral. 2 = happy and animated with warm and engaging smiles.			
5. Is sensitive and responsive to child's need for touch by stroking or touching baby in pleasurable ways and/or encourages child to explore textured toys.			
6. Provides pleasurable movement experiences to the child or encourages movement exploration.			
Total For Self-Regulation and Interest in the World			
FORMING RELATIONSHIPS, ATTACHMENT, AND ENGAGEMENT			
7. Is relaxed during interchange with child, not overly attentive to child's every action.			
8. Looks at child with affection, showing a warm connection.			
9. Enjoys being with and playing with the child through smiles or a joyful look and emits a sense of warmth by providing inviting gestures. Keep in mind cultural differences in how this may be expressed.			
10. Is overly anxious in attachment to child, overwhelming child with affectionate touching OR is not comfortable showing feelings and relating warmly and intimately with child, appearing overly vigilant toward child. (Circle which one.) *Scoring:* 0 = many times . 1 = sometimes. 2 = briefly or not at all.			
11. Maintains a verbal or visual connection with child, showing clear availability and interest in the child. Child may move away from caregiver to explore room, yet the caregiver stays connected to the child across space through gestures, vocalizations, and facial expressions.			
Total for Forming Relationships, Attachment, and Engagement			

	SYM	SENS	EXAM
TWO-WAY, PURPOSEFUL COMMUNICATION			

TWO-WAY, PURPOSEFUL COMMUNICATION

12. Opening circle of communication: Initiates interactions with child through vocalizations or gestures, creating interactive opportunities with child.

13. Responds to child's wishes, intentions, and actions in a contingent way, building on how the child wishes to play. For example, child may hand toy to parent, and parent responds by taking it and saying something about the toy, then gives the child an opportunity to respond to what parent just did.
    Scoring:
    0 = consistently does opposite to what baby seeks, misreads child's cues, changing activity from what child wants to do.
    1 = misreads child's signals 25 to 50% of time, changing activity or toy while at other times reads child's signals accurately.
    2 = responds to child's signals in appropriate way most of the time (up to 75% of time responsive to child), staying on the activity that the child has chosen.

14. Predominately handles toys, engaging in parallel play and removing attention from playing with child.
    Converted Score* Score of 0 converts to 2

15. Plays with child at developmentally appropriate level. Caregiver may play slightly above child's level of skill, modeling new ways to do things or labeling what child does or describing the functions of objects.

16. Stimulates child at pace that allows child to respond, waiting for child's responses. Avoids overstimulating child with language or actions.

17. Allows child to decide on the play topic, to initiate play and explore toys in ways that the child seeks or needs.

Total for Two-Way, Purposeful Communication

STOP HERE FOR PARENTS OF 7- TO 9-MONTH-OLDS

BEHAVIORAL ORGANIZATION, PROBLEM-SOLVING, AND INTERNALIZATION (A Complex Sense of Self)

18. Responds and initiates reciprocal back and forth chains of interactions with child, stringing together connected circles of communication or units of interaction. For example, caregiver introduces baby doll, baby touches doll's face, mother touches doll's hair, baby pats the doll, mother says "baby," and baby glances between mother and doll). The caregiver may imitate child (i.e., pushing car alongside child), then interject her turn by an action or verbalization related to the child's actions (i.e., "Oh, a bump!", then bumps her car into child's car).
    Scoring:
    0 = 0 to 2 circles.
    1 = 3 to 5 circles.
    2 = 6 or more circles.

	SYM	SENS	EXAM
19. Uses gestures and facial expressions as a modality to promote circles of communication.			
20. Uses touch or rough house play as a modality to promote circles of communication.			
21. Shows pleasure and excitement in playing with child in whatever way the child wishes to play. *Scoring:* 0 = little pleasure and excitement shown by caregiver. 1 = pleasure and excitement sustained by parent over the course of several (3 to 5) circles of communication. 2 = pleasure and excitement sustained for many (6 or more) circles of communication. *Note here if child is unable to sustain circles of communication if it affects caregiver's score:* Child can sustain circles: _____ Child cannot: _____			
22. Expresses appropriate limits on baby. The caregiver may redirect child not to leave room, not to hit her, or not to throw toy. If no need for limits arise during play, mark N/O and give 2 points.			
23. Elaborates on and builds complexity into the child's play behaviors while engaged in interactive sequences between parent and child. The parent expands on what the child does while remaining on the child's play topic (e.g., the parent does not introduce a completely new play idea). The parent provides a small challenge or interesting twist to the play that requires the child to respond slightly differently than before, thus creating a problem solving opportunity for the child. For example, the parent and child are pushing a car back and forth toward each other. The parent expands on this by creating a wall with her leg to prevent the car from rolling, then waits to see how the child will solve this situation.			
24. Allows child to assert self in play, exploring with confidence in what that he or she wishes (i.e., child expresses strong wish to play in a certain way such as banging toys, being silly, holding a doll, or running around room.) Parent supports the child's needs for dependency and closeness, assertiveness and curiosity, aggression, autonomy, or pleasure and excitement by admiring, showing interest, and/or by joining in to the child's play in whatever way the child seeks. Problems that may interfere with caregiver's capacity to support this area might be intrusiveness, withdrawal, overprotectiveness, or playing at level far above child's level of competence.			
Total for Behavioral Organization, Problem-Solving, and Internalization			
STOP HERE FOR PARENTS OF 10- TO 24-MONTH-OLDS			

	SYM	SENS	EXAM
REPRESENTATIONAL CAPACITY (Elaboration)			
25. Encourages child to engage in symbolic play by modeling or combining materials in ways that encourage representational actions (i.e., mother holds spoon near baby doll's mouth and says, "Feed baby?"). Parent appears comfortable in playing make believe.			
26. Elaborates on child's pretend play idea by building on child's ideas and adding some complexity to them. (e.g., child puts doll in car and pushes it and caregiver says "Oh, is Daddy going to the store?").			
27. Allows child to express pretend play themes involving closeness or dependency (e.g., nurturing doll) without competing for child's attention to be the one nurtured.			
28. Sustains pretend play, showing interest, pleasure, and excitement about the child's pretend play idea by asking questions, laughing or smiling, and joining into the child's play with enthusiasm (e.g., caregiver says "Oh, that's a good idea. What happens now? That's so funny!").			
29. Allows child to express themes of assertiveness in pretend play (i.e., child pretends he's a policeman and puts caregiver in jail; child pretends to go to work and tells caregiver to stay home).			
Total for Representational Capacity (Elaboration)			
STOP HERE FOR PARENTS OF 25- TO 35-MONTH-OLDS			
REPRESENTATIONAL DIFFERENTIATION (Building Bridges Between Ideas and Emotional Thinking)			
30. Elaborates on child's pretend play, creating opportunities to logically connect ideas in play. The caregiver accomplishes this by asking questions to give depth to the drama such as "how," "why," or "when." If the child strays off the topic, the caregiver asks questions to bridge the circle of communication back to the pretend play theme (i.e., "But what happened to the crocodile? He was ready to go for a swim and now you're playing with the truck.")			
31. Incorporates causality into pretend play by helping child to logically connect three or more ideas into a reality-based story sequence. For example, if the child is playing out how two animals fight, the caregiver might ask "How come they're fighting?", "Do they know each other?"			
32. Helps child to elaborate on a wide range of emotional themes, whatever they might be—assertiveness, pleasure and excitement, fearfulness, anger, or separation and loss. The caregiver is accepting of the child's expressions of different feelings and themes through play and shows no discomfort at the expression of different ideas from the child.			
Total for Representational Differentiation (Emotional Thinking)			
TOTAL CAREGIVER SCORE FOR SCALE			

Functional Emotional Assessment Scale

Administration and Scoring Form

Stanley I. Greenspan, M.D.
and
Georgia A DeGangi, Ph.D., OTR

Interdisciplinary Council on
Developmental and Learning Disorders
Bethesda, MD

Protocol Booklet - Research Version

Child Behaviors

Name of Child: _____   Date of Testing: _____

Age of Child: _____

Person Playing
With Child: Mother: ___   Father: ___
               Caregiver: ___   Examiner: ___

General Scoring

Scoring is on a two-point scale for most items, except where indicated, and is:
   0 = not at all or very brief
   1 = present some of time, observed several times
   2 = consistently present, observed many times
   Indicate N/O for behaviors that are not observed.

Where indicated to convert a score, transform the scoring as follows:
   0 becomes a 2
   1 = 1
   2 becomes a 0

Scores for symbolic play should be entered in the SYM column and scores for sensory play entered in the SENS column. When the examiner facilitates play with the child, enter scores in the EXAM column. The last column may be used for entering scores for additional caregivers (e.g., mother, father, foster parent, babysitter) observed playing with the child.

Scores are interpreted for the primary caregiver playing with the child for the symbolic and sensory play situations. If scores do not differ for symbolic and sensory play, then only one score is interpreted. However, if behaviors differ for the different play situations, then two scores are calculated, one for symbolic play, one for sensory play. These are interpreted using the cutoff scores presented in the profile form.

	SYM	SENS	EXAM
SELF-REGULATION AND INTEREST IN THE WORLD			
1. Is interested and attentive to play with toys.			
2. Explores objects freely without caution.			
3. Remains calm for play period with no signs of distress (crying or whining), showing appropriate frustration.			
4. Is comfortable touching textured toys and in being touched by caregiver.			
5. Enjoys moving on equipment or engaging in roughhouse play.			
6. Is overly visual, looking at toys rather than playing with them. *Converted Score* Score of 0 converts to 2			
7. Shows happy, content affect. *Scoring:* 0 = flat, somber, or depressed affect. 1 = content but neutral. 2 = happy and content, robust smiles, warm and engaging affect.			
NOTE: SCORE ONLY ITEM 8 OR 9, WHICHEVER APPLIES. 8. Underreactivity: Appears sluggish or withdrawn. *Scoring:* 0 = withdrawn, difficult to engage. 1 = sluggish or slow-paced in actions but can eventually be aroused or engaged. 2 = shows a bright, alert state with focused play throughout.			
9. Overreactivity: Appears overaroused by toys and environment. *Scoring:* 0 = very active, moves quickly from one toy to the next or wanders away from caregiver and toys constantly. 1= moderately active, occasional bursts of changing activity quickly or wandering away, then settles into play with one toy for short period. 2 = well-modulated in pace and activity level, focusing on a toy or caregiver for long periods before changing activity.			
Total For Self-Regulation and Interest in the World			
FORMING RELATIONSHIPS, ATTACHMENT, AND ENGAGEMENT			
10. Shows emotional interest and connection with caregiver by vocalizing and smiling at her.			
11. Anticipates with curiosity or excitement when caregiver presents an interesting object or game.			
12. Initiates physical closeness to caregiver but is not clingy; if child is active and moves away from caregiver, child maintains a visual or verbal connection with caregiver.			

	SYM	SENS	EXAM
13. Turns head away, averts gaze, moves away, or sits facing away from caregiver without social referencing caregiver. Appears indifferent, aloof, withdrawn, or avoidant of caregiver. *Converted Score* Score of 0 converts to 2			
14. Social references caregiver while playing with toys.			
15. Evidences a relaxed sense of security and/or comfort when near caregiver. If child is active and moves away from caregiver, he references her from across space and shows relaxed security in distal space.			
16. Displays signs of discomfort, displeasure, or sadness during interactive play if caregiver should become unresponsive or engage in anticontingent behaviors. *(If caregiver is responsive or contingent, note that this was not observed with "N/O," then assign 2 points.)*			
17. Initiates physical closeness to caregiver but is not clingy; if child is active and moves away from caregiver, child maintains a visual or verbal connection with caregiver.			
18. After moving away, communicates to caregiver from across space by looking, gestures, or vocalizations.			
Total for Forming Relationships, Attachment, and Engagement			
STOP HERE FOR 7- TO 9-MONTH-OLDS			
TWO-WAY, PURPOSEFUL COMMUNICATION			
19. Opens circles of communication: Initiates intentional actions with objects while also engaged in interactions with caregiver (i.e., manipulates object then looks at mother and smiles or vocalizes).			
20. Gives signals: Initiates purposeful and intentional actions in play with objects. *Scoring:* 0 = needs considerable help to get started in play or to engage in purposeful actions; no clear gestures or organized intent. 1 = initiates play but engages in stereotypic actions; i.e., lining toys up, mouthing toys for long periods of time, banging toys without engaging in any other actions with the same toy, OR initiates play but actions appear aimless or disorganized. 2 = play shows intentionality and variety, engaging in two or more different behaviors with a given toy or activity. Gestures are specific and activity is functionally tied to objects.			

	SYM	SENS	EXAM
21. Closes circles: Responds to caregiver's cues in contingent manner (i.e., mother offers toy, baby takes it and puts it in a container). *Scoring:* 0 = does not notice caregiver's response. 1 = notices caregiver's response and looks, but does not respond contingently through actions; instead does something that has nothing to do with what caregiver did (i.e., mother holds toy out for child; child looks at mother and toy, then returns to what he was doing before). 2 = notices caregiver's response, then responds contingently by elaborating on what caregiver did, by taking toy held by caregiver and examining it, by imitating her, or some other r sponse that is clearly linked to what caregiver did.			
22. Shows anger, frustration, aggressive behavior (e.g., hitting), or protest repeatedly *Converted Score* Score of 0 converts to 2			
23. Uses language (e.g., sounds, words, and/or gestures) during interactions. Circle which ones were used.			
Total for Two-Way, Purposeful Communication			
STOP HERE FOR 10- TO 18-MONTH-OLDS			
BEHAVIORAL ORGANIZATION, PROBLEM-SOLVING, AND INTERNALIZATION (A Complex Sense of Self)			
24. Engages in complex patterns of communication stringing together several circles of communication with caregiver (initiated and elaborated on by child) using gestures, vocalizations, and/or words. *Scoring:* 0 = 0 to 2 circles. 1 = 3 to 5 circles. 2 = 6 or more circles.			
25. Imitates or copies something new that the caregiver introduces, then incorporates idea into play (i.e., caregiver feeds doll; child copies this).			
Total for Behavioral Organization, Problem-Solving, and Internalization			
STOP HERE FOR 19- TO 24-MONTH-OLDS			
REPRESENTATIONAL CAPACITY (Elaboration)			
26. Engages in symbolic play with the various toys or equipment (e.g., plays out cars racing), going beyond simple concrete actions (e.g., feeding self with cup).			
27. Engages in pretend play patterns of at least one idea in collaboration with caregiver (e.g., one part of a script or scenario played out).			
28. Uses language or pretend play (e.g., playing out with doll figures) to communicate needs, wishes, intentions, or feelings.			
29. Uses pretend play to express themes around closeness or dependency (e.g., putting dolls to sleep next to one another; feeding caregiver and dolls).			

	SYM	SENS	EXAM
30. Allows child to express themes of assertiveness in pretend play (i.e., child pretends he's a policeman and puts caregiver in jail; child pretends to go to work and tells caregiver to stay home).			
31. Uses pretend play to express themes around pleasure and excitement around humorous theme (e.g., imitating humorous behaviors).			
32. Uses pretend play to express themes around assertiveness (e.g., cars racing).			
33. Creates pretend drama with two or more ideas that are not related or logically connected.			
Total for Representational Capacity (Elaboration)			
STOP HERE FOR 25- TO 35-MONTH-OLDS			
REPRESENTATIONAL DIFFERENTIATION (Building Bridges Between Ideas and Emotional Thinking)			
34. Pretend play, however unrealistic, involves two or more ideas that are logically tied to one another. Child may build on adult's pretend play idea.			
35. Elaborates on pretend play sequence of two or more ideas that are logically connected and grounded in reality. There is a planned quality and child can elaborate to "how," "why," or "when" questions, giving depth to drama.			
36. Uses pretend play or language to communicate themes containing two or more ideas dealing with closeness or dependency (e.g., doll gets hurt, then gets kiss from daddy, then plays ball together).			
37. Uses pretend play or language to communicate themes containing two or more ideas dealing with pleasure and excitement in humorous game (e.g., imitates funny word heard, watches how caregiver reacts, then laughs).			
38. Uses pretend play or language to communicate themes containing two or more ideas dealing with assertiveness (e.g., soldiers search for missing person, find her, then battle to save her again).			
Total for Representational Differentiation (Emotional Thinking)			
TOTAL CHILD SCORE FOR SCALE			

Functional Emotional Assessment Scale
Profile Form
For 7- to 9-Month-Olds

Subtest	Score		Normal	At Risk	Deficient
	SYM	SENS			
Caregiver					
Self–Regulation and Interest in the World			6–10	5	0–4
Forming Relationships, Attachment, and Engagement			6	5	0–4
Two–Way, Purposeful, Communication			8–10	7	0–6
Total Caregiver Score			20–26	18–19	0–17
Child					
Self–Regulation and Interest in the World			14–16	13	0–12
Forming Relationships, Attachment, and Engagement			8–10	7	0–6
Total Child Score			22–26	20–21	0–19
Total FEAS Scale			**41–52**	**38–40**	**0–37**

Key: SYM = Symbolic; SENS = Sensory

Functional Emotional Assessment Scale

Profile Form
For 10- to 12-Month-Olds

Subtest	Score		Normal	At Risk	Deficient
	SYM	SENS			
Caregiver					
Self-Regulation and Interest in the World			8–10	7	0–6
Forming Relationships, Attachment, and Engagement			8	7	0–6
Two-Way, Purposeful, Communication			9–10	8	0–7
Behavioral Organization, Problem-Solving, and Internalization			4–6	3	0–2
Total Caregiver Score			27–34	25–26	0–24
Child					
Self-Regulation and Interest in the World			14–16	13	0–12
Forming Relationships, Attachment, and Engagement			10	9	0–8
Two–Way, Purposeful, Communication			7–8	6	0–5
Total Child Score			31–34	29–30	0–28
Total FEAS Scale			61–68	54–56	0–53

Key: SYM = Symbolic; SENS = Sensory

Functional Emotional Assessment Scale

Profile Form
For 13- to 18-Month-Olds

Subtest	Score		Normal	At Risk	Deficient
	SYM	SENS			
Caregiver					
Self-Regulation and Interest in the World			6–8	5	0–4
Forming Relationships, Attachment, and Engagement			7–8	6	0–5
Two-Way, Purposeful, Communication			9–10	8	0–7
Behavioral Organization, Problem-Solving, and Internalization			7–10	6	0–5
Total Caregiver Score			*30–36*	*28–29*	*0–27*
Child					
Self-Regulation and Interest in the World			13–14	12	0–11
Forming Relationships, Attachment, and Engagement			9–10	8	0–7
Two-Way, Purposeful, Communication			7–8	6	0–5
Total Child Score			*29–32*	*27–28*	*0–26*
Total FEAS Scale			**60–68**	**55–59**	**0–54**

Key: SYM = Symbolic; SENS = Sensory

Functional Emotional Assessment Scale

Profile Form

For 19- to 24-Month-Olds

Subtest	Score		Normal	At Risk	Deficient
	SYM	SENS			
Caregiver					
Self-Regulation and Interest in the World			3–6		0–2
Forming Relationships, Attachment, and Engagement			6	5	0–4
Two-Way, Purposeful, Communication			9–10	8	0–7
Behavioral Organization, Problem-Solving, and Internalization			11–14	10	0–9
Total Caregiver Score			*28–36*	*26–27*	*0–25*
Child					
Self-Regulation and Interest in the World			13–16	12	0–11
Forming Relationships, Attachment, and Engagement			12–14	11	0–10
Two-Way, Purposeful, Communication			9–10	8	0–7
Behavioral Organization, Problem-Solving, and Internalization			3–4		0–2
Total Child Score			*36–44*	*34–35*	*0–33*
Total FEAS Scale			**64–80**	**60–63**	**0–59**

Key: SYM = Symbolic; SENS = Sensory

Functional Emotional Assessment Scale

Profile Form

For 25- to 35-Month-Olds

Subtest	Score		Normal	At Risk	Deficient
	SYM	SENS			
Caregiver					
Self-Regulation and Interest in the World			6–8	5	0–4
Forming Relationships, Attachment, and Engagement			7–8	6	0–5
Two-Way, Purposeful, Communication			9–10	8	0–7
Behavioral Organization, Problem-Solving, and Internalization			12–14	11	0–10
Representational Capacity			4–12		0–3
Total Caregiver Score			*38–52*	*36–37*	*0–35*
Child					
Self-Regulation and Interest in the World			15–18	14	0–13
Forming Relationships, Attachment, and Engagement			14–18	13	0–12
Two-Way, Purposeful, Communication			8–10	7	0–6
Behavioral Organization, Problem-Solving, and Internalization			2–4		0–1
Representational Capacity			2–8		0–1
Total Child Score			*42–58*	*40–41*	*0–39*
Total FEAS Scale			**77–110**	**75–76**	**0–74**

Key: SYM = Symbolic; SENS = Sensory

Functional Emotional Assessment Scale

Profile Form

For 3- to 4-Year-Olds

Subtest	Score		Normal	At Risk	Deficient
	SYM	SENS			
Caregiver					
Self-Regulation and Interest in the World			4–6		0–3
Forming Relationships, Attachment, and Engagement			7–8	6	0–5
Two-Way, Purposeful, Communication			9–10	8	0–7
Behavioral Organization, Problem-Solving, and Internalization			12–14	11	0–10
Representational Capacity			6–10	5	0–4
Representational Differentiation			2–6		0–1
Total Caregiver Score			*42–54*	*40–41*	*0–39*
Child					
Self-Regulation and Interest in the World			12–14	11	0–10
Forming Relationships, Attachment, and Engagement			14–16	13	0–12
Two-Way, Purposeful, Communication			8–10	7	0–6
Behavioral Organization, Problem-Solving, and Internalization			2–4		0–1
Representational Capacity			8–14	7	0–6
Representational Differentiation			2–10		0–1
Total Child Score			*48–66*	*46–47*	*0–45*
Total FEAS Scale			**93–120**	**86–92**	**0–85**

Key: SYM = Symbolic; SENS = Sensory

Appendix C

Protocol Booklets

Stanley I. Greenspan, M.D. and Georgia A DeGangi, Ph.D., OTR
Interdisciplinary Council on Developmental and Learning Disorders, Bethesda, MD

The Functional Emotional Assessment Scale Administration and Scoring Form

Age: **7-9 Months**

Behaviors: **Caregiver**

Name of Child: _____   Date of Testing: _____

Age of Child: _____

Person Playing
With Child: Mother: ___   Father: ___
               Caregiver: ___   Examiner: ___

General Scoring

Scoring is on a two-point scale for most items, except where indicated, and is:
  0 = not at all or very brief
  1 = present some of time, observed several times
  2 = consistently present, observed many times
  Indicate N/O for behaviors that are not observed.

Where indicated to convert a score, transform the scoring as follows:
  0 becomes a 2
  1 = 1
  2 becomes a 0

Scores for symbolic play should be entered in the SYM column and scores for sensory play entered in the SENS column. When the examiner facilitates play with the child, enter scores in the EXAM column. The last column may be used for entering scores for additional caregivers (e.g., mother, father, foster parent, babysitter) observed playing with the child.

Scores are interpreted for the primary caregiver playing with the child for the symbolic and sensory play situations. If scores do not differ for symbolic and sensory play, then only one score is interpreted. However, if behaviors differ for the different play situations, then two scores are calculated, one for symbolic play, one for sensory play. These are interpreted using the cutoff scores presented in the profile form.

Age: **7-9 Months** Child's Name: _____

Behaviors: **Caregiver**

Key: SYM = Symbolic; SENS = Sensory; EXAM = Examiner

	SYM	SENS	EXAM
SELF-REGULATION AND INTEREST IN THE WORLD			
1. Shows interest in toys through facial or verbal expressions of interest or by handling and touching toys, but not so absorbed by toys that the caregiver plays with toys alone, ignoring the child.			
2. Shows sustained interest in child, focuses on child's signals (gestures, vocalizations), keeping child involved in play.			
3. Shows pleasant or animated, happy affect throughout play. *Scoring:* 0 = flat, somber, or depressed affect. 1 = content, but neutral. 2 = happy and animated with warm and engaging smiles.			
4. Is sensitive and responsive to child's need for touch by stroking or touching child in pleasurable ways and/or encourages child to explore textured toys.			
5. Provides pleasurable movement experiences to the child or encourages movement exploration.			
Total For Self-Regulation and Interest in the World			
FORMING RELATIONSHIPS, ATTACHMENT, AND ENGAGEMENT			
6. Is relaxed during interchange with child, not overly attentive to child's every action.			
7. Looks at child with affection, showing a warm connection.			
8. Enjoys being with and playing with the child through smiles or a joyful look and emits a sense of warmth by providing inviting gestures. Keep in mind cultural differences in how this may be expressed.			
Total for Forming Relationships, Attachment, and Engagement			
TWO-WAY, PURPOSEFUL COMMUNICATION			
9. Opening circle of communication: Initiates interactions with child through vocalizations or gestures, creating interactive opportunities with child.			

Age: **7-9 Months**   Child's Name: _____

Behaviors: **Caregiver**

	SYM	SENS	EXAM

10. Responds to child's wishes, intentions, and actions in a contingent way, building on how the child wishes to play. For example, child may hand toy to parent, and parent responds by taking it and saying something about the toy, then gives the child an opportunity to respond to what parent just did.
   Scoring:
   0 = consistently does opposite to what baby seeks, misreads child's cues, changing activity from what child wants to do.
   1 = misreads child's signals 25 to 50% of time, changing activity or toy while at other times reads child's signals accurately.
   2 = responds to child's signals in appropriate way most of the time (up to 75% time responsive to child), staying on the activity that the child has chosen.			

11. Predominately handles toys, engaging in parallel play and removing attention from playing with child. *Converted Score** Score of 0 converts to 2			
12. Plays with child at developmentally appropriate level. Caregiver may play slightly above child's level of skill, modeling new ways to do things or labeling what child does or describing the functions of objects.			
13. Stimulates child at pace that allows child to respond, waiting for child's responses. Avoids overstimulating child with language or actions.			
Total for Two-Way, Purposeful Communication			
Total Caregiver Score			

The Functional Emotional Assessment Scale Administration and Scoring Form

Age: **7-9 Months**
Behaviors: **Child**

Name of Child: _____   Date of Testing: _____

Age of Child: _____

Person Playing
With Child: Mother: ___   Father: ___
                Caregiver: ___   Examiner: ___

<u>General Scoring</u>

Scoring is on a two-point scale for most items, except where indicated, and is:

0 = not at all or very brief
1 = present some of time, observed several times
2 = consistently present, observed many times
Indicate N/O for behaviors that are not observed.

Where indicated to convert a score, transform the scoring as follows:

0 becomes a 2
1 = 1
2 becomes a 0

Scores for symbolic play should be entered in the SYM column and scores for sensory play entered in the SENS column. When the examiner facilitates play with the child, enter scores in the EXAM column. The last column may be used for entering scores for additional caregivers (e.g., mother, father, foster parent, babysitter) observed playing with the child.

Scores are interpreted for the primary caregiver playing with the child for the symbolic and sensory play situations. If scores do not differ for symbolic and sensory play, then only one score is interpreted. However, if behaviors differ for the different play situations, then two scores are calculated, one for symbolic play, one for sensory play. These are interpreted using the cutoff scores presented in the profile form.

Age: **7-9 Months**   Child's Name: _____

Behaviors: **Child**

Key: SYM = Symbolic; SENS = Sensory; EXAM = Examiner

	SYM	SENS	EXAM
SELF-REGULATION AND INTEREST IN THE WORLD			
1. Is interested and attentive to play with toys.			
2. Explores objects freely without caution.			
3. Remains calm for play period with no signs of distress (crying or whining), showing appropriate frustration.			
4. Is comfortable touching textured toys and in being touched by caregiver.			
5. Enjoys moving on equipment or engaging in roughhouse play.			
6. Is overly visual, looking at toys rather than playing with them. *Converted Score** Score of 0 converts to 2			
7. Shows happy, content affect. *Scoring:* 0 = flat, somber, or depressed affect. 1 = content but neutral. 2 = happy and content, robust smiles, warm and engaging affect.			
NOTE: SCORE ONLY ITEM 8 OR 9, WHICHEVER APPLIES. 8. Underreactivity: Appears sluggish or withdrawn. *Scoring:* 0 = withdrawn, difficult to engage. 1 = sluggish or slow-paced in actions but can eventually be aroused or engaged. 2 = shows a bright, alert state with focused play throughout.			
9. Overreactivity: Appears overaroused by toys and environment. *Scoring:* 0 = very active, moves quickly from one toy to the next or wanders away from caregiver and toys constantly. 1= moderately active, occasional bursts of changing activity quickly or wandering away, then settles into play with one toy for short period. 2 = well-modulated in pace and activity level, focusing on a toy or caregiver for long periods before changing activity.			
Total For Self-Regulation and Interest in the World			
FORMING RELATIONSHIPS, ATTACHMENT, AND ENGAGEMENT			
10. Shows emotional interest and connection with caregiver by vocalizing and smiling at her.			
11. Anticipates with curiosity or excitement when caregiver presents an interesting object or game.			

Age: **7-9 Months**   Child's Name: _____

Behaviors: **Child**

	SYM	SENS	EXAM
12. Initiates physical closeness to caregiver but is not clingy; if child is active and moves away from caregiver, child maintains a visual or verbal connection with caregiver.			
13. Turns head away, averts gaze, moves away, or sits facing away from caregiver without social referencing caregiver. Appears indifferent, aloof, withdrawn, or avoidant of caregiver. *Converted Score** Score of 0 converts to 2			
14. Social references caregiver while playing with toys.			
Total for Forming Relationships, Attachment, and Engagement			
Total Child Score			
TOTAL FEAS SCALE SCORE (add Caregiver and Child scores)			

Functional Emotional Assessment Scale
Profile Form
For 7- to 9-Month-Olds

Subtest	Score			Normal	At Risk	Deficient
	SYM	SENS	EXAM			
Caregiver						
Self–Regulation and Interest in the World				6–10	5	0–4
Forming Relationships, Attachment, and Engagement				6	5	0–4
Two–Way, Purposeful, Communication				8–10	7	0–6
Total Caregiver Score				20–26	18–19	0–17
Child						
Self–Regulation and Interest in the World				14–16	13	0–12
Forming Relationships, Attachment, and Engagement				8–10	7	0–6
Total Child Score				22–26	20–21	0–19
Total FEAS Scale				41–52	38–40	0–37

Key: SYM = Symbolic; SENS = Sensory

Stanley I. Greenspan, M.D. and Georgia A DeGangi, Ph.D., OTR
Interdisciplinary Council on Developmental and Learning Disorders, Bethesda, MD

The Functional Emotional Assessment Scale Administration and Scoring Form

Age: **10-12 Months**

Behaviors: **Caregiver**

Name of Child: _____   Date of Testing: _____

Age of Child: _____

Person Playing
With Child: Mother: ___   Father: ___
               Caregiver: ___   Examiner: ___

General Scoring

Scoring is on a two-point scale for most items, except where indicated, and is:
  0 = not at all or very brief
  1 = present some of time, observed several times
  2 = consistently present, observed many times
  Indicate N/O for behaviors that are not observed.

Where indicated to convert a score, transform the scoring as follows:
  0 becomes a 2
  1 = 1
  2 becomes a 0

Scores for symbolic play should be entered in the SYM column and scores for sensory play entered in the SENS column. When the examiner facilitates play with the child, enter scores in the EXAM column. The last column may be used for entering scores for additional caregivers (e.g., mother, father, foster parent, babysitter) observed playing with the child.

Scores are interpreted for the primary caregiver playing with the child for the symbolic and sensory play situations. If scores do not differ for symbolic and sensory play, then only one score is interpreted. However, if behaviors differ for the different play situations, then two scores are calculated, one for symbolic play, one for sensory play. These are interpreted using the cutoff scores presented in the profile form.

Age: **10-12 Months** Child's Name: _____

Behaviors: **Caregiver**

Key: SYM = Symbolic; SENS = Sensory; EXAM = Examiner

	SYM	SENS	EXAM
SELF-REGULATION AND INTEREST IN THE WORLD			
1. Shows interest in toys through facial or verbal expressions of interest or by handling and touching toys, but not so absorbed by toys that the caregiver plays with toys alone, ignoring the child.			
2. Shows sustained interest in child, focuses on child's signals (gestures, vocalizations), keeping child involved in play.			
3. Shows pleasant or animated, happy affect throughout play. *Scoring:* 0 = flat, somber, or depressed affect. 1 = content, but neutral. 2 = happy and animated with warm and engaging smiles.			
4. Is sensitive and responsive to child's need for touch by stroking or touching child in pleasurable ways and/or encourages child to explore textured toys.			
5. Provides pleasurable movement experiences to the child or encourages movement exploration.			
Total For Self-Regulation and Interest in the World			
FORMING RELATIONSHIPS, ATTACHMENT, AND ENGAGEMENT			
6. Is relaxed during interchange with child, not overly attentive to child's every action.			
7. Looks at child with affection, showing a warm connection.			
8. Enjoys being with and playing with the child through smiles or a joyful look and emits a sense of warmth by providing inviting gestures. Keep in mind cultural differences in how this may be expressed.			
9. Is overly anxious in attachment to child, overwhelming child with affectionate touching OR is not comfortable showing feelings and relating warmly and intimately with child, appearing overly vigilant toward child. (Circle which one.) *Scoring:* 0 = many times. 1 = sometimes. 2 = briefly or not at all.			
Total for Forming Relationships, Attachment, and Engagement			
TWO-WAY, PURPOSEFUL COMMUNICATION			
10. Allows child to decide on the play topic, to initiate play and explore toys in ways that the child seeks or needs.			

Age: **10-12 Months**   Child's Name: _____
Behaviors: **Caregiver**

	SYM	SENS	EXAM

11. Responds to child's wishes, intentions, and actions in a contingent way, building on how the child wishes to play. For example, child may hand toy to parent, and parent responds by taking it and saying something about the toy, then gives the child an opportunity to respond to what parent just did.
    Scoring:
    0 = consistently does opposite to what baby seeks, misreads child's cues, changing activity from what child wants to do.
    1 = misreads child's signals 25 to 50% of time, changing activity or toy while at other times reads child's signals accurately.
    2 = responds to child's signals in appropriate way most of time (up to 75% time responsive to child), staying on the activity that the child has chosen.			

12. Predominately handles toys, engaging in parallel play and removing attention from playing with child. *Converted Score** Score of 0 converts to 2			
13. Plays with child at developmentally appropriate level. Caregiver may play slightly above child's level of skill, modeling new ways to do things or labeling what child does or describing the functions of objects.			
14. Stimulates child at pace that allows child to respond, waiting for child's responses. Avoids overstimulating child with language or actions.			
Total for Two-Way, Purposeful Communication			
BEHAVIORAL ORGANIZATION, PROBLEM-SOLVING, AND INTERNALIZATION (A Complex Sense of Self)			

15. Responds and initiates reciprocal back and forth chains of interactions with child, stringing together connected circles of communication or units of interaction. For example, caregiver introduces baby doll, baby touches doll's face, mother touches doll's hair, baby pats the doll, mother says "baby," and baby glances between mother and doll. The caregiver may imitate child (i.e., pushing car alongside child), then interject her turn by an action or verbalization related to the child's actions (i.e., "Oh, a bump!", then bumps her car into child's car).
    Scoring:
    0 = 0 to 2 circles.
    1 = 3 to 5 circles.
    2 = 6 or more circles.			

16. Uses gestures and facial expressions as a modality to promote circles of communication.			
17. Uses touch or roughhouse play as a modality to promote circles of communication.			
Total for Behavioral Organization, Problem-Solving, and Internalization			
Total Caregiver Score			

The Functional Emotional Assessment Scale Administration and Scoring Form

Age: **10-12 Months**

Behaviors: **Child**

Name of Child: _____   Date of Testing: _____

Age of Child: _____

Person Playing
With Child: Mother: ___   Father: ___
                Caregiver: ___   Examiner: ___

<u>General Scoring</u>

Scoring is on a two-point scale for most items, except where indicated, and is:
0 = not at all or very brief
1 = present some of time, observed several times
2 = consistently present, observed many times
Indicate N/O for behaviors that are not observed.

Where indicated to convert a score, transform the scoring as follows:
0 becomes a 2
1 = 1
2 becomes a 0

Scores for symbolic play should be entered in the SYM column and scores for sensory play entered in the SENS column. When the examiner facilitates play with the child, enter scores in the EXAM column. The last column may be used for entering scores for additional caregivers (e.g., mother, father, foster parent, babysitter) observed playing with the child.

Scores are interpreted for the primary caregiver playing with the child for the symbolic and sensory play situations. If scores do not differ for symbolic and sensory play, then only one score is interpreted. However, if behaviors differ for the different play situations, then two scores are calculated, one for symbolic play, one for sensory play. These are interpreted using the cutoff scores presented in the profile form.

Age: **10-12 Months**   Child's Name: _____

Behaviors: **Child**

Key: SYM = Symbolic; SENS = Sensory; EXAM = Examiner

	SYM	SENS	EXAM
SELF-REGULATION AND INTEREST IN THE WORLD			
1. Is interested and attentive to play with toys.			
2. Explores objects freely without caution.			
3. Remains calm for play period with no signs of distress (crying or whining), showing appropriate frustration.			
4. Is comfortable touching textured toys and in being touched by caregiver.			
5. Enjoys moving on equipment or engaging in roughhouse play.			
6. Is overly visual, looking at toys rather than playing with them. *Converted Score** Score of 0 converts to 2			
7. Shows happy, content affect. *Scoring:* 0 = flat, somber, or depressed affect. 1 = content but neutral. 2 = happy and content, robust smiles, warm and engaging affect.			
NOTE: SCORE ONLY ITEM 8 OR 9, WHICHEVER APPLIES. 8. Underreactivity: Appears sluggish or withdrawn. *Scoring:* 0 = withdrawn, difficult to engage. 1 = sluggish or slow-paced in actions but can eventually be aroused or engaged. 2 = shows a bright, alert state with focused play throughout.			
9. Overreactivity: Appears overaroused by toys and environment. *Scoring:* 0 = very active, moves quickly from one toy to the next or wanders away from caregiver and toys constantly. 1= moderately active, occasional bursts of changing activity quickly or wandering away, then settles into play with one toy for short period. 2 = well-modulated in pace and activity level, focusing on a toy or caregiver for long periods before changing activity.			
Total For Self-Regulation and Interest in the World			
FORMING RELATIONSHIPS, ATTACHMENT, AND ENGAGEMENT			
10. Shows emotional interest and connection with caregiver by vocalizing and smiling at her.			
11. Anticipates with curiosity or excitement when caregiver presents an interesting object or game.			
12. Initiates physical closeness to caregiver but is not clingy; if child is active and moves away from caregiver, child maintains a visual or verbal connection with caregiver.			

Age: **10-12 Months**   Child's Name: _____

Behaviors: **Child**

	SYM	SENS	EXAM
13. Turns head away, averts gaze, moves away, or sits facing away from caregiver without social referencing caregiver. Appears indifferent, aloof, withdrawn, or avoidant of caregiver. *Converted Score** Score of 0 converts to 2			
14. Social references caregiver while playing with toys.			
Total for Forming Relationships, Attachment, and Engagement			
TWO-WAY, PURPOSEFUL COMMUNICATION			
15. Opens circles of communication: Initiates intentional actions with objects while also engaged in interactions with caregiver (i.e., manipulates object then looks at mother and smiles or vocalizes).			
16. Closes circles: Responds to caregiver's cues in contingent manner (i.e., mother offers toy, baby takes it and puts it in a container). *Scoring:* 0 = does not notice caregiver's response. 1 = notices caregiver's response and looks, but does not respond contingently through actions; instead does something that has nothing to do with what caregiver did (i.e., mother holds toy out for child; child looks at mother and toy, then returns to what he was doing before). 2 = notices caregiver's response, then responds contingently by elaborating on what caregiver did, by taking toy held by caregiver and examining it, by imitating her, or some other response that is clearly linked to what caregiver did.			
17. Shows anger, frustration, aggressive behavior (e.g., hitting), or protest repeatedly. *Converted Score** Score of 0 converts to 2			
18. Uses language (e.g., sounds, words, and/or gestures) during interactions. Circle which ones were used.			
Total for Two-Way, Purposeful Communication			
Total Child Score			
TOTAL FEAS SCALE SCORE (add Caregiver and Child scores)			

Age: **10-12 Months**   Child's Name: _____

Behaviors: **Child**

Functional Emotional Assessment Scale

Profile Form
For 10- to 12-Month-Olds

Subtest	Score			Normal	At Risk	Deficient
	SYM	SENS	EXAM			
Caregiver						
Self-Regulation and Interest in the World				8–10	7	0–6
Forming Relationships, Attachment, and Engagement				8	7	0–6
Two-Way, Purposeful, Communication				9–10	8	0–7
Behavioral Organization, Problem-Solving, and Internalization				4–6	3	0–2
Total Caregiver Score				27–34	25–26	0–24
Child						
Self-Regulation and Interest in the World				14–16	13	0–12
Forming Relationships, Attachment, and Engagement				8–10	7	0–6
Two-Way, Purposeful, Communication				7–8	6	0–5
Total Child Score				22–26	20–21	0–19
Total FEAS Scale				41–52	38–40	0–37

Key: SYM = Symbolic; SENS = Sensory

Stanley I. Greenspan, M.D. and Georgia A DeGangi, Ph.D., OTR
Interdisciplinary Council on Developmental and Learning Disorders, Bethesda, MD

The Functional Emotional Assessment Scale Administration and Scoring Form

Age: **13-18 Months**

Behaviors: **Caregiver**

Name of Child: _____   Date of Testing: _____

Age of Child: _____

Person Playing
With Child: Mother: ___   Father: ___
               Caregiver: ___   Examiner: ___

General Scoring

Scoring is on a two-point scale for most items, except where indicated, and is:
   0 = not at all or very brief
   1 = present some of time, observed several times
   2 = consistently present, observed many times
   Indicate N/O for behaviors that are not observed.

Where indicated to convert a score, transform the scoring as follows:
   0 becomes a 2
   1 = 1
   2 becomes a 0

Scores for symbolic play should be entered in the SYM column and scores for sensory play entered in the SENS column. When the examiner facilitates play with the child, enter scores in the EXAM column. The last column may be used for entering scores for additional caregivers (e.g., mother, father, foster parent, babysitter) observed playing with the child.

Scores are interpreted for the primary caregiver playing with the child for the symbolic and sensory play situations. If scores do not differ for symbolic and sensory play, then only one score is interpreted. However, if behaviors differ for the different play situations, then two scores are calculated, one for symbolic play, one for sensory play. These are interpreted using the cutoff scores presented in the profile form.

Age: **13-18 Months**   Child's Name: _____

Behaviors: **Caregiver**

Key: SYM = Symbolic; SENS = Sensory; EXAM = Examiner

	SYM	SENS	EXAM
SELF-REGULATION AND INTEREST IN THE WORLD			
1. Shows sustained interest in child, focuses on child's signals (gestures, vocalizations), keeping child involved in play.			
2. Shows pleasant or animated, happy affect throughout play. *Scoring:* 0 = flat, somber, or depressed affect. 1 = content, but neutral. 2 = happy and animated with warm and engaging smiles.			
3. Is sensitive and responsive to child's need for touch by stroking or touching child in pleasurable ways and/or encourages child to explore textured toys.			
4. Provides pleasurable movement experiences to the child or encourages movement exploration.			
Total For Self-Regulation and Interest in the World			
FORMING RELATIONSHIPS, ATTACHMENT, AND ENGAGEMENT			
5. Is relaxed during interchange with child, not overly attentive to child's every action.			
6. Looks at child with affection, showing a warm connection.			
7. Enjoys being with and playing with the child through smiles or a joyful look and emits a sense of warmth by providing inviting gestures. Keep in mind cultural differences in how this may be expressed.			
8. Is overly anxious in attachment to child, overwhelming child with affectionate touching OR is not comfortable showing feelings and relating warmly and intimately with child, appearing overly vigilant toward child. (Circle which one.) *Scoring:* 0 = many times. 1 = sometimes. 2 = briefly or not at all.			
Total for Forming Relationships, Attachment, and Engagement			
TWO-WAY, PURPOSEFUL COMMUNICATION			
9. Allows child to decide on the play topic, to initiate play and explore toys in ways that the child seeks or needs.			

Age: **13-18 Months**   Child's Name: _____
Behaviors: **Caregiver**

	SYM	SENS	EXAM
10. Responds to child's wishes, intentions, and actions in a contingent way, building on how the child wishes to play. For example, child may hand toy to parent, and parent responds by taking it and saying something about the toy, then gives the child an opportunity to respond to what parent just did. *Scoring:* 0 = consistently does opposite to what baby seeks, misreads child's cues, changing activity from what child wants to do. 1 = misreads child's signals 25 to 50% of time, changing activity or toy while at other times reads child's signals accurately. 2 = responds to child's signals in appropriate way most of time (up to 75% time responsive to child), staying on the activity that the child has chosen.			
11. Predominately handles toys, engaging in parallel play and removing attention from playing with child. *Converted Score** Score of 0 converts to 2			
12. Plays with child at developmentally appropriate level. Caregiver may play slightly above child's level of skill, modeling new ways to do things or labeling what child does or describing the functions of objects.			
13. Stimulates child at pace that allows child to respond, waiting for child's responses. Avoids overstimulating child with language or actions.			
Total for Two-Way, Purposeful Communication			
BEHAVIORAL ORGANIZATION, PROBLEM-SOLVING, AND INTERNALIZATION (A Complex Sense of Self)			
14. Responds and initiates reciprocal back and forth chains of interactions with child, stringing together connected circles of communication or units of interaction. For example, caregiver introduces baby doll, baby touches doll's face, mother touches doll's hair, baby pats the doll, mother says "baby," and baby glances between mother and doll). The caregiver may imitate child (i.e., pushing car alongside child), then interject her turn by an action or verbalization related to the child's actions (i.e., "Oh, a bump!", then bumps her car into child's car). *Scoring:* 0 = 0 to 2 circles. 1 = 3 to 5 circles. 2 = 6 or more circles.			
15. Uses gestures and facial expressions as a modality to promote circles of communication.			
16. Uses touch or roughhouse play as a modality to promote circles of communication.			

Age: **13-18 Months**   Child's Name: _____

Behaviors: **Caregiver**

	SYM	SENS	EXAM
17. Shows pleasure and excitement in playing with child in whatever way the child wishes to play. *Scoring:* 0 = little pleasure and excitement shown by caregiver. 1 = pleasure and excitement sustained by parent over the course of several (3 to 5) circles of communication. 2 = pleasure and excitement sustained for many (6 or more) circles of communication. *Note here if child is unable to sustain circles of communication if it affects caregiver's score:* Child can sustain circles: _____ Child cannot: _____			
18. Expresses appropriate limits on baby. The caregiver may redirect child not to leave room, not to hit her, or not to throw toy. If no need for limits arises during play, mark N/O and give 2 points.			
Total for Behavioral Organization, Problem-Solving, and Internalization			
Total Caregiver Score			

The Functional Emotional Assessment Scale Administration and Scoring Form

Age: **13-18 Months**

Behaviors: **Child**

Name of Child: _____   Date of Testing: _____

Age of Child: _____

Person Playing
With Child: Mother: ___   Father: ___

Caregiver: ___   Examiner: ___

General Scoring

Scoring is on a two-point scale for most items, except where indicated, and is:

0 = not at all or very brief
1 = present some of time, observed several times
2 = consistently present, observed many times
Indicate N/O for behaviors that are not observed.

Where indicated to convert a score, transform the scoring as follows:

0 becomes a 2
1 = 1
2 becomes a 0

Scores for symbolic play should be entered in the SYM column and scores for sensory play entered in the SENS column. When the examiner facilitates play with the child, enter scores in the EXAM column. The last column may be used for entering scores for additional caregivers (e.g., mother, father, foster parent, babysitter) observed playing with the child.

Scores are interpreted for the primary caregiver playing with the child for the symbolic and sensory play situations. If scores do not differ for symbolic and sensory play, then only one score is interpreted. However, if behaviors differ for the different play situations, then two scores are calculated, one for symbolic play, one for sensory play. These are interpreted using the cutoff scores presented in the profile form.

Age: **13-18 Months**   Child's Name: _____

Behaviors: **Child**

Key: SYM = Symbolic; SENS = Sensory; EXAM = Examiner

	SYM	SENS	EXAM
SELF-REGULATION AND INTEREST IN THE WORLD			
1. Is interested and attentive to play with toys.			
2. Explores objects freely without caution.			
3. Remains calm for play period with no signs of distress (crying or whining), showing appropriate frustration.			
4. Is comfortable touching textured toys and in being touched by caregiver.			
5. Enjoys moving on equipment or engaging in roughhouse play.			

6.   Shows happy, content affect.
    Scoring:
    0 = flat, somber, or depressed affect.
    1 = content but neutral.
    2 = happy and content, robust smiles, warm and engaging affect.			

NOTE: SCORE ONLY ITEM 7 OR 8, WHICHEVER APPLIES.
7.   Underreactivity: Appears sluggish or withdrawn.
    Scoring:
    0 = withdrawn, difficult to engage.
    1 = sluggish or slow-paced in actions but can eventually be aroused or engaged.
    2 = shows a bright, alert state with focused play throughout.			

8.   Overreactivity: Appears overaroused by toys and environment.
    Scoring:
    0 = very active, moves quickly from one toy to the next or wanders away from caregiver and toys constantly.
    1= moderately active, occasional bursts of changing activity quickly or wandering away, then settles into play with one toy for short period.
    2 = well-modulated in pace and activity level, focusing on a toy or caregiver for long periods before changing activity.			

Total For Self-Regulation and Interest in the World			
FORMING RELATIONSHIPS, ATTACHMENT, AND ENGAGEMENT			
9. Shows emotional interest and connection with caregiver by vocalizing and smiling at her.			
10. Evidences a relaxed sense of security and/or comfort when near caregiver. If child is active and moves away from caregiver, he references her from across space and shows relaxed security in distal space.			
11. Anticipates with curiosity or excitement when caregiver presents an interesting object or game.			
12. Turns head away, averts gaze, moves away, or sits facing away from caregiver without social referencing caregiver. Appears indifferent, aloof, withdrawn, or avoidant of caregiver. *Converted Score** Score of 0 converts to 2			

Age: **13-18 Months**   Child's Name: _____

Behaviors: **Child**

	SYM	SENS	EXAM
13. Social references caregiver while playing with toys.			
Total for Forming Relationships, Attachment, and Engagement			
TWO-WAY, PURPOSEFUL COMMUNICATION			
14. Opens circles of communication: Initiates intentional actions with objects while also engaged in interactions with caregiver (i.e., manipulates object then looks at mother and smiles or vocalizes).			
15. Closes circles: Responds to caregiver's cues in contingent manner (i.e., mother offers toy, baby takes it and puts it in a container). *Scoring:* 0 = does not notice caregiver's response. 1 = notices caregiver's response and looks, but does not respond contingently through actions; instead does something that has nothing to do with what caregiver did (i.e., mother holds toy out for child; child looks at mother and toy, then returns to what he was doing before). 2 = notices caregiver's response, then responds contingently by elaborating on what caregiver did, by taking toy held by caregiver and examining it, by imitating her, or some other r esponse that is clearly linked to what caregiver did.			
16. Shows anger, frustration, aggressive behavior (e.g., hitting), or protest repeatedly. *Converted Score** Score of 0 converts to 2			
17. Uses language (e.g., sounds, words, and/or gestures) during interactions. Circle which ones were used.			
Total for Two-Way, Purposeful Communication			
Total Child Score			
TOTAL FEAS SCALE SCORE (add Caregiver and Child scores)			

Age: **13-18 Months**   Child's Name: _____

Behaviors: **Child**

Functional Emotional Assessment Scale
Profile Form
For 13- to 18-Month-Olds

Subtest	Score			Normal	At Risk	Deficient
	SYM	SENS	EXAM			
Caregiver						
Self-Regulation and Interest in the World				6–8	5	0–4
Forming Relationships, Attachment, and Engagement				7–8	6	0–5
Two-Way, Purposeful, Communication				9–10	8	0–7
Behavioral Organization, Problem-Solving, and Internalization				7–10	6	0–5
Total Caregiver Score				*30–36*	*28–29*	*0–27*
Child						
Self-Regulation and Interest in the World				13–14	12	0–11
Forming Relationships, Attachment, and Engagement				9–10	8	0–7
Two-Way, Purposeful, Communication				7–8	6	0–5
Total Child Score				*29–32*	*27–28*	*0–26*
Total FEAS Scale				**60–68**	**55–59**	**0–54**

Key: SYM = Symbolic; SENS = Sensory

Stanley I. Greenspan, M.D. and Georgia A DeGangi, Ph.D., OTR
Interdisciplinary Council on Developmental and Learning Disorders, Bethesda, MD

The Functional Emotional Assessment Scale Administration and Scoring Form

Age: **19-24 Months**

Behaviors: **Caregiver**

Name of Child: _____   Date of Testing: _____

Age of Child: _____

Person Playing
With Child: Mother: ___   Father: ___

                    Caregiver: ___   Examiner: ___

General Scoring

Scoring is on a two-point scale for most items, except where indicated, and is:

  0 = not at all or very brief
  1 = present some of time, observed several times
  2 = consistently present, observed many times
  Indicate N/O for behaviors that are not observed.

Where indicated to convert a score, transform the scoring as follows:

  0 becomes a 2
  1 = 1
  2 becomes a 0

Scores for symbolic play should be entered in the SYM column and scores for sensory play entered in the SENS column. When the examiner facilitates play with the child, enter scores in the EXAM column. The last column may be used for entering scores for additional caregivers (e.g., mother, father, foster parent, babysitter) observed playing with the child.

Scores are interpreted for the primary caregiver playing with the child for the symbolic and sensory play situations. If scores do not differ for symbolic and sensory play, then only one score is interpreted. However, if behaviors differ for the different play situations, then two scores are calculated, one for symbolic play, one for sensory play. These are interpreted using the cutoff scores presented in the profile form.

Age: **19-24 Months**   Child's Name: _____

Behaviors: **Caregiver**

Key: SYM = Symbolic; SENS = Sensory; EXAM = Examiner

	SYM	SENS	EXAM
SELF-REGULATION AND INTEREST IN THE WORLD			

1. Shows pleasant or animated, happy affect throughout play.
   Scoring:
   0 = flat, somber, or depressed affect.
   1 = content, but neutral.
   2 = happy and animated with warm and engaging smiles.			

2. Is sensitive and responsive to child's need for touch by stroking or touching child in pleasurable ways and/or encourages child to explore textured toys.			
3. Provides pleasurable movement experiences to the child or encourages movement exploration.			
Total For Self-Regulation and Interest in the World			
FORMING RELATIONSHIPS, ATTACHMENT, AND ENGAGEMENT			
4. Is relaxed during interchange with child, not overly attentive to child's every action.			
5. Looks at child with affection, showing a warm connection.			
6. Enjoys being with and playing with the child through smiles or a joyful look and emits a sense of warmth by providing inviting gestures. Keep in mind cultural differences in how this may be expressed.			
Total for Forming Relationships, Attachment, and Engagement			
TWO-WAY, PURPOSEFUL COMMUNICATION			
7. Allows child to decide on the play topic, to initiate play and explore toys in ways that the child seeks or needs.			

8. Responds to child's wishes, intentions, and actions in a contingent way, building on how the child wishes to play. For example, child may hand toy to parent, and parent responds by taking it and saying something about the toy, then gives the child an opportunity to respond to what parent just did.
   Scoring:
   0 = consistently does opposite to what baby seeks, misreads child's cues, changing activity from what child wants to do.
   1 = misreads child's signals 25 to 50% of time, changing activity or toy while at other times reads child's signals accurately.
   2 = responds to child's signals in appropriate way most of time (up to 75% time responsive to child), staying on the activity that the child has chosen.			

9. Predominately handles toys, engaging in parallel play and removing attention from playing with child. *Converted Score** Score of 0 converts to 2			

Age: **19-24 Months**   Child's Name: _____

Behaviors: **Caregiver**

	SYM	SENS	EXAM
10. Plays with child at developmentally appropriate level. Caregiver may play slightly above child's level of skill, modeling new ways to do things or labeling what child does or describing the functions of objects.			
11. Stimulates child at pace that allows child to respond, waiting for child's responses. Avoids overstimulating child with language or actions.			
Total for Two-Way, Purposeful Communication			
BEHAVIORAL ORGANIZATION, PROBLEM-SOLVING, AND INTERNALIZATION (A Complex Sense of Self)			
12. Responds and initiates reciprocal back and forth chains of interactions with child, stringing together connected circles of communication or units of interaction. For example, caregiver introduces baby doll, baby touches doll's face, mother touches doll's hair, baby pats the doll, mother says "baby," and baby glances between mother and doll. The caregiver may imitate child (i.e., pushing car alongside child), then interject her turn by an action or verbalization related to the child's actions (i.e., "Oh, a bump!", then bumps her car into child's car). *Scoring:* 0 = 0 to 2 circles. 1 = 3 to 5 circles. 2 = 6 or more circles.			
13. Uses gestures and facial expressions as a modality to promote circles of communication.			
14. Uses touch or roughhouse play as a modality to promote circles of communication.			
15. Elaborates on and builds complexity into the child's play behaviors while engaged in interactive sequences between parent and child. The parent expands on what the child does while remaining on the child's play topic (e.g., the parent does not introduce a completely new play idea). The parent provides a small challenge or interesting twist to the play that requires the child to respond slightly differently than before, thus creating a problem solving opportunity for the child. For example, the parent and child are pushing a car back and forth toward each other. The parent expands on this by creating a wall with her leg to prevent the car from rolling, then waits to see how the child will solve this situation.			
16. Allows child to assert self in play, exploring with confidence in what he or she wishes (i.e., child expresses strong wish to play in a certain way such as banging toys, being silly, holding a doll, or running around room). Parent supports the child's needs for dependency and closeness, assertiveness and curiosity, aggression, autonomy, or pleasure and excitement by admiring, showing interest, and/or by joining in to the child's play in whatever way the child seeks. Problems that may interfere with caregiver's capacity to support this area might be intrusiveness, withdrawal, overprotectiveness, or playing at level far above child's level of competence.			

Age: **19-24 Months**   Child's Name: _____
Behaviors: **Caregiver**

	SYM	SENS	EXAM
17. Shows pleasure and excitement in playing with child in whatever way the child wishes to play. *Scoring:* 0 = little pleasure and excitement shown by caregiver. 1 = pleasure and excitement sustained by parent over the course of several (3 to 5) circles of communication. 2 = pleasure and excitement sustained for many (6 or more) circles of communication. *Note here if child is unable to sustain circles of communication if it affects caregiver's score:* Child can sustain circles: _____ Child cannot: _____			
18. Expresses appropriate limits on baby. The caregiver may redirect child not to leave room, not to hit her, or not to throw toy. If no need for limits arises during play, mark N/O and give 2 points.			
Total for Behavioral Organization, Problem-Solving, and Internalization			
Total Caregiver Score			

The Functional Emotional Assessment Scale Administration and Scoring Form

Age: **19-24 Months**

Behaviors: **Child**

Name of Child: _____   Date of Testing: _____

Age of Child: _____

Person Playing
With Child: Mother: ___   Father: ___
                   Caregiver: ___   Examiner: ___

General Scoring

Scoring is on a two-point scale for most items, except where indicated, and is:
0 = not at all or very brief
1 = present some of time, observed several times
2 = consistently present, observed many times
Indicate N/O for behaviors that are not observed.

Where indicated to convert a score, transform the scoring as follows:
0 becomes a 2
1 = 1
2 becomes a 0

Scores for symbolic play should be entered in the SYM column and scores for sensory play entered in the SENS column. When the examiner facilitates play with the child, enter scores in the EXAM column. The last column may be used for entering scores for additional caregivers (e.g., mother, father, foster parent, babysitter) observed playing with the child.

Scores are interpreted for the primary caregiver playing with the child for the symbolic and sensory play situations. If scores do not differ for symbolic and sensory play, then only one score is interpreted. However, if behaviors differ for the different play situations, then two scores are calculated, one for symbolic play, one for sensory play. These are interpreted using the cutoff scores presented in the profile form.

Age: **19-24 Months**   Child's Name: _____

Behaviors: **Child**

Key: SYM = Symbolic; SENS = Sensory; EXAM = Examiner

	SYM	SENS	EXAM
SELF-REGULATION AND INTEREST IN THE WORLD			
1. Is interested and attentive to play with toys.			
2. Explores objects freely without caution.			
3. Remains calm for play period with no signs of distress (crying or whining), showing appropriate frustration.			
4. Is comfortable touching textured toys and in being touched by caregiver.			
5. Enjoys moving on equipment or engaging in roughhouse play.			
6. Shows happy, content affect. *Scoring:* 0 = flat, somber, or depressed affect. 1 = content but neutral. 2 = happy and content, robust smiles, warm and engaging affect.			
7. Remains focused on objects or caregiver without being distracted by sights or sounds. *Scoring:* 0 = distracted frequently; no focused play for more than a few seconds at a time. 1 = distracted some of the time with brief periods of focused play. 2 = remains focused in play most of the time with only brief distractibility.			
NOTE: SCORE ONLY ITEM 8 OR 9, WHICHEVER APPLIES. 8. Underreactivity: Appears sluggish or withdrawn *Scoring:* 0 = withdrawn, difficult to engage. 1 = sluggish or slow-paced in actions but can eventually be aroused or engaged. 2 = shows a bright, alert state with focused play throughout.			
9. Overreactivity: Appears overaroused by toys and environment. *Scoring:* 0 = very active, moves quickly from one toy to the next or wanders away from caregiver and toys constantly. 1= moderately active, occasional bursts of changing activity quickly or wandering away, then settles into play with one toy for short period. 2 = well-modulated in pace and activity level, focusing on a toy or caregiver for long periods before changing activity.			
Total For Self-Regulation and Interest in the World			
FORMING RELATIONSHIPS, ATTACHMENT, AND ENGAGEMENT			
10. Shows emotional interest and connection with caregiver by vocalizing and smiling at her.			

Age: **19-24 Months**   Child's Name: _____

Behaviors: **Child**

	SYM	SENS	EXAM
11. Evidences a relaxed sense of security and/or comfort when near caregiver. If child is active and moves away from caregiver, he references her from across space and shows relaxed security in distal space.			
12. Anticipates with curiosity or excitement when caregiver presents an interesting object or game.			
13. Initiates physical closeness to caregiver but is not clingy; if child is active and moves away from caregiver, child maintains a visual or verbal connection with caregiver.			
14. Turns head away, averts gaze, moves away, or sits facing away from caregiver without social referencing caregiver. Appears indifferent, aloof, withdrawn, or avoidant of caregiver. *Converted Score** Score of 0 converts to 2			
15. Social references caregiver while playing with toys.			
16. After moving away, communicates to caregiver from across space by looking, gestures, or vocalizations.			
Total for Forming Relationships, Attachment, and Engagement			
TWO-WAY, PURPOSEFUL COMMUNICATION			
17. Opens circles of communication: Initiates intentional actions with objects while also engaged in interactions with caregiver (i.e., manipulates object then looks at mother and smiles or vocalizes).			
18. Gives signals: Initiates purposeful and intentional actions in play with objects. *Scoring:* 0 = needs considerable help to get started in play or to engage in purposeful actions; no clear gestures or organized intent. 1 = initiates play but engages in stereotypic actions; i.e., lining toys up, mouthing toys for long periods of time, banging toys without engaging in any other actions with the same toy OR initiates play but actions appear aimless or disorganized. 2 = play shows intentionality and variety, engaging in two or more different behaviors with a given toy or activity. Gestures are specific and activity is functionally tied to objects.			

Age: **19-24 Months**   Child's Name: _____

Behaviors: **Child**

	SYM	SENS	EXAM
19. Closes circles: Responds to caregiver's cues in contingent manner (i.e., mother offers toy, baby takes it and puts it in a container). *Scoring:* 0 = does not notice caregiver's response. 1 = notices caregiver's response and looks, but does not respond contingently through actions; instead does something that has nothing to do with what caregiver did (i.e., mother holds toy out for child; child looks at mother and toy, then returns to what he/she was doing before). 2 = notices caregiver's response, then responds contingently by elaborating on what caregiver did, by taking toy held by caregiver and examining it, by imitating her, or some other response that is clearly linked to what caregiver did.			
20. Shows anger, frustration, aggressive behavior (e.g., hitting), or protest repeatedly. *Converted Score** Score of 0 converts to 2			
21. Uses language (e.g., sounds, words, and/or gestures) during interactions. Circle which ones were used.			
Total for Two-Way, Purposeful Communication			
BEHAVIORAL ORGANIZATION, PROBLEM-SOLVING, AND INTERNALIZATION (A Complex Sense of Self)	/////	/////	/////
22. Engages in complex patterns of communication stringing together several circles of communication with caregiver (initiated and elaborated on by child) using gestures, vocalizations, and/or words. *Scoring:* 0 = 0 to 2 circles 1 = 3 to 5 circles 2 = 6 or more circles			
23. Imitates or copies something new that the caregiver introduces, then incorporates idea into play (i.e., caregiver feeds doll; child copies this).			
Total for Behavioral Organization, Problem-Solving, and Internalization			
Total Child Score			
TOTAL FEAS SCALE SCORE (add Caregiver and Child scores)			

Age: **19-24 Months**   Child's Name: _____

Behaviors: **Child**

Functional Emotional Assessment Scale

Profile Form
For 19- to 24-Month-Olds

Subtest	SYM	SENS	EXAM	Normal	At Risk	Deficient
		Score				
Caregiver						
Self-Regulation and Interest in the World				3–6		0–2
Forming Relationships, Attachment, and Engagement				6	5	0–4
Two-Way, Purposeful, Communication				9–10	8	0–7
Behavioral Organization, Problem-Solving, and Internalization				11–14	10	0–9
Total Caregiver Score				*28–36*	*26–27*	*0–25*
Child						
Self-Regulation and Interest in the World				13–16	12	0–11
Forming Relationships, Attachment, and Engagement				12–14	11	0–10
Two-Way, Purposeful, Communication				9–10	8	0–7
Behavioral Organization, Problem-Solving, and Internalization				3–4		0–2
Total Child Score				*36–44*	*34–35*	*0–33*
Total FEAS Scale				**64–80**	**60–63**	**0–59**

Key: SYM = Symbolic; SENS = Sensory

Stanley I. Greenspan, M.D. and Georgia A DeGangi, Ph.D., OTR
Interdisciplinary Council on Developmental and Learning Disorders, Bethesda, MD

The Functional Emotional Assessment Scale Administration and Scoring Form

Age: **25-35 Months**

Behaviors: **Caregiver**

Name of Child: _____   Date of Testing: _____

Age of Child: _____

Person Playing
With Child: Mother: ___   Father: ___
              Caregiver: ___   Examiner: ___

General Scoring

Scoring is on a two-point scale for most items, except where indicated, and is:
   0 = not at all or very brief
   1 = present some of time, observed several times
   2 = consistently present, observed many times
   Indicate N/O for behaviors that are not observed.

Where indicated to convert a score, transform the scoring as follows:
   0 becomes a 2
   1 = 1
   2 becomes a 0

Scores for symbolic play should be entered in the SYM column and scores for sensory play entered in the SENS column. When the examiner facilitates play with the child, enter scores in the EXAM column. The last column may be used for entering scores for additional caregivers (e.g., mother, father, foster parent, babysitter) observed playing with the child.

Scores are interpreted for the primary caregiver playing with the child for the symbolic and sensory play situations. If scores do not differ for symbolic and sensory play, then only one score is interpreted. However, if behaviors differ for the different play situations, then two scores are calculated, one for symbolic play, one for sensory play. These are interpreted using the cutoff scores presented in the profile form.

Age: **25-35 Months**   Child's Name: _____

Behaviors: **Caregiver**

Key: SYM = Symbolic; SENS = Sensory; EXAM = Examiner

	SYM	SENS	EXAM
SELF-REGULATION AND INTEREST IN THE WORLD			
1. Interacts calmly with child, able to wait for child's responses.			
2. Shows pleasant or animated, happy affect throughout play. *Scoring:* 0 = flat, somber, or depressed affect. 1 = content, but neutral. 2 = happy and animated with warm and engaging smiles.			
3. Is sensitive and responsive to child's need for touch by stroking or touching child in pleasurable ways and/or encourages child to explore textured toys.			
4. Provides pleasurable movement experiences to the child or encourages movement exploration.			
Total For Self-Regulation and Interest in the World			
FORMING RELATIONSHIPS, ATTACHMENT, AND ENGAGEMENT			
5. Is relaxed during interchange with child, not overly attentive to child's every action.			
6. Looks at child with affection, showing a warm connection.			
7. Enjoys being with and playing with the child through smiles or a joyful look and emits a sense of warmth by providing inviting gestures. Keep in mind cultural differences in how this may be expressed.			
8. Is overly anxious in attachment to child, overwhelming child with affectionate touching OR is not comfortable showing feelings and relating warmly and intimately with child, appearing overly vigilant toward child. (Circle which one.) *Scoring:* 0 = many times. 1 = sometimes. 2 = briefly or not at all.			
Total for Forming Relationships, Attachment, and Engagement			
TWO-WAY, PURPOSEFUL COMMUNICATION			
9. Allows child to decide on the play topic, to initiate play and explore toys in ways that the child seeks or needs.			

Age: **25-35 Months**   Child's Name: _____

Behaviors: **Caregiver**

	SYM	SENS	EXAM
10. Responds to child's wishes, intentions, and actions in a contingent way, building on how the child wishes to play. For example, child may hand toy to parent, and parent responds by taking it and saying something about the toy, then gives the child an opportunity to respond to what parent just did. *Scoring:* 0 = consistently does opposite to what baby seeks, misreads child's cues, changing activity from what child wants to do. 1 = misreads child's signals 25 to 50% of time, changing activity or toy while at other times reads child's signals accurately. 2 = responds to child's signals in appropriate way most of time (up to 75% time responsive to child), staying on the activity that the child has chosen.			
11. Predominately handles toys, engaging in parallel play and removing attention from playing with child. *Converted Score** Score of 0 converts to 2			
12. Plays with child at developmentally appropriate level. Caregiver may play slightly above child's level of skill, modeling new ways to do things or labeling what child does or describing the functions of objects.			
13. Stimulates child at pace that allows child to respond, waiting for child's responses. Avoids overstimulating child with language or actions.			
Total for Two-Way, Purposeful Communication			
BEHAVIORAL ORGANIZATION, PROBLEM-SOLVING, AND INTERNALIZATION (A Complex Sense of Self)			
14. Responds and initiates reciprocal back and forth chains of interactions with child, stringing together connected circles of communication or units of interaction. For example, caregiver introduces baby doll, baby touches doll's face, mother touches doll's hair, baby pats the doll, mother says "baby," and baby glances between mother and doll. The caregiver may imitate child (i.e., pushing car alongside child), then interject her turn by an action or verbalization related to the child's actions (i.e., "Oh, a bump!", then bumps her car into child's car). *Scoring:* 0 = 0 to 2 circles. 1 = 3 to 5 circles. 2 = 6 or more circles.			
15. Uses gestures and facial expressions as a modality to promote circles of communication.			
16. Uses language or vocalizations as a modality to promote circles of communication.			

Age: **25-35 Months**   Child's Name: _____

Behaviors: **Caregiver**

	SYM	SENS	EXAM
17. Elaborates on and builds complexity into the child's play behaviors while engaged in interactive sequences between parent and child. The parent expands on what the child does while remaining on the child's play topic (e.g., the parent does not introduce a completely new play idea). The parent provides a small challenge or interesting twist to the play that requires the child to respond slightly differently than before, thus creating a problem solving opportunity for the child. For example, the parent and child are pushing a car back and forth toward each other. The parent expands on this by creating a wall with her leg to prevent the car from rolling, then waits to see how the child will solve this situation.			
18. Allows child to assert self in play, exploring with confidence in what he or she wishes (i.e., child expresses strong wish to play in a certain way s uch as banging toys, being silly, holding a doll, or running around room.) Parent supports the child's needs for dependency and closeness, assertiveness and curiosity, aggression, autonomy, or pleasure and excitement by admiring, showing interest, and/or by joining in to the child's play in whatever way the child seeks. Problems that may interfere with caregiver's capacity to support this area might be intrusiveness, withdrawal, overprotectiveness, or playing at level far above child's level of competence.			
19. Shows pleasure and excitement in playing with child in whatever way the child wishes to play. *Scoring:* 0 = little pleasure and excitement shown by caregiver. 1 = pleasure and excitement sustained by parent over the course of several (3 to 5) circles of communication. 2 = pleasure and excitement sustained for many (6 or more) circles of communication. *Note here if child is unable to sustain circles of communication if it affects caregiver's score:* Child can sustain circles: _____ Child cannot: _____			
20. Expresses appropriate limits on child. The caregiver may redirect child not to leave room, not to hit her, or not throw toy. If no need for limits arises during play, mark N/O and give 2 points.			
Total for Behavioral Organization, Problem-Solving, and Internalization			
REPRESENTATIONAL CAPACITY (Elaboration)			
21. Encourages child to engage in symbolic play by modeling or combining materials in ways that encourage representational actions (i.e., mother holds spoon near baby doll's mouth and says, "Feed baby?"). Parent appears comfortable in playing make believe.			

Age: **25-35 Months**   Child's Name: _____

Behaviors: **Caregiver**

	SYM	SENS	EXAM
22. Elaborates on child's pretend play idea by building on child's ideas and adding some complexity to them (e.g., child puts doll in car and pushes it and caregiver says, "Oh, is Daddy going to the store?").			
23. Allows child to express pretend play themes involving closeness or dependency (e.g., nurturing doll) without competing for child's attention to be the one nurtured.			
24. Sustains pretend play, showing interest, pleasure, and excitement about the child's pretend play idea by asking questions, laughing or smiling, and joining into the child's play with enthusiasm (e.g., caregiver says, "Oh, that's a good idea. What happens now? That's so funny!").			
25. Allows child to express themes of assertiveness in pretend play (i.e., child pretends he's a policeman and puts caregiver in jail; child pretends to go to work and tells caregiver to stay home).			
Total for Representational Capacity (Elaboration)			
Total Caregiver Score			

The Functional Emotional Assessment Scale Administration and Scoring Form

Age: **25-35 Months**

Behaviors: **Child**

Name of Child: _____   Date of Testing: _____

Age of Child: _____

Person Playing
With Child: Mother: ___   Father: ___

                 Caregiver: ___   Examiner: ___

General Scoring

Scoring is on a two-point scale for most items, except where indicated, and is:

    0 = not at all or very brief
    1 = present some of time, observed several times
    2 = consistently present, observed many times
    Indicate N/O for behaviors that are not observed.

Where indicated to convert a score, transform the scoring as follows:

    0 becomes a 2
    1 = 1
    2 becomes a 0

Scores for symbolic play should be entered in the SYM column and scores for sensory play entered in the SENS column. When the examiner facilitates play with the child, enter scores in the EXAM column. The last column may be used for entering scores for additional caregivers (e.g., mother, father, foster parent, babysitter) observed playing with the child.

Scores are interpreted for the primary caregiver playing with the child for the symbolic and sensory play situations. If scores do not differ for symbolic and sensory play, then only one score is interpreted. However, if behaviors differ for the different play situations, then two scores are calculated, one for symbolic play, one for sensory play. These are interpreted using the cutoff scores presented in the profile form.

Age: **25-35 Months**   Child's Name: _____

Behaviors: **Child**

Key: SYM = Symbolic; SENS = Sensory; EXAM = Examiner

	SYM	SENS	EXAM
SELF-REGULATION AND INTEREST IN THE WORLD			
1. Is interested and attentive to play with toys.			
2. Explores objects freely without caution.			
3. Remains calm for play period with no signs of distress (crying or whining), showing appropriate frustration.			
4. Is comfortable touching textured toys and in being touched by caregiver.			
5. Enjoys moving on equipment or engaging in roughhouse play.			
6. Is overly visual, looking at toys rather than playing with them. *Converted Score** Score of 0 converts to 2			
7. Shows happy, content affect. *Scoring:* 0 = flat, somber, or depressed affect. 1 = content but neutral. 2 = happy and content, robust smiles, warm and engaging affect.			
8. Remains focused on objects or caregiver without being distracted by sights or sounds. *Scoring:* 0 = distracted frequently; no focused play for more than a few seconds at a time. 1 = distracted some of the time with brief periods of focused play. 2 = remains focused in play most of the time with only brief distractibility.			
NOTE: SCORE ONLY ITEM 9 OR 10, WHICHEVER APPLIES. 9. Underreactivity: Appears sluggish or withdrawn. *Scoring:* 0 = withdrawn, difficult to engage. 1 = sluggish or slow-paced in actions but can eventually be aroused or engaged. 2 = shows a bright, alert state with focused play throughout.			
10. Overreactivity: Appears overaroused by toys and environment. *Scoring:* 0 = very active, moves quickly from one toy to the next or wanders away from caregiver and toys constantly. 1= moderately active, occasional bursts of changing activity quickly or wandering away, then settles into play with one toy for short period. 2 = well-modulated in pace and activity level, focusing on a toy or caregiver for long periods before changing activity.			
Total For Self-Regulation and Interest in the World			

Age: **25-35 Months** Child's Name: _____

Behaviors: **Child**

	SYM	SENS	EXAM
FORMING RELATIONSHIPS, ATTACHMENT, AND ENGAGEMENT			
11. Shows emotional interest and connection with caregiver by vocalizing and smiling at her.			
12. Evidences a relaxed sense of security and/or comfort when near caregiver. If child is active and moves away from caregiver, he references her from across space and shows relaxed security in distal space.			
13. Anticipates with curiosity or excitement when caregiver presents an interesting object or game.			
14. Displays signs of discomfort, displeasure, or sadness during interactive play if caregiver should become unresponsive or engage in anticontingent behaviors. *(If caregiver is responsive or contingent, note that this was not observed with "N/O," then assign 2 points.)*			
15. Recovers from distress when caregiver provides social overtures to reengage child. *(If no distress is observed, note "N/O," then assign 2 points)*			
16. Initiates physical closeness to caregiver but is not clingy; if child is active and moves away from caregiver, child maintains a visual or verbal connection with caregiver.			
17. Turns head away, averts gaze, moves away, or sits facing away from caregiver without social referencing caregiver. Appears indifferent, aloof, withdrawn, or avoidant of caregiver. *Converted Score** Score of 0 converts to 2			
18. Social references caregiver while playing with toys.			
19. After moving away, communicates to caregiver from across space by looking, gestures, or vocalizations.			
Total for Forming Relationships, Attachment, and Engagement			
TWO-WAY, PURPOSEFUL COMMUNICATION			
20. Opens circles of communication: Initiates intentional actions with objects while also engaged in interactions with caregiver (i.e., manipulates object then looks at mother and smiles or vocalizes).			

Age: **25-35 Months** Child's Name: _____

Behaviors: **Child**

	SYM	SENS	EXAM
21. Gives signals: Initiates purposeful and intentional actions in play with objects. *Scoring:* 0 = needs considerable help to get started in play or to engage in purposeful actions; no clear gestures or organized intent. 1 = initiates play but engages in stereotypic actions; i.e., lining toys up, mouthing toys for long periods of time, banging toys without engaging in any other actions with the same toy OR initiates play but actions appear aimless or disorganized. 2 = play shows intentionality and variety, engaging in two or more different behaviors with a given toy or activity. Gestures are specific and activity is functionally tied to objects.			
22. Closes circles: Responds to caregiver's cues in contingent manner (i.e., mother offers toy, baby takes it and puts it in a container). *Scoring:* 0 = does not notice caregiver's response. 1 = notices caregiver's response and looks, but does not respond contingently through actions; instead does something that has nothing to do with what caregiver did (i.e., mother holds toy out for child; child looks at mother and toy, then returns to what he was doing before). 2 = notices caregiver's response, then responds contingently by elaborating on what caregiver did, by taking toy held by caregiver and examining it, by imitating her, or some other response that is clearly linked to what caregiver did.			
23. Shows anger, frustration, aggressive behavior (e.g., hitting), or protest repeatedly. *Converted Score** Score of 0 converts to 2			
24. Uses language (e.g., sounds, words, and/or gestures) during interactions. Circle which ones were used.			
Total for Two-Way, Purposeful Communication			
BEHAVIORAL ORGANIZATION, PROBLEM-SOLVING, AND INTERNALIZATION (A Complex Sense of Self)			
25. Engages in complex patterns of communication stringing together several circles of communication with caregiver (initiated and elaborated on by child) using gestures, vocalizations, and/or words. *Scoring:* 0 = 0 to 2 circles. 1 = 3 to 5 circles. 2 = 6 or more circles.			
26. Imitates or copies something new that the caregiver introduces, then incorporates idea into play (i.e., caregiver feeds doll; child copies this).			
Total for Behavioral Organization, Problem-Solving, and Internalization			

Age: **25-35 Months**   Child's Name: _____

Behaviors: **Child**

	SYM	SENS	EXAM
REPRESENTATIONAL CAPACITY (Elaboration)	/////	/////	/////
27. Engages in symbolic play with the various toys or equipment (e.g., plays out cars racing), going beyond simple concrete actions (e.g., feeding self with cup).			
28. Engages in pretend play patterns of at least one idea in collaboration with caregiver (e.g., one part of a script or scenario played out).			
29. Uses language or pretend play (e.g., playing out with doll figures) to communicate needs, wishes, intentions, or feelings.			
30. Uses pretend play to express themes around closeness or dependency (e.g., putting dolls to sleep next to one another; feeding caregiver and dolls).			
Total for Representational Capacity (Elaboration)			
Total Child Score			
TOTAL FEAS SCALE SCORE (add Caregiver and Child scores)			

Age: **25-35 Months**   Child's Name: _____

Behaviors: **Child**

Functional Emotional Assessment Scale
Profile Form
For 25- to 35-Month-Olds

Subtest	Score SYM	SENS	EXAM	Normal	At Risk	Deficient
Caregiver						
Self-Regulation and Interest in the World				6–8	5	0–4
Forming Relationships, Attachment, and Engagement				7–8	6	0–5
Two-Way, Purposeful, Communication				9–10	8	0–7
Behavioral Organization, Problem-Solving, and Internalization				12–14	11	0–10
Representational Capacity				4–12		0–3
Total Caregiver Score				*38–52*	*36–37*	*0–35*
Child						
Self-Regulation and Interest in the World				15–18	14	0–13
Forming Relationships, Attachment, and Engagement				14–18	13	0–12
Two-Way, Purposeful, Communication				8–10	7	0–6
Behavioral Organization, Problem-Solving, and Internalization				2–4		0–1
Representational Capacity				2–8		0–1
Total Child Score				*42–58*	*40–41*	*0–39*
Total FEAS Scale				**77–110**	**75–76**	**0–74**

Key: SYM = Symbolic; SENS = Sensory

Stanley I. Greenspan, M.D. and Georgia A DeGangi, Ph.D., OTR
Interdisciplinary Council on Developmental and Learning Disorders, Bethesda, MD

The Functional Emotional Assessment Scale Administration and Scoring Form

Age: **3-4 Years**
Behaviors: **Caregiver**

Name of Child: _____   Date of Testing: _____

Age of Child: _____

Person Playing
With Child: Mother: ___   Father: ___
               Caregiver: ___   Examiner: ___

General Scoring

Scoring is on a two-point scale for most items, except where indicated, and is:
   0 = not at all or very brief
   1 = present some of time, observed several times
   2 = consistently present, observed many times
   Indicate N/O for behaviors that are not observed.

Where indicated to convert a score, transform the scoring as follows:
   0 becomes a 2
   1 = 1
   2 becomes a 0

Scores for symbolic play should be entered in the SYM column and scores for sensory play entered in the SENS column. When the examiner facilitates play with the child, enter scores in the EXAM column. The last column may be used for entering scores for additional caregivers (e.g., mother, father, foster parent, babysitter) observed playing with the child.

Scores are interpreted for the primary caregiver playing with the child for the symbolic and sensory play situations. If scores do not differ for symbolic and sensory play, then only one score is interpreted. However, if behaviors differ for the different play situations, then two scores are calculated, one for symbolic play, one for sensory play. These are interpreted using the cutoff scores presented in the profile form.

Age: **3-4 Years**   Child's Name: _____
Behaviors: **Caregiver**

Key: SYM = Symbolic; SENS = Sensory; EXAM = Examiner

	SYM	SENS	EXAM
SELF-REGULATION AND INTEREST IN THE WORLD			
1. Interacts calmly with child, able to wait for child's responses.			
2. Shows pleasant or animated, happy affect throughout play. *Scoring:* 0 = flat, somber, or depressed affect. 1 = content, but neutral. 2 = happy and animated with warm and engaging smiles.			
3. Is sensitive and responsive to child's need for touch by stroking or touching child in pleasurable ways and/or encourages child to explore textured toys.			
Total For Self-Regulation and Interest in the World			
FORMING RELATIONSHIPS, ATTACHMENT, AND ENGAGEMENT			
4. Is relaxed during interchange with child, not overly attentive to child's every action.			
5. Looks at child with affection, showing a warm connection.			
6. Enjoys being with and playing with the child through smiles or a joyful look and emits a sense of warmth by providing inviting gestures. Keep in mind cultural differences in how this may be expressed.			
7. Maintains a verbal or visual connection with child, showing clear availability and interest in the child. Child may move away from caregiver to explore room, yet the caregiver maintains connection to the child across space through gestures, vocalizations, and facial expressions.			
Total for Forming Relationships, Attachment, and Engagement			
TWO-WAY, PURPOSEFUL COMMUNICATION			
8. Allows child to decide on the play topic, to initiate play and explore toys in ways that the child seeks or needs.			
9. Responds to child's wishes, intentions, and actions in a contingent way, building on how the child wishes to play. For example, child may hand toy to parent, and parent responds by taking it and saying something about the toy, then gives the child an opportunity to respond to what parent just did. *Scoring:* 0 = consistently does opposite to what baby seeks, misreads child's cues, changing activity from what child wants to do. 1 = misreads child's signals 25 to 50% of time, changing activity or toy while at other times reads child's signals accurately. 2 = responds to child's signals in appropriate way most of time (up to 75% time responsive to child), staying on the activity that the child has chosen.			

Age: **3-4 Years**   Child's Name: _____
Behaviors: **Caregiver**

	SYM	SENS	EXAM
10. Predominately handles toys, engaging in parallel play and removing attention from playing with child. *Converted Score** Score of 0 converts to 2			
11. Plays with child at developmentally appropriate level. Caregiver may play slightly above child's level of skill, modeling new ways to do things or labeling what child does or describing the functions of objects.			
12. Stimulates child at pace that allows child to respond, waiting for child's responses. Avoids overstimulating child with language or actions.			
Total for Two-Way, Purposeful Communication			
BEHAVIORAL ORGANIZATION, PROBLEM-SOLVING, AND INTERNALIZATION (A Complex Sense of Self)			
13. Responds and initiates reciprocal back and forth chains of interactions with child, stringing together connected circles of communication or units of interaction. For example, caregiver introduces baby doll, baby touches doll's face, mother touches doll's hair, baby pats the doll, mother says "baby," and baby glances between mother and doll. The caregiver may imitate child (i.e., pushing car alongside child), then interject her turn by an action or verbalization related to the child's actions (i.e., "Oh, a bump!", then bumps her car into child's car). *Scoring:* 0 = 0 to 2 circles. 1 = 3 to 5 circles. 2 = 6 or more circles.			
14. Uses gestures and facial expressions as a modality to promote circles of communication.			
15. Uses language or vocalizations as a modality to promote circles of communication.			
16. Elaborates on and builds complexity into the child's play behaviors while engaged in interactive sequences between parent and child. The parent expands on what the child does while remaining on the child's play topic (e.g., the parent does not introduce a completely new play idea). The parent provides a small challenge or interesting twist to the play that requires the child to respond slightly differently than before, thus creating a problem solving opportunity for the child. For example, the parent and child are pushing a car back and forth toward each other. The parent expands on this by creating a wall with her leg to prevent the car from rolling, then waits to see how the child will solve this situation.			

Age: **3-4 Years**   Child's Name: _____

Behaviors: **Caregiver**

	SYM	SENS	EXAM
17. Allows child to assert self in play, exploring with confidence in what he or she wishes (i.e., child expresses strong wish to play in a certain way such as banging toys, being silly, holding a doll, or running around room.) Parent supports the child's needs for dependency and closeness, assertiveness and curiosity, aggression, autonomy, or pleasure and excitement by admiring, showing interest, and/or by joining in to the child's play in whatever way the child seeks. Problems that may interfere with caregiver's capacity to support this area might be intrusiveness, withdrawal, overprotectiveness, or playing at level far above child's level of competence.			
18. Shows pleasure and excitement in playing with child in whatever way the child wishes to play. *Scoring:* 0 = little pleasure and excitement shown by caregiver. 1 = pleasure and excitement sustained by parent over the course of several (3 to 5) circles of communication. 2 = pleasure and excitement sustained for many (6 or more) circles of communication. *Note here if child is unable to sustain circles of communication if it affects caregiver's score:* Child can sustain circles: _____ Child cannot: _____			
19. Expresses appropriate limits on baby. The caregiver may redirect child not to leave room, not to hit her, or not to throw toy. If no need for limits arises during play, mark N/O and give 2 points.			
Total for Behavioral Organization, Problem-Solving, and Internalization			
REPRESENTATIONAL CAPACITY (Elaboration)			
20. Encourages child to engage in symbolic play by modeling or combining materials in ways that encourage representational actions (i.e., mother holds spoon near baby doll's mouth and says, "Feed baby?"). Parent appears comfortable in playing make believe.			
21. Elaborates on child's pretend play idea by building on child's ideas and adding some complexity to them. (e.g., child puts doll in car and pushes it and caregiver says, "Oh, is Daddy going to the store?").			
22. Allows child to express pretend play themes involving closeness or dependency (e.g., nurturing doll) without competing for child's attention to be the one nurtured.			
23. Sustains pretend play, showing interest, pleasure, and excitement about the child's pretend play idea by asking questions, laughing or smiling, and joining into the child's play with enthusiasm (e.g., caregiver says, "Oh, that's a good idea. What happens now? That's so funny!").			

Age: **3-4 Years**   Child's Name: _____

Behaviors: **Caregiver**

	SYM	SENS	EXAM
24. Allows child to express themes of assertiveness in pretend play (i.e., child pretends he's a policeman and puts caregiver in jail; child pretends to go to work and tells caregiver to stay home).			
Total for Representational Capacity (Elaboration)			
REPRESENTATIONAL DIFFERENTIATION **(Building Bridges Between Ideas and Emotional Thinking)**			
25. Elaborates on child's pretend play, creating opportunities to logically connect ideas in play. The caregiver accomplishes this by asking questions to give depth to the drama such as "how," "why," or "when." If the child strays off the topic, the caregiver asks questions to bridge the circle of communication back to the pretend play theme (i.e., "But what happened to the crocodile? He was ready to go for a swim and now you're playing with the truck.")			
26. Incorporates causality into pretend play by helping child to logically connect three or more ideas into a reality-based story sequence. For example, if the child is playing out how two animals fight, the caregiver might ask "How come they're fighting?", "Do they know each other?"			
27. Helps child to elaborate on a wide range of emotional themes, whatever they might be—assertiveness, pleasure and excitement, fearfulness, anger, or separation and loss. The caregiver is accepting of the child's expressions of different feelings and themes through play and shows no discomfort at the expression of different ideas from the child.			
Total for Representational Differentiation (Emotional Thinking)			
Total Caregiver Score			

The Functional Emotional Assessment Scale Administration and Scoring Form

Age: **3-4 Years**
Behaviors: **Child**

Name of Child: _____   Date of Testing: _____

Age of Child: _____

Person Playing
With Child: Mother: ___   Father: ___
               Caregiver: ___   Examiner: ___

General Scoring

Scoring is on a two-point scale for most items, except where indicated, and is:
  0 = not at all or very brief
  1 = present some of time, observed several times
  2 = consistently present, observed many times
  Indicate N/O for behaviors that are not observed.

Where indicated to convert a score, transform the scoring as follows:
  0 becomes a 2
  1 = 1
  2 becomes a 0

Scores for symbolic play should be entered in the SYM column and scores for sensory play entered in the SENS column. When the examiner facilitates play with the child, enter scores in the EXAM column. The last column may be used for entering scores for additional caregivers (e.g., mother, father, foster parent, babysitter) observed playing with the child.

Scores are interpreted for the primary caregiver playing with the child for the symbolic and sensory play situations. If scores do not differ for symbolic and sensory play, then only one score is interpreted. However, if behaviors differ for the different play situations, then two scores are calculated, one for symbolic play, one for sensory play. These are interpreted using the cutoff scores presented in the profile form.

Age: **3-4 Years** Child's Name: _____ Behaviors: **Child** Key: SYM = Symbolic; SENS = Sensory; EXAM = Examiner	SYM	SENS	EXAM
SELF-REGULATION AND INTEREST IN THE WORLD	///////	///////	///////
1. Is interested and attentive to play with toys.			
2. Explores objects freely without caution.			
3. Remains calm for play period with no signs of distress (crying or whining), showing appropriate frustration.			
4. Is comfortable touching textured toys and in being touched by caregiver.			
5. Shows happy, content affect. *Scoring:* 0 = flat, somber, or depressed affect. 1 = content but neutral. 2 = happy and content, robust smiles, warm and engaging affect.			
6. Remains focused on objects or caregiver without being distracted by sights or sounds. *Scoring:* 0 = distracted frequently; no focused play for more than a few seconds at a time. 1 = distracted some of the time with brief periods of focused play. 2 = remains focused in play most of the time with only brief distractibility.			
NOTE: SCORE ONLY ITEM 7 OR 8, WHICHEVER APPLIES. 7. Underreactivity: Appears sluggish or withdrawn. *Scoring:* 0 = withdrawn, difficult to engage. 1 = sluggish or slow-paced in actions but can eventually be aroused or engaged. 2 = shows a bright, alert state with focused play throughout.			
8. Overreactivity: Appears overaroused by toys and environment. *Scoring:* 0 = very active, moves quickly from one toy to the next or wanders away from caregiver and toys constantly. 1= moderately active, occasional bursts of changing activity quickly or wandering away, then settles into play with one toy for short period. 2 = well-modulated in pace and activity level, focusing on a toy or caregiver for long periods before changing activity.			
Total For Self-Regulation and Interest in the World			
FORMING RELATIONSHIPS, ATTACHMENT, AND ENGAGEMENT	///////	///////	///////
9. Shows emotional interest and connection with caregiver by vocalizing and smiling at her.			

Age: **3-4 Years**   Child's Name: _____
Behaviors: **Child**

	SYM	SENS	EXAM
10. Evidences a relaxed sense of security and/or comfort when near caregiver. If child is active and moves away from caregiver, he references her from across space and shows relaxed security in distal space.			
11. Anticipates with curiosity or excitement when caregiver presents an interesting object or game.			
12. Displays signs of discomfort, displeasure, or sadness during interactive play if caregiver should become unresponsive or engage in anticontingent behaviors. *(If caregiver is responsive or contingent, note that this was not observed with "N/O," then assign 2 points.)*			
13. Initiates physical closeness to caregiver but is not clingy; if child is active and moves away from caregiver, child maintains a visual or verbal connection with caregiver.			
14. Turns head away, averts gaze, moves away, or sits facing away from caregiver without social referencing caregiver. Appears indifferent, aloof, withdrawn, or avoidant of caregiver. *Converted Score** Score of 0 converts to 2			
15. Social references caregiver while playing with toys.			
16. After moving away, communicates to caregiver from across space by looking, gestures, or vocalizations.			
Total for Forming Relationships, Attachment, and Engagement			
TWO-WAY, PURPOSEFUL COMMUNICATION			
17. Opens circles of communication: Initiates intentional actions with objects while also engaged in interactions with caregiver (i.e., manipulates object then looks at mother and smiles or vocalizes).			
18. Gives signals: Initiates purposeful and intentional actions in play with objects. *Scoring:* 0 = needs considerable help to get started in play or to engage in purposeful actions; no clear gestures or organized intent. 1 = initiates play but engages in stereotypic actions; i.e., lining toys up, mouthing toys for long periods of time, banging toys without engaging in any other actions with the same toy OR initiates play but actions appear aimless or disorganized. 2 = play shows intentionality and variety, engaging in two or more different behaviors with a given toy or activity. Gestures are specific and activity is functionally tied to objects.			

Age: **3-4 Years**   Child's Name: _____

Behaviors: **Child**

	SYM	SENS	EXAM
19. Closes circles: Responds to caregiver's cues in contingent manner (i.e., mother offers toy, baby takes it and puts it in a container). *Scoring:* 0 = does not notice caregiver's response. 1 = notices caregiver's response and looks, but does not respond contingently through actions; instead does something that has nothing to do with what caregiver did (i.e., mother holds toy out for child; child looks at mother and toy, then returns to what he was doing before). 2 = notices caregiver's response, then responds contingently by elaborating on what caregiver did, by taking toy held by caregiver and examining it, by imitating her, or some other response that is clearly linked to what caregiver did.			
20. Uses language (e.g., sounds, words, and/or gestures) during interactions. Circle which ones were used.			
Total for Two-Way, Purposeful Communication			
BEHAVIORAL ORGANIZATION, PROBLEM-SOLVING, AND INTERNALIZATION (A Complex Sense of Self)			
21. Engages in complex patterns of communication stringing together several circles of communication with caregiver (initiated and elaborated on by child) using gestures, vocalizations, and/or words. *Scoring:* 0 = 0 to 2 circles. 1 = 3 to 5 circles. 2 = 6 or more circles.			
22. Imitates or copies something new that the caregiver introduces, then incorporates idea into play (i.e., caregiver feeds doll; child copies this).			
Total for Behavioral Organization, Problem-Solving, and Internalization			
REPRESENTATIONAL CAPACITY (Elaboration)			
23. Engages in symbolic play with the various toys or equipment (e.g., plays out cars racing), going beyond simple concrete actions (e.g., feeding self with cup).			
24. Engages in pretend play patterns of at least one idea in collaboration with caregiver (e.g., one part of a script or scenario played out).			
25. Uses language or pretend play (e.g., playing out with doll figures) to communicate needs, wishes, intentions, or feelings.			
26. Uses pretend play to express themes around closeness or dependency (e.g., putting dolls to sleep next to one another; feeding caregiver and dolls).			
27. Uses pretend play to express themes around pleasure and excitement around humorous theme (e.g., imitating humorous behaviors).			

Age: **3-4 Years**   Child's Name: _____
Behaviors: **Child**

	SYM	SENS	EXAM
28. Uses pretend play to express themes around assertiveness (e.g., cars racing).			
29. Creates pretend drama with two or more ideas that are not related or logically connected.			
Total for Representational Capacity (Elaboration)			
REPRESENTATIONAL DIFFERENTIATION (Building Bridges Between Ideas and Emotional Thinking)			
30. Pretend play, however unrealistic, involves two or more ideas, which are logically tied to one another. Child may build on adult's pretend play idea.			
31. Elaborates on pretend play sequence of two or more ideas, which are logically connected and grounded in reality. There is a planned quality and child can elaborate to "how," "why," or "when" questions, giving depth to drama.			
32. Uses pretend play or language to communicate themes containing two or more ideas dealing with closeness or dependency (e.g., doll gets hurt, then gets kiss from daddy, then plays ball together).			
33. Uses pretend play or language to communicate themes containing two or more ideas dealing with pleasure and excitement in humorous game (e.g., imitates funny word heard, watches how caregiver reacts, then laughs).			
34. Uses pretend play or language to communicate themes containing two or more ideas dealing with assertiveness (e.g., soldiers search for missing person, find her, then battle to save her again)			
Total for Representational Differentiation (Emotional Thinking)			
Total Child Score			
TOTAL FEAS SCALE SCORE (add Caregiver and Child scores)			

Age: **3-4 Years**   Child's Name: _____

Behaviors: **Child**

Functional Emotional Assessment Scale
Profile Form
For 3- to 4-Year-Olds

Subtest	Score			Normal	At Risk	Deficient
	SYM	SENS	EXAM			
Caregiver						
Self-Regulation and Interest in the World				4–6		0–3
Forming Relationships, Attachment, and Engagement				7–8	6	0–5
Two-Way, Purposeful, Communication				9–10	8	0–7
Behavioral Organization, Problem-Solving, and Internalization				12–14	11	0–10
Representational Capacity				6–10	5	0–4
Representational Differentiation				2–6		0–1
Total Caregiver Score				*42–54*	*40–41*	*0–39*
Child						
Self-Regulation and Interest in the World				12–14	11	0–10
Forming Relationships, Attachment, and Engagement				14–16	13	0–12
Two-Way, Purposeful, Communication				8–10	7	0–6
Behavioral Organization, Problem-Solving, and Internalization				2–4		0–1
Representational Capacity				8–14	7	0–6
Representational Differentiation				2–10		0–1
Total Child Score				*48–66*	*46–47*	*0–45*
Total FEAS Scale				**93–120**	**86–92**	**0–85**

Key: SYM = Symbolic; SENS = Sensory

About the Authors

Stanley I. Greenspan, M.D. is Clinical Professor of Psychiatry, Behavioral Sciences, and Pediatrics at the George Washington University Medical School; a supervising child psychoanalyst at the Washington Psychoanalytic Institute in Washington, DC; and is Chairman of the Interdisciplinary Council on Developmental and Learning Disorders. He's a founder and former president of ZERO TO THREE: The National Center for Infants, Toddlers, and Families. He also served as chief of the Mental Health Studies Center and director of the Clinical Infant Development Program at the National Institute of Mental Health. A recipient of the American Psychiatric Association's Ittleson Prize for outstanding contributions to Child Psychiatry Research, Dr. Greenspan is the author of more than one hundred scholarly articles and chapters, and author or editor of over thirty books.

Georgia A. DeGangi, Ph.D., OTR, FAOTA is a clinical psychologist and an occupational therapist in private practice at ITS (Integrated Therapy Services) for Children and Families, Inc., in Kensington, MD. Among her publications are the *Test of Sensory Functions in Infants*, the *Infant/Toddler Symptom Checklists*, and the *Test of Attention in Infants*. She has recently published a book entitled *Disorders of Regulation in Affect and Behavior: A Therapist's Guide to Assessment and Treatment*. She was the 1992 recipient of the A. Jean Ayres Award from the American Occupational Therapy Foundation. She is also co-director of the Infant Mental Health program of the Washington School of Psychiatry.

Serena Wieder, Ph.D., is a clinical psychologist in private practice, specializing in the diagnosis and treatment of infants and young children. She is associate chair of the Interdisciplinary Council on Developmental and

Learning Disorders and associate editor of its journal. Dr. Wieder is on the faculty of the Infant mental Health Program at the Washington (DC) School of Psychiatry and is a co-chair of the Diagnostic Classification Committee and a board member of ZERO TO THREE: The National Center for Infants, Toddlers, and Families. She has published widely in the professional literature, including coauthoring with Dr. Greenspan *The Child with Special Needs*, and has conducted more than thirty major training workshops in the diagnosis and treatment of complex developmental problems.

Index